Front cover photograph "Mannequins" © Thomas Edwards (www.thomasedwards.co.uk). Back cover collage: "North Beach Tree" © Mauro Lo Conte and "Hand X-Ray" © Trace Meek (http://tracemeek.com). "Mannequins" and "Hand X-Ray" used in compliance with the terms of a Creative Commons Attribution license: creativecommons.org/licenses/by/2.0; "North Beach Tree" used by permission of the photographer.

Some of the pieces in *Blue, Too* have been previously published and are used by kind permission of the author or publisher. A version of "Walls" appeared in *Countrycide: Stories* by L. A. Fields (Lethe Press, 2014). Judy Grahn's "Boys at the Rodeo" was reprinted in *The Judy Grahn Reader* (Aunt Lute Books, 2009). "Men Without Bliss" appeared in Rigoberto González's collection of the same name (University of Oklahoma Press, 2008). "Lowest of the Low" appeared in Keith Banner's collection, *Next to Nothing: Stories* (Lethe Press, 2014). Andrej Longo's *Tanto peggio di così mica può andare* appeared in Italian in the literary magazine, *linus*. "Heaven" by Royston Tester appeared in his collection, *Summat Else* (Porcupine's Quill, 2004). "advancedELVIScourse" appeared in a different form in CAConrad's book of the same name (Soft Skull Press, 2009). A version of "My Blue Midnights" appeared in the late Rane Arroyo's collection, *How to Name A Hurricane* (Tucson: University of Arizona Press, 2005). A version of "Middle-Class Drag: A Performance Piece" by Renny Christopher appeared in *Resilience: Queer Professors from the Working Class* (SUNY Press, 2008). Carter Sickels' "Saving" first appeared in *The Collection: Short Fiction from the Transgender Vanguard* (Topside Press, 2012).

Published in the United States by FourCats Press
ISBN: 978-0989980012
LCCN: 2014913951

Book design by FourCats Press.
First FourCats Press Edition: August 2014
www.FourCatsPress.com
Editor@FourCatsPress.com

Blue, Too

More Writing by (for or about) Working-Class Queers

Edited by Wendell Ricketts

PRAISE FOR *EVERYTHING I HAVE IS BLUE*

"This book serves up feisty, sharp stories that stretch and challenge stagnant notions of class, masculinity, and gay identity." (D. Travers Scott, author of *Execution, Texas* and *One of These Things is Not Like the Other*)

"The edgy, surprising stories in *Everything I Have Is Blue* are a tonic: they make an important contribution in terms of bringing to our attention characters and themes we seldom see explored in gay contemporary fiction." (Jaime Manrique, author of *Besame Mucho: New Gay Latino Fiction* and *Eminent Maricones: Arenas, Lorca, Puig, and Me*)

"This book gives us what no contemporary TV program, movie, or magazine has even come close to—the tender, angry, funny emotional innards of the embattled daily life of working-class gay men. These could be the stories of the guys on the corner in my neighborhood—or yours!" (Minnie Bruce Pratt, author of *S/He*)

"This anthology by queer working class men is utterly necessary and beautifully curated—a real gift to our ever-growing library." (Kirk Reader, author of *How I Learned to Snap*)

Table of Contents

Section I

Section II

SECTION III

Blue, Too:

More Writing by (for or about)
Working-Class Queers

EDITED BY WENDELL RICKETTS

Foreword
Wendell Ricketts

In 2005, I began the Foreword to *Everything I Have Is Blue: Short Fiction by Working-Class Men about More-or-Less Gay Life* with these words:

> The book you hold in your hand took six years to come into being. It was rejected by fifty-seven publishers.
>
> Should I ever own a home—or maybe just live in an apartment where I don't care about getting the deposit back—I really do intend to paper the bathroom walls with the rejection slips I've collected over more than twenty years as a writer. A wall of distinction—not to say honor—will have to be reserved for the rejections *Blue* received.
>
> Ironically, many of them say the same thing: "This is a terrific (important, much-needed, exciting, valuable) project, but we could never do it." I was told that publishing short stories would be "professional suicide"; I was told that gay fiction was dead.
>
> The best rejection for *Blue*, if I can say it that way, was the one from the publisher who admired the writing but "remain(ed) unconvinced of the validity of the category." (The category, that is, of working-class queer.) It might have been fun to introduce her to the gay publisher who told me, in his plummy British accent, that the writers in this book couldn't "really" be working class because, as far as I was able to follow his argument, they were writers.

Since I wrote that, ten years have passed. *Everything I Have Is Blue* had two printings, was released in a hardback edition as a "Featured Selection" by the Insight Out book club, and was nominated for a Lambda Literary Award (which, though it was the first and only anthology dedicated to the voices of gay men from the working classes, it didn't win).

Blue received serious reviews in *Xtra* (Canada) and *Stonewall News* (Spokane, WA) (whose critics loved it) and in the journal, *Western American Literature* (whose critic didn't). A few bloggers wrote respectfully about *Blue*. There was a mention of *Blue* (thanks to Kirk Read) among the "Favorites and Bests for 2005" on the now-defunct Books to Watch Out For site and as one of the "Books of the Year" for 2005 (thanks to Jesse Monteagudo) on the site of the now-defunct *The Weekly News* (*TWN*) (South Florida).

On the other hand, more than a few reviewers missed the point entirely. Take the one who wrote "Lend [*Everything I Have Is Blue*] to the cute guy who delivers bottled water to your office every month. Or your hunky garbage man. Basically, anyone hot with a blue collar." Because, of course, "hot and hunky" blue collar guys probably wouldn't buy their own books, and it might help you—you big, bottled-water-drinking corporate exec, you—get laid.

The field of working-class studies politely ignored the book, as did queer and gay studies programs, though at least one academic took *Everything I Have Is Blue* all the way to the Modern Language Association conference in 2006, where he discussed the anthology's potential to "complicate the 'is class a subject position or an economic relation?' question." In other words, he understood the book perfectly.

After that, like the vast majority of writing that isn't published by big houses with major distribution contracts and large advertising budgets, *Everything I Have Is Blue* sank out of sight. In fairness, I should make clear that I contributed significantly to its disappearance: After a third year passed in which the publisher refused to pay royalties, I asked for *Everything I Have Is Blue* to be taken out of print.

And then I started over.

Blue, Too includes the "Reader's, Writer's, and Scholar's Guide" and the Annotated Bibliography I had always hoped would be part of this project, but which couldn't be included the first time around. And, like *Everything I Have Is Blue* before it, *Blue, Too* is entirely self-financed. Not everyone will agree, but I think it's important to make that clear. It's one of the things I learned as a boy in my working-class family: only the wealthy pretend to be too embarrassed to talk about money.

Blue, Too reprints some reader favorites from *Everything I Have Is Blue* and, in that sense, bears a passing resemblance to a second edition. On the other hand, half the pieces in Section I are new (*Blue, Too* expanded to include work by writers of all genders and sexual orientations); the Afterword has been completely revamped, updated, and expanded; and the Reader's Guide and Annotated Bibliography (with more than 500 entries) are original to this volume. So *Blue, Too* is also something like a sequel. What it really is, is a hybrid.

I continue to be proud of the work in *Everything I Have Is Blue* and *Blue, Too* and I remain committed to what the books represent: the effort to add colors to the palette of American identity, rebut the reductionisms of "multiculturalism," confuse categories that deserve to be confused, propagandize where propaganda is well warranted. Though I spent years wandering queer literature in search of something like home, I now know that the writers in this collection are the people I needed to find.

FLOWERS, FLAMES
C. Bard Cole

Frankie's boy Raj is all like, what are you doing hangin' out with that fucker man, he don't care shit for you, what you bein' stupid for man dats ill. Frankie's all like, you my man okay and dats the truth but you don't know okay so don't be talking shit when you don't know.

Raj is, you know what they be sayin' bout chu now man and Frankie's you tell me okay—you tell me. Nobody says this shit to my face. That's the thing man, when bitch asses be talking behind your back nobody says shit to your face. If I need to know you tell me.

Raj is, don't fuck wit' me man.

Frankie's if you can't say it man, then fuck dat shit. People talk shit, that's their deal not mine. Frankie looks him in the eye. So whatchu have to say man?

They say you down wit' dat faggot, man.

His name David okay? I'm down with him, he's my man. You my man, okay?

You know what I'm sayin', Raj goes. They sayin' you gay together and shit.

Damn, says Frankie. They sayin' it, must be true.

Naw, Raj goes. I don't think so. I don't believe it man. I know you ain't a fag. I'm just sayin'.

Damn, says Frankie, waving his hand. You know it all man. You don't think so, must not be true. You say so, I guess I ain't.

David Florian's walking home from the F train, his laptop and portfolio slung over his shoulder. A menthol cigarette between his lips, he fumbles one-handed with a pack of matches. Looking up, he sees Frankie sitting on his stoop, kicked back, a bottle of ice tea resting between his big, immaculate white sneakers. David smiles, wonders how long he's been sitting there.

"Yo paps," Frankie says. "Where you been at today?"

"I was in the city," David says, sliding the padded shoulder strap down his arm. "I had a meeting. You been sitting here all day?"

Frankie shrugs. "I been lookin' in every now and then. You didn't say you were going to Manhattan."

David's a designer, he does illustration and graphics for a couple music labels, some independent, some corporate. Most of the time he works at home. Today he's wearing baggy khaki pants, a white button-down shirt, a gold and red striped tie, no baseball cap. He could dress sharper if he wanted but it's not worth it. The art directors he deals with wouldn't care if he came in wearing cutoff sweatpants and a T-shirt, his tattoos showing. They would actually expect that—it's what he looks like. The tie just gets him past the security guards and receptionists, stops people from showing him the messengers' entrance.

"They had some work I had to do in the office," he says, and then, remembering that Frankie dislikes his avoiding details, adds, "The color keys came in for a whole bunch of c.d. booklets and it's shit they had to send back to the printer ASAP."

Frankie nods seriously. David is sure Frankie doesn't know what color keys are, but if he cares enough he'll ask. Giving his portfolio an emphatic shake, David says, "Plus I got some sketches for the next job I'm doing."

"Warner?" Frankie asks with apparent casual indifference.

David nods. "This is my Rhino shit."

Frankie snorts. "Rhino?" he says. "You doin' the fuckin' Monkees?"

Rhino's a label that repackages old music into compilations, box sets, and collector's editions. They do, actually, have all the old Monkees albums on their list. Frankie thumbed through the catalogue one day and made fun of its contents. David is working on a "breakdancing" theme boxed set, early eighties hip-hop. Graffiti-style text illustration is a specialty of his.

"I ain't doin' the Monkees," David says. Then, from the corner in of his mouth, in a stage aside, he mutters, "Dumbass kid trippin' this Monkees shit like he knows somethin'. His mother doin' the fuckin' Monkees."

This sends Frankie into ecstasies of boyish laughter.

He gathers himself together. "You say somethin' about my mother, yo?"

David's smile is slightly cockeyed. "Yeah. She Davy Jones's bitch. Don't be ashamed of your mamma, Davy Jones keep the food on your table."

David pushes past Frankie to unlock his front door.

"I know who keeps the food on my table," Frankie says, play-sulking. David doesn't turn around but he stands in the door frame, his back facing the street, until Frankie gathers up his backpack to follow him inside.

David has lived in this apartment for five years, pretty much since he graduated from college, working as a sales clerk at Pearl Paint in Manhattan and going out Thursday, Friday, Saturday nights to hip-hop clubs in the outer boroughs, tagging walls, subway posters, and sketchbooks with a nice variety of fat art markers he'd stolen from work. He didn't find the job in a magazine art department—the job he'd promised his parents he could get easy—but he hadn't cared. He was happy to be on his own and thoughtless, happy not to have to move home to his childhood bedroom like some of his high school friends. He made friends with club promoters and kids running indie labels; he started up a little T-shirt company—nothing that made money, until it started to.

Frankie came with the building. He came with the stoop. He watched David move his possessions in five years ago, watched him run to the store for cigarettes and food three or four times a day. Maybe after the first year they finally started talking. The first thing David recalls Frankie saying to him was: "Yo kid, whassup? Donchoo never go to work or nothin'?"

David raised a supercilious eyebrow: "You're—asking me—if I ever go to work?"

"Damn ... dats cold," Frankie said, approving. "I am workin', kid." Frankie's uncle was supposed to be the Super of a couple of buildings on the block, but whether that really was his uncle, or whether Frankie ever helped him out with anything, David couldn't say for sure.

David shook his head as he trotted off. "Workin' my nerves, maybe."

From that day on, whenever David was working in the front room of his apartment—he had his office set up there because it was too noisy and bright at night to use as his bedroom—Frankie might come by, reach up and rattle the window grill. If the window were left open even a crack, David might find himself interrupted by an instant conversation. "Hey kid, whatchu cookin' in there? Damn, that smells good." It would be, for example, macaroni and cheese. Or Campbell's soup, simmering on the kitchen stovetop. Frankie had an extraordinary nose for food.

David had been reluctant to allow Frankie into his life. He did not credit Frankie with any strong appreciation of subtlety. He wondered what would happen if Frankie finally figured out that he was gay, for example, or, more practically, if it was a good idea to allow a neighborhood boy like this to see that he had six, seven thousand dollars of irreplaceable computer equipment in his street-level apartment—secondhand hardware it'd taken him years to put together and expensive software he'd pirated from various temp assignments. He had no idea what kind of shit Frankie was up to. One day you'd see him in some raggedy-ass shorts and T-shirt, drinking a forty of cheap Midnight Dragon, a few days later in a new hip-length leather coat and new jeans, new Walkman, mixing Guinness with St. Ides and bragging about his "mad loot."

"I don't wanna hear whatchu do for that loot, kid," David said.

"You wanna know, man?" Frankie said, winking slyly. "I'll tell ya."

What it was, was: Frankie had a girl friend who worked as a prostitute, a "role play therapist" at a West Side escort service. All the clients had secret desires they'd confess, eventually or right off the bat, and more than one wanted to be beaten up by a homeboy. "And she beeped me, said I got this faggot wants to be beaten up, and I go kick the shit out of this guy for like an hour and come back home with two hundred bucks in my pocket."

David had let Frankie into his home for this story. They were in his back room, the living room where he sleeps—futon folded into a couch—watching TV, smoking weed. The story made him uncomfortable. "I'm a fag, Frankie," he said finally.

"This one dude," Frankie continued indifferently. "He paid me two hundred bucks just to stand with my foot on his face."

"You really do all that shit?" David asked.

Frankie shrugged, looking down at his sneakers. "Don't tell me you wouldn't." After a moment he laughed, covering his mouth with his hand.

That was a long time ago. A couple years but a long time. David doesn't remember now that he was ever scared of Frankie. He remembers the fact, and they joke about it, but he doesn't remember the feeling.

"Hey bitch," Frankie says, flopping down on David's couch as David unloads his bags. "What's for dinner?"

"You the bitch," David says, grabbing a beer from the refrigerator. "You the one I keep around 'cuz you look pretty."

Frankie turns on the TV. *Roseanne* reruns. "Come on Flores, I'm hungry, man." He calls David "Flores," refuses to believe in "this 'Florian' shit,'" as he likes to say. This secretly delights David. He fears the opposite—that one day Frankie might regard him as a phony homeboy wanna-be. When he gets down to it, David's not really sure which is the truth. His life's always been about passing for something he isn't. Maybe he really is a Flores. Maybe it's just Frankie can see it.

"Serious man," Frankie says, "What's for dinner?"

David grunts, walking into the room. "Shit, man. I've been on my feet all day. I wanted to come home and take a bath."

"And not eat nothing?"

"Man, you are the all-time bitch," David says, taking his wallet from his back pocket. "I was gonna order Chinese or pizza or shit. Chinese. Broccoli with garlic sauce." He flips a twenty onto the coffee table.

"You taking a shower?" Frankie says, snatching the bill up. "I'll run down the street, get us some pork chops an' shit. You don't want Chinese food."

"Don't tell me what I don't want," David says, knowing full well he's going to be eating pork chops in the next hour.

"Do you," Frankie says, scrunching his brow. "Do you ... The thing I don't get about, you know, you being gay an' shit. Is you know a woman's body is...." He outlines the standard curvaceous form with his hands. "Is beautiful. And a guy's body is all flat here...." He smacks his chest. "And all knotty here...." He grabs a handful of haunch through his jeans. "And hairy an' shit. It's ugly, man."

David shakes his head, coughing instead of laughing. "I don't think so. I mean, you got your idea of what a woman looks like, how many women look like that?" He mimics the hourglass gesture. "What is that shit? I seen the girls you go with. Skinny like boys, they got muscles in their arms. In a bra and everything their tits are up here but take that off"—he indicates an area towards the bottom of his rib cage—"they don't stay up there like pretty little oranges."

"Oranges," Frankie laughs.

"Eggplants, whatever. Just don't bullshit me. Like you don't ever look at a guy and say, 'Damn, I wish I looked like that.'"

Frankie shrugged. "That's different."

"It's not different," David said. "That's what I like."

"Who?" Frankie says.

"Not who," David says. "What."

"No man. You said you look at a guy and say 'damn,'" Frankie says. "So who do you look at?"

David's not happy about finding himself right here. To explain this properly requires revealing more of himself than he'd like to do. The answer is: Any guy who can walk down a city street holding his head up, looking like he believes the glances coming his way show admiration or fear or respect, not contempt—that makes David say "damn." That's what David wants to be.

It took him years to understand, and to truly believe, that the men he saw and desired, men who advertised their manhood with their stance or walk, with telling gestures like overlong belts hitching up oversized jeans, the long leather strap folded over to dangle cock-like at the crotch, or one sweatpants leg pushed up over a tight knot of calf muscle—that these were, precisely, gestures, consciously made, and that David could imitate them if he wanted, that imitating men he desired and admired made him strong like them, and not merely an imitation, that imitating and admiring was what these desirable men themselves did with their stances and walks and telling gestures.

But David can't always believe this. Acknowledging the consciousness of his inspiration makes him feel like a phony. So he doesn't answer Frankie.

"Who do you look at, Frankie?" he asks instead.

Frankie doesn't hesitate. "You," he says. "I wish I had green eyes."

"My mom's Irish," David says.

"I always wanted to be one of them green-eyed Puerto Ricans."

"My dad's Cuban," David says.

"Whatever," Frankie says. "You look like somebody."

"Who do I look like?" David asks.

"No, man. You look like yourself. You look like somebody. That's what I thought when I first saw you. 'Who's this kid? He got something going on.'"

"Oh, you did not." David pushes away his plate—stray clumps of yellow rice and a stripped pork chop bone. "You're full of shit."

"Fuck off yo. I'm serious. I had to nose around after you. I had to know what the deal was."

David smirks. "So this is it," he says, gesturing loosely with his arm. "This is what the deal is." He thinks he's gesturing at a messy apartment, a pile of chaos signifying nothing. David doesn't recognize that he has made choices in his life.

"I don't know whas wrong wit' you, man," Frankie says.

Frankie understands more than David thinks.

They're watching TV, bellies full of pork chop and yellow rice, stretched out on the couch, David as close to Frankie as he dares place himself, close but far enough to seem like he doesn't mean to be close. Frankie understands more than David thinks. He puts his arm around David's neck. He's not going to kiss David. David is wondering. David is thinking, well, if I was less of a fag I wouldn't be afraid and we would kiss and make love and we'd never have to say that it meant anything in particular except we love each other. Frankie starts kneading the muscles of David's shoulder, saying, "Man, you gotta learn to relax." David wonders if Frankie means something metaphysical.

Frankie doesn't. He just means David's got to learn to relax. It doesn't bother him to touch David. It's not—well, first of all: his friendship with David is something unique in his life, almost a fantasy, in the sense that it changes nothing except the way he looks at the world. Second of all: he has a hard time thinking of David as a guy. David isn't what a guy is, as far as the rest of Frankie's life goes, so it isn't necessary to think of him as one. David with his small features, his olive skin just light enough to show freckles, just dark enough to set off his green eyes—his yellow eyes, Frankie thinks, yellow and blue. They look green but the two colors don't actually blend, they are blue shot through with gold. David's hair's cut in a fade, perfect, with no scars on his scalp. All the guys Frankie knows show scars beneath their buzz cuts.

It's not that he sees David as a girl. He's a fag and his features are soft but that's not enough to blur Frankie's basic understanding of gender. Frankie likes pussy and tits and sex with girls a lot more hard-assed than David. It's easy enough to say, but when you're in David's position you never quite accept things like this, especially when you're in this boy's arms and you're wondering if he's going to kiss you, ever. If he wants to.

Frankie knows that David thinks he is beautiful and Frankie likes this. There is no one else in the world that thinks Frankie is beautiful. His mom says he is handsome. His girlfriends say he is cute. The guy who paid him two hundred dollars to be punched said he was hot. But beautiful is different. Beautiful is wanting to look without touching because the fact that he exists provides a true and sufficient pleasure. They watch TV and Frankie's dark irises dart to the corner of his eyes, catching David in the act of this contemplation. "What are you lookin' at man," he says in feigned annoyance.

"I'm not looking at shit," David says, turning back towards the television screen.

"Well," Frankie says. "Alright then."

Frankie's uncle Manny snaps, irritated. "*¡Oye, hazme caso!* I don't need any more of your fucking suggestions!"

Frankie's supposed to be helping Manny with repairs to a newly vacated apartment. They're ripping up the bathroom and kitchen, putting in some new fixtures—this makes the place "remodeled," takes it out of rent stabilization. Carroll Garden's getting gentrified, a landlord can easily pull down twelve hundred dollars a month for a one bedroom on the open market. Manny's got basic super-slash-handyman repair skills; installing a stove or repairing drywall's kind of a challenge. Manny stands, rubbing his chin, legs apart, muttering at the new stove and the incomprehensible tangle of wires and tubing at its back. Frankie has just suggested, for the third or fourth time this morning, that he can find a "how-to" guide on the World Wide Web—if he can take ten to go over his friend's place.

But Manny's not muttering to elicit suggestions. He's just thinking. He can usually figure shit out. Frankie showed up an hour late this morning and that's already primed Manny to be pissed off. He doesn't want to hear any more bullshit about computers.

"Bendito, I'm just trying to help," Frankie says. "I don't want to be all day at this."

Manny scrapes his hand on a metal edge of the back of the stove. "Coño fuckin' ... Jesus Christ, Frankie, will you shut up and do what I ask you? Go get my ratchet set outta the truck."

David never studied computers at school, Frankie knows. They've talked about it. He says his teachers were too old and they never thought computers would turn out to be important, and anyhow they're not too hard to learn just by playing on one. But Manny doesn't care, and Raj didn't seem too impressed either when Frankie told him if he got a laptop instead of a PlayStation he could download all the music he wanted and play it through his stereo speakers. ("What are you, on crack?" Raj had said. "I'm getting a PlayStation with my Christmas money. A computer is like five thousand dollars or some shit.") Frankie doesn't get it. Computers are the future, but nobody wants to educate themselves about it because nobody wants to see that Frankie knows shit that they don't know nothing about.

Chainsmoking Newports, David's staring numb-headed at a layout of a menu he's doing—a couple-hundred-dollar job for a restaurant on Smith Street that's opening in a few weeks: logo, menu, flyers, stationery. It just sort of fell in his lap and it's money but it's boring as fuck, he doesn't really give a shit how it turns out so it's hard to judge whether one font choice makes a difference over another, or whether tight letter spacing looks better than loose.

He's both relieved and annoyed when the doorbell starts buzzing frantically. It's almost ten in the evening so he knows it's Frankie. Walking to the door he's deciding whether it's better to look annoyed, to justify sending Frankie away so he can finish, or to look pleased and relieved, which he is. It's bad though. He does need to finish this job. He opens the door before deciding and Frankie's already in, hugging him violently, and he's got no choice but to smile and squeeze back. "Hey man," he says. "Whassup?"

"Fuckin' shit, man," Frankie says. "A lot of motherfuckin' bullshit's what's up. Damn."

Frankie's giving off disjointed vibes. "Are you stoned or something? Man, you are stoned."

"Whatever, man. I was just hanging out with my friend Angela. The whore—you know, I told you about her."

"Oh," David says, letting the door slam as he follows Frankie to the couch. "What were you—stepping on some old faggots again?"

Frankie shakes his head. "No man, we were just hanging out and shit. She wadn't working or nothin. Hey you know," Frankie says, grabbing David around the waist and pulling him down on the couch in a kind of wrestling more. "Hey, I met this friend of hers, this kid Orlando. He's a fag, man. He's pretty good looking. Come out wit' me sometime, I'll hook you up."

"What," David says, forcing a laugh. "You're picking guys for me now?"

Frankie puts his weight on David's chest. "Fuck," he says. "You ain't gettin' it off me, you gotta get it somewhere, right?"

"That's cute," David says, pushing back. Frankie's roughhousing with too much strength, David can't force him off. He's obviously really stoned, David thinks. "You're a good matchmaker, I bet. This kid's a fag and I'm a fag, so we'll get together and fuck or something. 'cuz we fags."

"Well man," Frankie says. "It's the start, right?"

David manages to wriggle free, sits upright. "I didn't know it bothered you, man," he says.

Frankie's legs are lying across David's lap so he folds his arms behind his head, acts like he meant to spread out that way. "What?" he says. "What bothers me?"

David grabs the remote, turns the TV on. "Nothing." David shrugs. "I mean, I thought you liked what we got going."

Frankie folds his eyebrows down, looking confused. He moves his hands to his chest. "What the fuck are you talking about man? Orlando's a cool kid, man. He's smart. He's funny as shit. You'd like him. He fucks guys."

David makes an unintelligible, sullen-sounding noise. He's sitting under Frankie real rigid, like he's afraid to feel comfortable like that.

"What do we got going, man," Frankie asks, serious.

David kind of sighs.

"Tell me, alright? It's cool, just tell me."

"I think you know what I feel," David says.

"I ain't your psychic friend," Frankie says.

He's looking at David, eyes wide, waiting.

"You fuckin' know," David says.

Frankie closes his eyes and feels the velour of the seat cushion at the back of his neck. He inhales the smell of David's apartment. "Tell me your words for it," he says.

David grabs for his cigarettes and lights one.

He checks Frankie's face to see if he believes in it.

"My life's kind of a mess right now," David says. "I don't wanna worry about dating somebody, all the bullshit and game playing. I just gotta—you know—have my life be solid. It's good to have someone around I can talk to. It's good to have someone I can touch."

"Uh-huh," Frankie says, uncertain. He almost understands but the words you choose for things matter and he wants to hear it.

"I mean, shit," David says. "You know I'm in love with you and you know I'm never going to pull anything on you you don't want. I don't want anything off you, you know that. I just like being with you."

David's right, Frankie felt this. But he didn't think that David would be able to say it. He'd thought maybe David didn't even know it for himself. It feels weird, and it hurts. "My uncle got real mad at me today," Frankie says, quiet. "It's such fuckin' bullshit to have to follow him around and carry his goddamn toolbox and shit all over the fuckin' place. I gotta find a better job than that."

"Frankie, you heard what I said, right?"

He shrugs. "So fuckin' what, you jack off at night thinkin' 'bout me or something. So fucking what? You don't need my okay."

David's not looking him in the face anymore. "But," he says. "But, do you ever think about it? What it would be like? I mean…. Come on, you told me to tell you what I was thinking."

Frankie ain't going to be what someone wants him to be, one more time: a disappointment. It's not my fault, he thinks—why don't they want something I can give? "You wanna know if I ever thought about us fucking?" he asks.

David nods.

"Yeah. I thought you'd probly like it and I probly wouldn't."

"All right."

"I mean, you want us to be boyfriends?" Frankie says. "Or you just want to suck my dick sometime?"

"I don't want to suck your dick," David says defensively.

"I'm not offering," Frankie says. "I just want to know."

"I'm sorry," says David. "I'm sorry I brought this up at all. I'm an asshole, okay. I'm fucked up. I don't want anything from you. It just makes me feel good when I'm around you and I don't know why. I don't want to have sex with you and I don't want to fuck some fag you just met. I'm sorry. We shouldn't be talking about this."

"Man, you just crazy, what's with you?"

David's folded his arms. He's staring straight ahead, wanting Frankie to disappear now. Or to shut up. Or something.

"'We shouldn't be talking about this'?" Frankie repeats.

It's been a while since David has hated himself this consciously. This isn't the first time he's made a relationship like this for himself. It's not the second or the third. Used to just be casual acquaintances, stupid crushes, always on straight boys. That he's made Frankie his friend, tied their lives together in various, sophisticated, tiny ways—he's appalled at himself. He didn't know he could be that devious.

He says, out loud, "I wish I could die or something and get it over with." And just hearing himself say that, seeing the look on Frankie's face, makes him wish it harder 'cuz he can see Frankie's upset.

"David, man," Frankie says in a whisper. "Why the fuck would you say that?"

David doesn't answer.

"Man, that makes me feel real fucked up. Don't say that, alright? I love you, okay? You're my brother. If you think you're a piece of shit, what does that make me?" With some effort Frankie works his hand into David's clenched fist. David doesn't relax. "Come on, man," Frankie says. "I don't know why you gotta be like this."

David shakes his head. "Okay," he says, putting his feet back on the floor. "All right." His hand relaxes, but it's just in Frankie's grip. He's not holding back. "Yeah. I want you to be my boyfriend. I want you to be my lover. This whole time, I think, that's what I've wanted. I'm friends with you because it turns me on to be near you."

"That's cool," Frankie says gently. "That doesn't bother me."

"It bothers me, alright?" David says. "That's the problem. It bothers me."

Frankie's stoop-sitting in front of his aunt's house when his friend Raj goes by. Raj says, Frankie, man, whassup?

Frankie thinks of a beer commercial, whassup? Frankie starts to say, jes chillin', but stops, and thinks about it, and laughs. Chillin'. What the fuck does that mean? So Frankie goes, I'm sittin' on the stoop in front of my aunts.

Raj is like, what're you, laughin' like a mutherfuckin' idiot.

Yeah, Frankie says, I'm a mutherfuckin' idiot. You wanna sip of this?

Raj laughs, takes the bagged forty. Frankie's in the doghouse, he says. What's up, kid?

Frankie just shakes his head, shrugs. Smiles.

Out on the street on a Friday night, Raj says. You ditched your man, huh?

Frankie's lip curls. Yeah, he says.

For real?

Yeah, Frankie says.

Raj is waiting for the punch line, or something. For real? he says again.

We decided, Frankie says wistfully, head held low. We decided we should see other people.

For five seconds Frankie can keep a straight face.

Man, Raj says.

Wha-a-a-ssup! Frankie says, like the beer commercial.

You are serious retarded, man, Raj says, laughing, sitting down.

MY BLUE MIDNIGHTS
Rane Arroyo

The trees which grew along the broken arches
Waved dark in the blue midnight, and the stars
Shone through the rents of ruin
—Lord Byron, *Manfred*

1.

My ears are ringing so I can't help but think my family is already talking about me.

I don't think I'm that interesting once I get out of other people's beds.

The country of my own bed is only for invited tourists.

I stop at Little Jim's for a drink before I go to the family party for yet another cousin who is engaged.

It's only four o'clock in a Gemini afternoon but already the bar is crowded.

I see lots of businessmen eyeing unemployed (or unemployable, as my friend Linc insists) men in cowboy suits.

How has the gay world become so full of uniforms?

A younger man nonchalantly stares at me.

I look away and see one of the suits staring at him.

In the beginning was the triangle and it is still holy.

I walk over to the jukebox to see if there are any new Spanish songs and I find the same old one: "Feliz Navidad."

Jesus, why is there a Christmas song on this jukebox in the middle of June?

I swallow my warm Budweiser and hurry out of the bar before I have to reject a skinny man with an eye patch who is seeking rejection, and probably wouldn't believe that I'm late for a family party.

It's so strange but the inside of a gay bar is like being inside an imaginary country; rarely are there clocks or even clues to which city you might be in.

It's a no-man's land filled with men.

It's as if we're all amnesiacs without any other I.D.s other than what hangs between our legs.

I'm an exile who isn't an exile.

I think of my parents arriving in Chicago not knowing any words of English, their Puerto Rico becoming only Puerto Pobre.

I remember how they used to bundle us up in the winters as if we were going out to play in a new ice age.

My boots hit the sidewalks in a regular rhythm and I think of that song that Uncle Israel, used to sing, before he became Uncle Rachel: *There is a rose / that grows / in Spanish Harlem.*

He got the words almost right.

I arrive at the party, take a deep breath and ring the doorbell.

The cousin who is pregnant and fifteen is being honored for trapping her man, an electrician who is even in a union.

She shrugs at me and cousin Tony embraces me and I'm pushed into the living room.

He is one of the family's heroes because he has been a rich banker's (I've never seen a poor banker) personal chauffeur for over ten years.

Tony's tragedy is that he hasn't had enough free time to make children, or at least "legal ones" as Mami whispered to me at another party for another pregnant cousin.

In our family, sometimes we had celebrations to celebrate the fact that nothing bad had happened in a long time.

Tony's wife, Rosa, kisses me on the cheek and sighs, "Ricky, you've finally got here. It's you and me against them. I've been doing my part."

It's a well-established, if undiscussed, fact in the family that I will have no children either.

Rosa finds this a more important link than I do, but it provides me an entry, or reentry, into the family.

Bells cut out of white tissue paper are taped everywhere so it feels like I'm inside a hot church.

My secret life is no secret anymore.

It's supposed to be my secret love.

Where is he?

Will I never sing: *eres tú / como el agua de mi …?*

Cousin Blanca walks into the living room, her body stuffed into a white Christian Dior yacht-dress, and rushes forward to embrace me.

"I told your mother this morning you would show up," she purrs. "Your parents told me that you wouldn't. That you had to go to the ballet or something that you—you know—you like to do."

"I like to do everything," I smile back. "That's how I get in trouble."

Rosa chokes and Blanca beams.

Sometimes I wish either of these women had been my mother.

"Where are Mami and Papi?" I ask.

"They'll be here. You know your mother. She's like a daughter of the tides. She only leaves the suburbs when there isn't any traffic. She wasn't that nervous when she was young. But who is young anymore? Not even you. I see gray hairs, hijo."

"That's because I am very good on some very bad nights." I feel drunk, strangely happy.

I like the sound of Spanish and English filling the room.

Some of the men are huddled, talking about the Cubs vs. The White Socks, that ancient argument where there are no clear-cut winners.

I join the women in the kitchen who are never more than a few steps away from the liquor.

I grab a beer, look at it in case it's on the latest boycott list— it's not!

Blanca hits my hand. "Put that back, you barbarian. I have a surprise for you."

She pushes me through the hallway into the dining room where a bar has been set up. "See something you like?"

I follow her gaze and see a handsome bartender. "Blanca, are you trying to get me in trouble?"

"Let's just say I'm trying to manage the trouble you're already in."

Jesus, I have a sudden taste for a cigarette even though I don't really smoke except when I'm drunk or nervous or sexed-out.

I rarely smoke.

I kiss Blanca. "Is this like a late graduation present?"

"It's up to you to make it a party. I know it's a fact the stud is suffering from a broken heart. So just keep it below the waist, you get me, huh? You'd be surprised what can crawl from down there to up here." She pounds her chest and then dramatically winks then walks away.

I savor the moment.

I feel as if I'm in *Brideshead Revisited*, but with a mambo soundtrack.

"Hola, hermano." I'm a fucking idiot, I think to myself.

Why am I calling such a stud my brother?

The bartender smiles back. "Are you my tip?"

I pull back. "What do you mean?"

"You're the Ricky that Blanca told me about."

I nod, "The little she knows to tell you."

He extends his hand, "I'm Pablo."

I hold his hand, "And I'm very happy that you are Pablo."

He breaks into a smile. "Ah, they warned me that you could be charming."

I smile back. "This is going to sound crazy, but I feel happy today. I mean, just being with my family—look at these criminals. I'm ... here and you're...."

"Also ... happy."

"Right," I wink back. "Happy."

"But you haven't asked me about my broken heart!"

"Tell me about your broken heart," I ask even as I offer my best *GQ* scowl.

Pablo gestures toward a drink, "You're too sober and I'm working."

"Can I ask just one thing?"

"As long as it's not the kind of question that is too inspirational."

"Was he Spanish or American?"

"He was Spanish-American. A Latino. I only sleep with our kind. Who do you sleep with?"

The robot in me can't be stopped once again. "Usually myself."

Pablo puts his hand over mine. "Look, I've been hearing about you for nearly a month. And you are handsome. And you might even be sweet. I don't want to talk about me, OK? I want to talk about spending next summer in Madrid. Or some other adventure we might have. Stupid, right?"

I cock my head. "Are you a professional bartender?"

He shrugs, "I'm licensed. God, that makes me sound like James Bond, no? Did you see Rob Lowe, no wait, it was Tom Cruise in that terrible movie where he serves drinks in the Caribbean?"

"No, but I'll have to rent it now."

Rosa shows up. "Sorry to interrupt whatever this is but I need your help. The uncles are arguing about who will be godfather to our children."

Pablo points, "You two....?"

I shake my head, "No, it's a joke...."

Rosa yells, "We're two of a kind."

I'm dragged off into the living room.

I wave goodbye to Pablo and he waves back.

Forgive me this literary theft, but I'm surfing one of Virginia Woolf's waves and drunk on adrenaline: the waves, the waves.

Uncle Tony grabs me, "Am I or am I not your favorite uncle?"

I nod my head, "No."

Everyone laughs.

Uncle only pats me on my back, "America is still a land of choices, right?"

"Right," I laugh. "But you're always going to be my uncle. I have no choice!"

Uncle Tony playfully pushes me away and I watch the conversation slowly descend into a series of private concerns and confessions.

I can't help but think of Uncle Rachel and wonder what he is doing right now, at this very moment.

How many times have I tried to find him but it seems he has legally changed his last name too.

A transvestite in the family still has no place at the table during prayers, for our god is a jealous god and wants the spotlight all to himself.

Ask me about Spanish men I admire and I'll tell you of my Uncle Rachel, he who taught me how to dance to Aretha Franklin records, whose last words to me before he disappeared (los lost desperados in America): *Honey, I'm taking a slow boat to China and I may never see you again but think of me each time you open a fortune cookie.*

Those were his last words.

Then he was gone.

I wonder if I'll disappear just like that someday.

I need a new drink, a new bartender.

Funny word—"bartender."

Tender bar.

Father Time, love me tender and I'll be so good to you.

I think of escaping my family, of making my way back to Little Jim's and be picked up.

I want to be seduced tonight and not be the seducer.

I avoid Pablo, feeling as unsexy as an old bean burrito in a 7-Eleven microwave.

2.

I call Pablo and he meets me at the Chicago Diner, a trendy vegetarian restaurant blocks from the bars.

I'm a creature of habit, feeling safe only with the familiar, the explored, the tamed.

Christopher Columbus I am not.

I always have to know where the emergency exit is in the theater, the skyscraper, the airplane, and on first dates.

Little Jim's is two blocks from here and French Kissing is three.

Pablo shows up, looking a little older than he did at the party.

Perhaps that's because he is dressed more informally, in a jeans and a tank top.

Or maybe I'm just sober.

We smile at each other, stumble through orders, and face each other without saying much of anything.

He breaks the silence. "So your lovers—Americans?"

I smile back, but not so as to reveal much of anything. "You and I are Americans, too."

Pablo laughs and the tension breaks.

I like this man, although I don't know if I can love this man.

Why am I thinking about this over lentil soup, with a side of hand-shredded carrots?

He says, "When I was young I wanted to change the colors of my eyes. I wanted them to be sea blue."

I stare at his brown eyes, the eyes of a Marc Anthony before his encounter with destiny.

God, I have to stop reading personal ads.

I smile, "There are contacts for that now."

Pablo shrugs. "But I've changed. I came to realize that blue eyes wouldn't help me look like James Dean."

"I wanted to look like Sal Mineo, the smart one in *Rebel Without a Cause*."

Pablo pats my hand. "At least, you pick a dark hero."

"So what do you think?"

Pablo understands. He shakes his head. "It won't work. You, hijo, are too Americanized to live in my world. You know your family's party. Well, I belong there."

"I don't."

Pablo plays at twirling his pretend mustache. "And someday you'll succeed.

And you'll get away from them, too."

"What do you mean?"

"Ricky, I watched you watch them. I'm not even sure if you know how far away you've placed everyone from you."

I must have been crazy, but I just put my right hand in his crotch and rubbed him.

"I'm right here, baby."

Pablo lifts the hand, kisses the open palm and puts it gently in my own lap. "No matter how you try, you can't make the United States your real bed. You'll be Puertorriqueño again soon. I'm not talking about your body. I'm sure it knows how to sleep almost anywhere."

There is a pause and we're both laughing.

I feel so good.

I want to love this man.

"I want to love you, Pablo."

"I want to love you too, Ricky, but...."

I stop him from talking.

The dinner is excellent as usual.

I walk Pablo to Belmont Avenue and flag down a taxi for him, but before he enters it I kiss him slowly on the lips.

His hands wrap around my hips.

He pulls me to him.

We can't let go.

We don't let go.

I jump into the taxi and we go to his place near the Taco Bell in Andersonville.

We walk up the stairs past stoners in black T-shirts and underwear munching on tacos.

I think how the neighborhood looks like a Mexican Disneyland.

Pablo's apartment is crazier than I thought it would be because he seemed so damn polite and not the free spirit he feels free to be at home.

There are cacti painted on the wall; orange chairs are all over the place.

They're like pumpkins that no one will carve with human faces.

There are different colored light bulbs in the lamps throughout his place.

Pablo has filled an aquarium with broken wine glasses.

"Souvenirs of parties?" I ask in an amused voice, "or glass slippers that didn't fit?"

He gives me a look that makes him look like a brat, a mischievous little boy, a sideshow barker.

I thank Pablo for being my new brother, though I want and need him to be my lover.

I thank the men whose names I don't remember for giving me memories I'll never forget.

We mess up his place as our shadows rub against each other.

Making love with him is both silly and beautiful.

His brown skin covers me and it feels like I'm falling into the sun head first.

I wake up at midnight, my heart racing.

I look at the man next to me and Pablo looks uncannily like me; we're not twins, but we do look as if we come from the same planet.

I wake him up and insist we walk naked to his balcony.

"Los vecinos will call the cops, hombre," he half-protests.

"Fuck your neighbors," I growl.

"Dios, you're not going to be very faithful, are you, Ricky?"

He pulls me to him and soon I get him to look out at a city of lights.

Chicago, Chicago, Chicago.

We don't say anything.

We don't need to speak in Spanish or English about this moment as the weight of his body and mine are burdens we share.

Puerto Rico, my heart's devotion, let it sink back in the ocean.

I quote musicals at the worst times.

Hell, whatever scars I might have are only causes of celebration—that I've made it to the present, this now which is as naked as we are.

Pablo asks me where the North Star is but what do I know of space, of cosmic forms?

I kiss him slowly and he rubs his face against me.

I don't care if we are ghosts among ruins.

Right now, we're dreaming without even having to close our eyes.

"What will happen to us in the morning?" I stutter.

"That's a million years away," he whispers.

"But in the morning?"

"We'll see."

I nod my head.

In daylight, one can trust one's eyes.

In the dark, the body knows the route to survival.

We have instincts that have developed within us after millions of years of living and dying on Earth.

I become cold and we go back to bed where earlier our forms have been etched out in the sheets.

Our desires are explicit.

3.

Over the next year, Pablo and I become friends and stop sleeping with each other.

I'm a little surprised one March night to see him waiting for me as I stagger home from Little Jim's.

I'm alone, broke, and tired of my clothes smelling like smoke.

I smell like a goddamn fireman; the bars are becoming more and more like the hearts of volcanoes.

The truth is that I spent most of the night hugging the jukebox.

I didn't really want sex.

I do right now.

Only, it's Pablo who is here and we are just amigos.

Pablo is as gone as I am, but I sense he is here for a safe place from some internal storm.

He loves my apartment because if you open up the balcony door you can smell Lake Michigan.

Not that you can see it!

My building is one of the last rental units in the lake shore area of New Chinatown.

Daily, I see yuppies shopping for $100,000 condos right in this building.

Soon I will have to move out, replaced by a young banker, a pretty actor, a successful photographer, or a dedicated accountant.

"Hola, El Cid," I smile. "Come inside. If you want to be cold, I'll put some ice in your wine."

He follows me inside, holds me, takes a deep breath.

"What are you doing?" I ask gently.

He holds me even harder. "I want to never forget how you smell like. The nose is one way that a poor man takes his revenge on a rich man's garden."

"Sit down. You're drunk."

"Ricky, you've been trying to pick someone up tonight. Why don't you take the bull by the horns instead? You know what I mean?"

Many glasses of wine later, we stop talking.

We grow sullen as we next finish off the rum.

Maybe this is what I miss most about not having a lover anymore: two bodies in one space not having to say anything to each other.

Pablo is still young, too young to be this unhappy. "So why are you here tonight?"

He becomes animated, as if a spell has been broken.

"You know about Chino. I mean, you know he's dead. You went to his funeral. They never caught the guys who did it, you know."

I move over by him. "I know, honey. Chino's probably in heaven looking down on us right now. Jerking off, I hope."

Pablo pushes me away. "Ricky, he tried awfully hard to go to hell."

We say nothing for the next ten minutes.

Chino stole Pablo from me even though Pablo was never mine.

My family asks about Pablo although they are afraid that if I find a companion then I will demand for them to treat us as a couple.

A couple of thugs.

A couple of what?

Pablo starts talking and I know it's going to be one of his monologues; I'm right but first, "Stop, let me piss and get bigger glasses for the vodka."

He follows me into the bathroom. "Why do you always know the right thing to say to me?"

"Pablo, a man needs his privacy sometimes."

"I've seen you at the Belmont Rocks doing God knows what. It was hard to tell from where I was but your butt...."

I zip up.

Glasses, vodka, ice, radio tuned to a classical station.

It's the *New World Symphony*; I'd laugh at the selection but Pablo might think I'm laughing at him.

He speaks slowly, deliberately. "It's my anniversary. Chino has forgotten all about me. The dead are putas, no. We went out just a couple of months. Then he got killed. And today is the fifth month anniversary of our first date. Chino was something special. That's why he got stolen from me. You liked him, I know you did because you didn't make jokes around him. You listened to him. Not anymore. Chino doesn't have a tongue. He doesn't have hands. He doesn't have those beautiful legs. He doesn't have a cock. He doesn't have a neck I wanted to bite tonight like I was Dracula or something."

He cries so hard that he is no longer saying words and I hold him.

Pablo's Chino was killed in a drive-by shooting.

He had been in the wrong place and in the wrong time.

Pablo's Chino.

Will I never belong to anyone?

I don't know what to say and end up making Pablo angry with these words, "Honey, you celebrate the sixth month, a year, twenty five years. But the fifth month, well...."

"Ricky, we have five fingers on each hand. Five. You should know. You jerk-off enough. You should know that five is important. Five. Five."

He paces the room like a trapped animal.

I open the balcony door. "Take a deep breath."

Pablo almost says something, stops and takes a long look into my tired face.

He then takes that deep breath.

"Lake Michigan!" I prompt. "There are some things you can't see even if they're there."

Pablo leans forward, throws his glass of vodka in my face.

Startled, I fall back. "What?"

"I want to lick it off."

He does and we end up kissing.

"Let's just sleep tonight, OK?"

Pablo nods.

"Sometimes, Ricky, I have sex with a guy just to sleep next to him. To breathe in the air he's just breathed out."

I push him towards the bedroom. "You're sick and you are the most perfect friend for me."

"I think I'm going to be sick in the morning."

"If you're human," I add.

He whispers in my ear, "I love you, Ricky Ricardo, Jr."

"I wish you did."

I put Pablo to bed and he floats away to some safe place in his head.

Why do I always feel like I'm being left behind?

Again.

My body is my true family.

My soul is the orphan that I've adopted.

My mother and father are sleeping in each other's arms and why can't I have the same refuge?

Is my Uncle Rachel going to make his cameo in a séance soon?

Again, I'm alone.

I am no loner and that is my tragedy.

I can't sleep.

I want to guard my friend against some invisible enemy tonight.

I sit on the couch, listening to my neighbors argue about alternative music not being alternative since it's so mainstream now.

Stupid shits.

I shake off my blue mood by thinking of someone I slept with (Did he even have a name?) who stayed over on a night when these very neighbors were going for each other's throats.

My boyfriend (who hadn't been a boy in a long time) cooed, "They sound like jazz musicians without instruments."

He didn't know what a poet he was.

I remember him listening to the arguing couple some more, cocking his head like a dog that is left alone very often.

"Just listen to them go up and down the scale, baby."

I remember that much of him.

I still appreciate that much of him.

Is love possible?

I don't remember orgasm with him, just that moment listening to the neighbors.

Curious how the body is an amnesiac.

Are we all men of the mancha, our lances erect against windmills?

I'm glad to laugh at myself.

I turn on the television and fall asleep watching, of all things, *It's A Wonderful Life*.

It's not "La Vida Loca," is it?

Pablo talks in his sleep.

He talks in Spanish.

Angels gets wings on the television every time a bell rings.

Is it a wonderful life?

The blue midnight blows out my candles, one by one.

I end up in the dark, face down.

I spite the gods by dreaming about reality.

There Are No Pretty Girls At the Tabernacle
Marcel Devon

When Ma opens the door for me and Terry, it comes as no surprise that Pa is one of the first sights we see, enthroned in his usual place on the dingy brown sofa. His once-white T-shirt hikes up in rolls, exposing a pale, distended belly which one thick-fingered hand enthusiastically rubs. His other hand, complete with a half-moon of black axle grease under each nail, loosely grips a can of Coors. A Saturday afternoon college football game bleats from the old TV.

Ma smiles warmly at me. "Who's this with you, son?" she asks.

"Terry, my roomie from the U." That's the University of Houston. My major—Architectural Engineering. I've just finished my first year.

Terry thrusts out his hand and Ma takes it limply. "My pleasure, Terry," she says with little interest. She turns to yell over her shoulder to Pa. "Dan! Scotty's brought his roommate from the university with him. Name's Terry." Ma motions for Terry and me to enter. As we do, we hear Pa's commentary.

"'Terry?' Thatta boy or a girl? Sounds like a girl's name. Thatchyur girlfriend, boy?"

No one bothers to answer him. Instead, Ma escorts us into the kitchen where Terry and I plop into uncomfortable wooden chairs. Ma pours out two glasses of warm orange juice. "I'll make you boys some sandwiches," she says, opening the bread box and moving several loaves to the cracked countertop "Did Scotty tell you he's going to be a pastor?" she asks Terry. Uh-oh, here we go.

Terry looks to me for confirmation. I roll my eyes. Ma needs to maintain her delusions, apparently unable to accept the fact that her son is godless.

"He took that class in ... umm ... Christian Science," she begins.

"Philosophy of Religion," I interrupt.

"... and right off I could tell a big difference in his spirit after that. The Lord reached him through that class. Terry, you want white or wheat?"

"Huh? Oh, wheat, please," Terry says. Ma already knows I like my bread wheat, my PB creamy, and my jelly strawberry.

"When Scotty came up to visit during Christmas Break, we all saw a new boy. Creamy or Crunchy?"

"Creamy," says Terry.

"He's thinking about joining that big church in Dallas," Ma continues. "What's it called? Strawberry, grape, or cherry?"

"Grape, please."

"Yes, Lord!" Mom raises her eyes to the ceiling, swaying a little. "My son!" She lets her words fade and sets two plates of sandwiches on the table.

"Ma, Terry needs a place to stay for the summer," I tell her, picking the crusts off my bread.

"You should eat your crusts, Scotty. Well, Terry can stay here. It's the best part of the bread. You shouldn't waste it, honey, eat it. Is he gonna ... are you gonna be working, Terry?" she asks. Terry shrugs casually. "I mean, you'll have to buy your own stuff. See, Scott, Terry eats his crusts. Not rent, just pitch in with the groceries is all I ask." Terry nods between bites of sandwich.

Ma watches us eat in silence for a moment. Then: "Terry, you know how to work on cars?"

"Yes, ma'am."

"Then you can help out at the shop." Half of my parents' two-acre lot is a car shop.

I give mom a smile, my mouth full of PBJ, a small mountain of peeled crusts on my plate.

"Well, Terry," Ma says, picking up my empty glass for a refill, "we also have a great congregation nearby that you can go to. Our pastor—oh! Don't get me started." No one was trying to, I think to myself. "He's fire and brimstone, I tell ya! Sorta scares the young kids, but it's good for them to fear God."

As Ma goes deeper into her "Christian Mode," her sixth-grade education becomes ever more embarrassingly apparent. My head is bobbing on my neck like a hood ornament as I nod at things I struggle not to hear. At least this time I get the satisfaction of watching Terry's head wobbling in synch with mine.

"And he's a rowdy one, too!" Ma is saying. "Get t' jumpin' and hollerin' and speakin' in tongues! Lord's always there with the pastor. You can feel it in your heart. Ain't that right, Scotty?"

I don't answer.

"Lord all *mighty*!" she says. "I can feel the Spirit as we speak! You'll just love Pastor Rick. He went to U of H, too. Maybe you know him?" Here it comes. Terry feels it coming, too, as tangible as the taste of peanut butter against the roof of his mouth. "Are you saved, Terry?"

Squirming on the hook, Terry looks to me, pleading with his eyes for me to help him off. I like the show, but I also like Terry, so I do.

"To tell you the truth, Ma, Terry's going through some real hard times right now. His fiancée just ran off with someone else." I lean toward her over the table and whisper conspiratorially. "A Negro."

Ma gasps. Suddenly she's full of warmth and sympathy for Terry's plight. Terry, meanwhile, is displaying his very best trying-to-be-brave face, a product of the drama class where we met. My fable continues.

"You can imagine how much it's upset him," I say. "He was really in love with her. And, to make matters worse, Ma, she'd been fornicating with the Negro the whole time Terry thought she loved him!" With difficulty I manage not to smile in satisfaction. I knew, if I tried hard enough, I could fit "fornicate" into this speech.

"And Ma...." I lean even closer. "The Negro Terry's fiancée ran off with—it was another girl!"

I might as well have punched Ma in the solar plexus. She's choking and wheezing out her sounds of protest and outrage.

My mind wanders to Pastor Rick, whose favorite sins are fornication and sodomy. I managed to cover them both. Ma, meanwhile, despises lesbians and is convinced that Tipper Gore, Janet Reno, and Hilary Clinton are in a kinky sex triangle. "That's why she doesn't care if Slick Willie sleeps with his interns," she has explained to me in the past, as confident as if she were declaring her discovery that the earth was round.

"So, Ma," I continue when she catches her breath. "I decided I should bring Terry home with me—to get him away from those disgusting girls." That statement is actually completely true, but not for reasons I'm about to tell Ma.

"Anybody want a cold soda?" Ma ventures. As she stands to go to the refrigerator, one of the dogs in the back yard begins to yelp. In a flash, Pa is up from his chair, his bouncing belly exposed under his beer-stained T-shirt. The floor shakes as Pa stomps to the rear door and straight-arms it, causing the door to fly back and crash against the side of the house. We listen as he kicks the shit out of one of the dogs, fuming and snarling, cursing the name of every god ever invented by the human mind. Ma covers her ears, squeezing her eyes shut against the blasphemy.

As quickly as it began, it's over. Pa returns from the back yard, stopping to retrieve another beer from the refrigerator, which stands open because Ma has frozen in the act of getting our sodas. "Scotty," he says, "his brow furrowing, "where's your girlfriend?"

The three of us look at him stupidly. He snorts and trudges back to the sofa. The cushions hiss violently as his three hundred pounds displace the air inside.

Ma puts the three sodas on the table, one for each of us. "As disgusting as it is, Dan," she says, popping open her can of RC, the squelching sound a tiny echo of the sofa's more violent version, "you don't have to take our Lord's name in vain! Swear to your heart's content if you want, but I will not tolerate you blaspheming the Lord!"

Pa's only response is a belch. Ma covers her face with her hands. I see the edges of her ears turn red, as they do when she is about to cry.

"Ma," I ask, "*what's* disgusting?"

"Those damn dogs!" she huffs, rising to pace the sticky linoleum. Her "inside" sandals slap against her heels with every step. "We got four boys, and one of 'em, the one we call Popper, can't tell the difference from a boy and a girl. I told Pa a long time ago to get a bitch, but Popper decided he can't wait on a bitch to come along so he's just gonna make himself one outta one of the other boys. It ain't natural. Like those Catholic priests going sebb-i-late."

"Celibate."

"Yes. Just ain't natural. It ain't in God's plan—that's why they molest those altar boys all the time. Same goes for the dogs, too. Pa says, 'Get 'em fixed,' and I say, 'We can't afford to, Dan,' and that's that."

"So Pa beats Popper?" I ask.

"You heard the other dog whimperin'. What's he supposed to do?"

"How much can it cost to neuter them? Just for Popper it can't be that much."

"Eighty bucks if we only get Popper done, but Pa says we have to do 'em all because it ain't fair if we only fix Popper."

"So why don't you just give Popper away?"

It must be half-time, because Pa has apparently been listening in on our conversation. "You know, we oughta get rid of that faggot mutt at that. Fact, Bernice has been bugging me forever to have one of these piece-of-shit dogs. I'll take 'im over to her house and she can deal with old fudge-packing Popper from now on." He digs a finger into his navel, wriggling it around before withdrawing it and wiping it on his shirt. "Shoulda done that a long fucking time ago. Dunno why I didn't."

In my mind I give the answer I would never say out loud. *Maybe it is because—although you can recite every college and NFL football player's jock-strap size; know how to dismantle any model vehicle and reassemble it, bolt by bolt, practically while blindfolded; can discourse on the differences between ale, lager, malt, stout, and bitters—you dropped out with Ma in junior high in order to become a mechanic in East Texas and have never been much of a one for taking action to solve your problems.*

Pa continues to watch the games, flipping through the channels whenever he is bored, while Terry, Ma, and I sip sodas at the kitchen table. Ma snaps out of "Christian Mode" and moves into "Gossip Mode," which I like better since it means Terry and I get to learn all our neighbors' dirty secrets.

First, Ma is absolutely certain that the teenaged girl across the street has had no less than three abortions. The girl's older brother had to leave town because he got two junior high girls pregnant, so that kind of behavior runs in the family. The neighbors to the right of our place are definitely swingers because another couple visits them for entire nights and all the lights go off as soon as they arrive. "With children in the house!" Ma exclaims. I suspect it must trouble her that they darken the house, making it impossible for her to watch.

The people on the corner smoke pot and continuously play loud "black devil music" (Ma is convinced that heavy metal is both African and Satanic in origin). The family across from them is a bunch of crack dealers who have frequent orgies.

"I'm sure their kids participate," I offer. Terry cuts his green eyes at me, but Ma only nods distractedly. Her densely curled bouffant, shellacked into hardpan by repeated applications of hair spray, rides her skull like a blonde helmet.

Down the street lives a married woman who must be a prostitute because of her miniskirts, high heels, and makeup. Ma believes the alleged whore made a move on Pa, but he refuses to talk about it. Ma moves on to other topics.

It enrages her that schools are mandated by law to teach sex education yet don't teach how God created the world in six days. "It's a liberal conspiracy," she says. "I know it. Because they're also teaching kids that homosexuality is acceptable. Yes! It's okay to be an abomination unto the Lord, and anyone who disagrees is a bigot. And they're even brainwashing babies still in the cradle!" She's preaching now, and the tendons in her neck stand out like tent cords. "Teletubbies! Ever heard of them? Well, the purple one is queer. You can tell because of the way he just prances around. Plus he carries a purse! And, Scotty, this is a show watched by babies and toddlers!"

I keep bobbing my head, tuning out, as best I can, Ma's diatribes about the things she claims to hate yet is obsessed with, about the wickedness she spends hours observing throughout the dusty blinds. I recall how Ma was among the group of local women who were scandalized by the "oversized" bulge in the pants of a Sam Houston statue downtown. The same women who scaled the monument with ladders and ground down the offending swelling. But now she has moved on to abortion.

"Murder is murder," she's saying. "In those sexual education classes they teach ten-year-old kids that it's all right to kill the unborn. Get this—as a form of birth control! The world is overcrowded, they say, so it's not only okay to do it, it's necessary!"

I don't bother to remind her of her belligerent support for the state of Texas's frequent application of the death penalty. Or of how, each time an unlucky, unforgiven murderer is executed, she drives to Huntsville to be among the throngs of picnicking "Christian" families carrying posters that read, "Score One For The State."

"Ma," I interrupt, "Terry and I need to fix up our room. We'll be back down in a little while, okay?"

The relief on Terry's face is a bit too evident. I wonder if he's still as eager as he was to attend the Pentecostal Tabernacle with Ma each Sunday for an entire summer. We excuse ourselves, thank Ma for the food and drinks, and walk past Pa, beached and immobile upon the sofa.

"Nice to meet you, sir," Terry says. A waste of breath. Pa does no more than grunt with impatience as we momentarily obstruct his view of spandex-clad college boys butting helmeted heads and tossing around an animal-hide bag.

We reach my old room, which, to Ma's credit, is spotless. Terry leaps onto the bed, test-driving the springs, grinning lecherously. I lock the door behind me.

"I'm sorry about all that, Terry," I tell him. "It's really embarrassing. Ma's a little lost in space, and Pa...."

"Did you have to tell her that crap about my girlfriend running off with some black girl?"

"Don't act like you didn't get a kick out of seeing the look on her face. Besides, she's got mucho sympathy for you now, Terry. You'll be her project for the summer. Sure you can handle the Tabernacle tomorrow?"

"Sure," he says without hesitation. "I'll just find some girl and give her the same sob story you told your mom."

"No, you won't," I answer back, perhaps a little too forcefully. "This summer, you're all mine. We agreed, remember? I'm not sharing you with any more girls."

Terry motions me to him where he sits on the edge of the bed. He wraps his arms around my hips, butting his head against my crotch. He gives me the same, charming shrug he gave my mom when she asked him whether he had a job. I already know I'll have to keep an eye on him.

"What would your mom say if she caught us like this?" Terry asks as he unbuckles my belt.

"She won't."

"What if?" he insists, sliding my zipper down.

"Saw what Pa did to Popper, didn't you?"

"Well.... When I go to the Tabernacle with your mom tomorrow, I'll make a good show of looking at all the pretty girls."

"No, 'cuz then Ma will just think you're a pervert."

"I am," Terry laughs, hooking his thumbs into the waistband of my jeans and my shorts and shucking the whole package down to my ankles.

"Anyway," I tell him, "there are no pretty girls at the Tabernacle."

SKINS
Rick Laurent Feely

> *"Let me also wear such deliberate disguises, rat's coat, crow skin, crossed staves in a field...."* (T. S. Eliot, The Hollow Men)

I slap him across the face.

"But Rat," he says to me.

He's got a slippery voice that Crow. It's good for telling stories, or singing whiskey-slurred lullabies in those haunting hours between night and morning. When you finally nod off you can still hear it, subliminal and ceaseless, like the backbeat in a song. This time I'm not listening.

I look up, away, anywhere. The sky is the color of a grainy photograph left too long in the back pocket of your only pair of jeans. Jeans cured to ancient blue and frayed at the knees. One day you reach in, lookin' for a quarter, maybe a cigarette butt, and you come across this photo you been keeping, but you can't tell what it's a picture of anymore. That's what the sky looks like. A memory condemned to a smear of gray. Somehow the sunlight bleeds through, so I know it ain't yet night.

My gaze jumps from grainy sky to duct-taped boots to the tarpaper rooftop where he's sprawled, all jutting ribs and skinned elbows and black feather pants. His eyes are twice as black and just as shiny. So is what's left of his hair, a few clumps hanging ropy from the top, hanging like his wings would if he had any. I watch them flutter, a feeble, first-instinct response, like raising your arm before a machete. Makes me wanna hold him, promise it'll all be okay. It won't. He looks back up at me, underlip caught between his teeth. Crow.

Get up," I says. His eyes gloss over like spit-polished thrift store buttons. Like maybe he don't wanna see me, so he'll see through me instead. He's got an arrogant nose that Crow, sharper and straighter than a switchblade. A slag-like spurt of blood from one nostril. He licks it away.

"Rat. Please." I flinch at the word. My gaze scurries over the rooftop's cinderblock edge, reels at the dizzying drop that ends in a gutted alley twenty-one stories below us. There, squad cars howl red blue spirals and circle like wild dogs before a kill. I close my eyes. The pressure builds behind them, like a pipe before it busts. I wish I could believe.

Runnels of fresh sweat cut tracks beneath my leather, through last week's dirt and cheap cologne. "I'm sorry," I says.

And I am. Like it matters.

Let me tell you 'bout Crow. I was tanked on vodka and methedrine the night I found him on Crescent Boulevarde. He wasn't hustling then, just hanging out. All the boys wore jeans and maybe leather. He had on them black feather pants, and more Mardi Gras beads than a Bourbon Street lamppost. It must not a been Mardi Gras or I woulda been drunker. I thought he was a boy, but I weren't too sure. He's like that, Crow. He wears his skin in such a way as you can't tell, smudging the lines everyone else takes for granted. But I guess that's what I was drawn to. That sense of limitless possibility. Me, I stay close to the ground.

But the one thing I was sure of. He was beautiful and outta place, like somethin' sprouted from out a crack in the sidewalk. I felt my tail twitch, even though I didn't have one. I told myself it was just the drugs. Maybe even I believed it.

Thing is, most of the other queers I'd met that weren't on the boulevard were calling councils, begging the city for a few crumbs of civil rights. They wore their skins beneath their suits, if they still wore them at all. They came down to the strip sometimes, bearing gifts. The condoms found their way into greedy pockets. Sometimes we even remembered to use them. The instruction pamphlets, crumpled in junk-hungry fists, fell unread into the gutter. They always brought us more.

A couple of them invited me to council once, asked my name. I says my name's Rat. That's not a name, they says. Well that was it. They could keep their votes and rights and suits as far as I cared. I cussed 'em all as the worst kinda whores. They says, child you're the one we found on Crescent Boulevarde. I says I guess it takes one to know. Well I never went back to council after that, and I avoided them when I saw them in the street. Unless they were handing out condoms.

But this one wasn't getting into any cars and he wasn't a suit. More like a bright tangle of cheap beads and smeared lipstick and ragged black feathers, flinging gestures through the swears and spit and sully like he were fearless, or maybe just reckless. I saw through his beads, saw through to his wings, which trembled beneath my fingers later that night in my tunnel beneath the Atlantic building. Mouths running hot with rich, narcotic secrets. Skins rubbed raw by feather and fur.

"I love you," he says, afterwards.

I was digging through my crumpled jeans for a cigarette. My stomach dropped, like when that sixth-precinct rookie hit me in the ribs with his nightstick. But then I got this crazy idea that if I didn't say something, he'd maybe disappear. Don't ask me how. It ain't like he could fly.

Maybe it was just the skins we wore. But when I looked up from my cigarette and into his black-bulb eyes, I saw they weren't at all afraid. Of me, of anything. I thought, that is one reckless Crow. And suddenly I wanted to be reckless with him, wanted to shed the shit-skin of my only pair of jeans, festoon myself with Mardi Gras beads, part the spit-strewn sidewalks and lay him like a sacrament beneath the thrumming neon lights.

But I couldn't. Maybe it was the fear that started talking. Fear of the swears and spit and sully, fear of a nightstick in the ribs. Maybe it was that fear what told him flaunting his feathers would get him nothing but killed, that the going price of love was sixty bucks an hour. That he should ask for seventy and let them bargain him down. You ain't in bum-fucked Kansas anymore, Dorothy.

It's funny how the softest, most secret noises sound crazy loud down in the tunnels. His sobs echoed something eerie, like when an animal dies. It was so dark it was safe for me to reach out in silent apology. I held him soft and raw and shaking naked 'til he'd cried himself to sleep, skin sticky with tears and sweat and god knows, maybe blood. I mean, I wasn't sure whether or not he was a virgin. It was too late to ask.

"Y'ever have rat dreams?" he says.

This was weeks later. He'd been staying with me in the tunnel. It was a while 'til he stopped feeling claustrophobic. Or maybe he just stopped complaining.

Hiking down to the beach was his idea. My knuckle grip turned white when he stood up on the Ferris wheel, spread his wings. We fed each other cotton candy, took our pictures in the one-dollar booth. Then we climbed down the broken spine of boardwalk. Crow, he ain't so good at climbing, so he jumped, and I caught him, and we fell laughing in the sand. There wasn't a soul or skin around. Molt-stricken seagulls fought over scraps, and oil-slick tide pools sucked at empty plastic bags. The ocean hissed a fierce brown spray of sewer and salt.

"Rat dreams, huh?"

I picked a half-smoked cigarette from the sand. It was crusted with lipstick. I shoved it between my teeth, lit a match. Maybe I'd scavenge enough to fill my pockets. The sky was the color of the sea. The one bled into the other, erasing the horizon. I thought it was goddamn beautiful, like something you'd see on a flyer for the art museum. Only real.

Crow crouched down, plucked a feather from the sand, and I saw then that his fist was full of them. And I thought he had been scrounging for cigarette butts with me. I wrapped my arms around him 'til we stood chest to chest. Skin to skin. His hair was in two braids, like a schoolgirl, or a warrior. His thoughts soared above us, picking at things I couldn't see. I knew when we got back to the tunnel he would tell erratic stories by the flicker of a match while I fixed us up. Sad, wild stories of talking beasts and ancient forests and doomed love. They couldn't shake the acrid chemical reek of boiled meth and scorched tinfoil. There's not much that can.

The gulls wheeled. His eyes followed. They looked dull and dry, like he'd forgotten to polish them. Face pinched and eyes unpolished he looked more like a rat himself—not the kind you'd find in a tunnel, but some child's sleek, miserable pet.

"I mean like, do you ever dream that you're a rat?" he asked.

The gulls were calling and he called back, but his call was something awful, like a throat full of twigs

"I don't have dreams," I says.

It wasn't like I turned him out or anything. I just didn't make enough for the both of us to cop. He didn't wanna be picking scabs all hellish night while I got straight. So it was his choice, as much as it ever is anyone's. I just made the connections, from skin to cash to meth to skin. A closed circuit, like this tattoo I saw once of a snake eating its tail. Ain't no end or beginning.

I don't remember when it was he got the lice. We'd been together less than half a year, but it's different out here. A day on the street is like a week anywhere else. A week is a month; a month is a year. A year is forever....

The lice eggs clumped in the crook between his braids, a live colony speckled white and itching mad. He crouched before me on a broken milk crate behind the 7-Eleven as I cut them free with my switchblade. I could count every button of his spine. The braids fell flapping to the blacktop, the lice scattered, the spine sagged. I tried to keep the blade's edge from touching his scalp, but we'd run out of needles sometime before sunrise and my hands jerked in withdrawal, laying open skin to blood. The blood sluiced tributaries down the shorn nape of his neck. My tongue caught the runnels, lapped him clean like I'd seen an alley cat do to all her kittens, but he only bled faster. Head wounds are like that.

We headed down to a new needle exchange at Thirteenth and Washington. It'd been awhile since I'd seen Crow in the stark glare of daylight. The sharp spokes of his hipbones fought with gravity to keep his pants on. Most of the feathers had fallen off. Long fingernails scratched at the sores that clung to his lips. He'd tried to cover them with lipstick. It made him look both sultry and ridiculous, but I wasn't gonna tell him. He was still beautiful, in a relentless sort of way, like an autumn leaf before the wind rattles it free.

We straggled down Thirteenth Street, past flat glass stares and hidden slurs, his dirty fingers laced in mine. I didn't care who saw. The van where they gave you fresh works squatted on one corner, across from a Dunkin Donuts and a twenty-one-story parking garage. Random street folks scuttled toward it, past skyscrapers and wind-blown bags and pinstripes driving silver bullet BMWs, too rich or too bored to follow common traffic laws. I thought of when I'd light a candle down in the tunnels, how some of the bugs were drawn toward it. Funny how only the ones with wings felt the pull, fluttered dangerously close. The smart ones scurried for cover, slid quick and deep into cracks to finish out their lives in subterranean obscurity. When you don't have to look at them, it's easier to pretend they ain't there.

He didn't wanna go with me to the van to get the needles. He's a shy one, that Crow. I dug a fistful of loose change outta my pocket. The window of the Dunkin Donuts was tinted dark. It turned our reflections to faceless shadows, one all shoulders and stubble and scuffed leather, the other a skinny smudge of beads and tattered black.

"Here." I spilled nickels and pennies into the cup of his palm. "Go get a coffee or somethin'. I won't be long."

I crossed the avenue and got in line behind a woman old enough to be my grandmother, but she was wearing hot pink jeans and plastic hair clips. Made her look like a wrinkled little girl with knowing eyes. The eyes were pus-yellow shot with red, like a sunset. I looked away. My knuckles tapped a nervous rhythm on the leg of my only pair of jeans.

The guy handing out the fresh needles smiled at me in recognition. I didn't know who the hell he was. A terrible ridiculousness struck me, that he coulda been someone I tricked with once, and my face went near bloodless at the thought. Then I remembered.

"It's Rat, isn't it?"

That was why I didn't recognize him. When people dress in suits, you never really see them. Today he slummed in pleated khakis and a green polo shirt. It looked as if it'd never seen a stain. The button pinned above his left pec caught my eye with white block letters. *Plant A Tree.*

I chewed the inside of my lip, turned my eyes to cobble.

"I'm Matt," he says to me. Pretending not to notice my curled lip, slit eyes. I guess that's the polite thing to do when you're a suit. Expert hands shove condoms and vacuum-wrapped syringes into brown paper. Like a check-out clerk at some fantasy headshop where no one has to pay. I let out a bark of laughter. For some reason, he doesn't look at me like I'm insane.

"Listen, I'm sorry about what Gary said to you at council. He gets too big for himself sometimes, y'know? Thinks he's the king of Sodom." It was his turn to laugh alone now. "There's a council tonight at six.... We'll be opening a gay-specific drop-in center soon. Y'know, somewhere to watch TV, eat hot food, take a shower. You should stop by tonight to give us input. The Center for Civil Rights, first floor, second door on the left. Bring your friend with if you want."

He handed me the brown paper bag. "I'll see ya later, Rat."

I walked to the corner, wondering whether this Matt guy was hot for my tail or just retarded. Maybe it was neither, maybe he'd just got off a bus from Idaho or bum-fucked Kansas, maybe some other ludicrous place where people planted trees and voted and smiled too much at drug-addicted strangers. I realized I never even said anything back to him. What the hell was I supposed to say?

"Fucking faggot piece of shit!"

My head snapped up as if they'd called my name, but the fight was already in action and the name was not for me. I heard the sickening thwap of fists cracking connective tissue. The blond had on one of them amber Cuervo T-shirts they give you at Shenanigan's for your twenty-first birthday. The other wore a backwards baseball cap and a gut-ugly sneer. Maybe once he had been beautiful. They looked as big and dumb and angry as cattle.

I dunno why I noticed the one standing in a widening pool of spilled coffee last. Maybe because he was more like a shadow than an opponent, bird-boned and shrinking backward until the wall of the parking garage left him nowhere else to go. Maybe because he was absorbing all the light as they reflected it— black clothes, black tufts of hair, black eyes in a white face smeared lolly red with lipstick and blood. Crow.

My first thought was that he had it coming to him, but that didn't stop me from jerking forward into the street. Beetle-like cars honked and swerved, whished rushing past like racing monsters and I stutter-stepped back to the curb. Red light.

I watched powerless while drunken knuckles pummeled shots into his stomach. It bent him over double so he couldn't see the next blow coming from the side. Steel-toed shit-kickers met with a thunk against the flower stem of his spine. Crow staggered, raised both arms over his head like they would stop the blows, like they would fly him away, but of course they didn't and the fuckers just went for his torso. I felt almost responsible. I mean, I never thought to teach him how to fight.

There was the green light, arms piston pumping at sides, boots carrying me quick over blacktop and boulevard. There was the last one to hit him, knuckles busted and half out of breath, blond hair plastered with sweat against his forehead. Then there was the terrifying thrill of my adrenaline funneling into a fist, the satisfying crunch of cartilage beneath my knuckles, the sluggish spurt of blood from a nose that had been broken one too many times.

His breath popped like a busted condom. The one behind me hit me sharp in the kidneys, threw an arm across my throat. I slammed my heel into his shin, snapped my head back. Lips split warm like bruised fruit against my skull and the arm dropped.

But the blond had recovered. *Cocksucker*, he spat, nose bleeding and bent at a crazy angle. His fist met with my jaw something terrific. I heard a crack and blood burst on my tongue. I flailed, gulped air, tried to call for Crow, but something from behind hit me in the ribs first. I reeled gasping to my knees. My vision flickered like a broken neon light. I thought I heard sirens in the distance. Maybe my ears were ringing. Either way it was a bad sign. My hand went for the switchblade in my boot.

Someone yelped. The one in the baseball cap, cheek raked open. I swerved my gaze to Crow. His nails clumped with blood and shreds of skin. His eyes were polished, glinting bright with fear or madness. "You'll die of AIDS!" he shrieked. But I didn't get to see the guy's reaction. His friend kicked me in the head.

The world turned black around the edges, like a tunnel. I could see the blond guy's waist before me and beyond it the light at the end. No way I could let it end like this. No goddamn way. The blade trembled in my palm. They hadn't noticed. Blood dripped into my eyes, but it wasn't like I had to aim. I plunged it hilt deep into his belly, through the fragile cotton layer. Through the skin. A dark stain blossomed on his Cuervo T-shirt and my knuckles drowned in blood.

I staggered to my feet. Still gripping the knife in his guts. Bile rose into my throat. My tongue pushed it back down, pushed up against loosened teeth, and an even deeper loosening, the loosening of that crucial stitch that sets a sweater to unravel.

I wrenched the blade and tore it free. The blood gushed slippery and dark down his jeans, down my arm. His hand went to the wound, pressing in his slick guts. Everything stopped. The stabbed guy's eyes went wild with sudden clarity. He cursed beneath his breath. They all looked at me in vague horror and awe, jaws slack and eyes gleaming, like I'd done something impossible and wrong. Even Crow. Especially Crow.

The sirens wailed louder closer faster. I shoved blood-slick knife back into boot and drug Crow to his feet. There was nothing to say. We ran into the shelter of the parking garage, pounding blood and breath and bones, hurtling over the candy-striped gate and into the elevator's hull.

He looked supreme. Forget the bruise and blood and lipstick. Forget the feathers and the scabs. His eyes glittered with a frightening peace. I couldn't meet them.

"Rat," he began.

"Just press a goddamn button!"

His blood-caked fingernail touched plastic square twenty-one. Magic number when boys become men in smoky downtown bars, friends and fathers nudging amber bottles past their teeth down their throats chug it down nice and easy 'til they throw up die pass out fall over get up go out and beat up a faggot. The orange numbers glowing as the elevator moved.

I want to ask Crow how old he is but I'm too scared of the answer. Up on the rooftop anything seems possible, he could be sixteen, fourteen, ten, or older than this city. Like some fairy tale he wove us into while I was sleeping. The sun bleeds stronger through the sky's grainy photo paper lens, melts it open like a cigarette's hot cherry. The wailing sirens die away below us, but the lights still pulse their red blue skywrite. There's nowhere to hide up here, nowhere to disappear to.

I look over. Standing two feet in from the edge I can't see much, but I'm afraid to get too close. Crow's not. Gray roof meets with gray sky under a drizzling of sunlight, flecking it all with tiny spots of gold. The gold's already there, in the cement; it's just that it needs the light to bring it out.

When I turn back to Crow, he's gone.

"I love you," he says to me.

My head swivels to his voice. He stands on the concrete ledge, the sun shooting fiery rays at his form, highlighting blood and bruise and beads. The wind ripples through what's left of his hair and torn T-shirt, sets what few feathers he's got left to dancing. The panic sends my heart thudding like a terrific shot of speed. Neurons fire at machine-gun speed from brain to battered body. I lurch forward, duct-taped boots crossing a tarpaper forever and the beat of the blood in my mouth in my veins like the beating of wings in the distance. Open eyes mouth fists guts heart and I'm split open gushing like a cracked glass bottle.

He spreads his arms. His face is turned up toward the sun. Still beautiful.

I lunge. He rocks back on his heels. The scuffed black leather of my arm stretches between us. My fingers, slick with straight-boy blood, clutch at ropes of plastic beads. For one brief still of a second the beads hold against the weight of his body in the sky, before the strain of gravity pops them open to rattle free in my fist.

I want to fling myself after him, tell him all the things I could never bring myself to say. Tell him how beautiful he is, how it takes guts to be beautiful, how I would do anything, fight for him, die for him. It doesn't happen. My heart is beating, my lungs are breathing, I am alive.

I step back, close my fingers tighter around the beads. I can't bring myself to watch. I'm afraid to get too close, afraid of falling. I haven't had my fix. Spastic shrieks echo up from the passersby twenty-one floors below me.

The sun will not stop shining. My eyes tear. Mouth ratchets open to birth some sob or scream. Nothing comes out but I can hear it anyway, silent and spiraling and endless.

Crow will only distract them for so long. I must get moving. I sneak slowly back into the building, scurry quick down through the floors, between the cars, between the cracks. They'll never find me.

I'm out on the street six blocks away when I reach into my pocket for a cigarette. That's when my fingers slide across it. Edges stained rusty brown and torn ragged in one corner. I can't make out the image at first, but then I remember—the beach, the booth, the buck, the blinding flash. It's a picture of him.

Six o'clock. The Center for Civil Rights. My reflection in the plate-glass window. Leather jacket. Beaded necklace. Broken teeth. I push the door open, follow the hallway, second room on the left. A milling of people, gray and tan and pinstripe blue, faces aghast and who can blame them. I spot the khakis and green polo shirt, stop. Matt. His eyes blink in startled recognition, face pale with however much he knows. I mean, he was less than a block away.

He starts across the room. I want to run but I can't move. My tongue curls dead and limp behind loose teeth. Matt says something soothing. A Styrofoam cup of coffee appears like magic in my hand. My hand starts shaking. He takes the cup away.

"I'm so glad you could make it." He's using that voice that people do when they're trying to get their cat to come back in, but I can tell he really wants to help me. It's not that I don't want him to. I'm just not sure he can.

I don't know where to sit. The table is a circle. Ain't no end or beginning. It reminds me what I done. He was so unreal to start with. I shoulda never tied his arm off. Shoulda never let him trick. The pain stretches open its claws. I pull out a chair next to Matt's.

"We usually begin by going around and introducing ourselves," Matt explains. Sitting this close, I can see the scars the track marks left in the crook of his elbow. The scars look old, faded. I wonder if any of the others here have noticed. Doubt it. I guess it takes one to know.

"I'll go first," he says. "I'm Matt, and I'm facilitating this evening."

My turn.

I feel the beads beneath the dried blood, beneath my leather, against my skin. I remind myself that under all their suits their skin's the same as mine.

"My name's Rat," I says.

FINANCIAL AID
Wendell Ricketts

The guy sitting across the narrow table is a grim, efficient little queen, blinking at me through expensive glasses that feature a tiny YSL logo and stems no thicker than a cocktail straw. His pale green shirt is tight over his bird chest; his voice is tight; on the small card he has just given me, his handwriting is tight, with meticulously formed letters and every dot and comma in place.

I know his type because I've encountered them so many times before. I know he isn't going to let me do what I want. It doesn't matter that he's gay and I know it or that I'm gay and he knows it. I'm not one of his friends, and I'm certainly not someone he's ever noticed out in public, meaning at one of the clubs he frequents with his clique. If I did have the gall to show up at one of those places, I'm the guy they'd be laughing at behind their hands—hair-challenged, they'd say, because mine is long and shaggy and thick, and has never been "styled" in my adult life, unless you count whatever they do for you at SuperCuts. Right now, it's looking more than a little nappy, held down behind a bandana that I'm wearing to keep it from flying all over the place and not as a fashion statement. I worked at the bar until four in the morning, went home for a bowl of cereal and a pot of coffee, rode my bike to campus for my eight o'clock and ten o'clock classes, dropped off my already-late rent check, and then went home again for a three-hour nap before coming to campus one last time today to meet with this asshole. Who kept me waiting for forty-five minutes.

He's younger than me by at least a half-dozen years, but someone has given him the authority to disburse financial aid checks, and he has decided I can't have mine. "You have to have a current university ID," he keeps saying. I haven't gone to get one yet. It's the end of the afternoon on a Friday, and I won't have time to make it across campus, stand in that line, get my picture taken, wait for the photo to develop and the laminator to do its work, and then come back to the Financial Aid building which, for no good reason, closes on Fridays an hour earlier than all the other campus offices.

"But does the ID card really matter that much?" I ask. "If I show up over there, they still have to check my name on some computer record to make sure I'm a student or else they won't give me a card, right? Can't you do the same thing? I have my driver's license." I take out my license and extend it across the table. He ignores the object in my hand the way polite people ignore bad breath.

"Our computer system isn't networked with the admissions and records computers," he says.

"Well, couldn't you call and verify that I'm registered as a student?" I slide my license back into the plastic window in my wallet, massaging the frayed Velcro strips together until the closure holds.

"I'm not authorized to do that."

Now I know, and he knows that I know, that he could get authorized if he got off his ass and asked his supervisor, or he could be a nice guy and just give me the check. It's not like he'd be facing a lot of jail time for breaking that particular rule. But he isn't going to do it. He doesn't *have* to do it, I suppose is the sticking point. Plus the fact that I'm just not his kind. He decided on sight that he didn't like me, which is probably fair, because I decided I didn't like him, either. You can never tell, in situations like this, whether the other queen is being hateful because he's attracted to you, because he *isn't* attracted to you, or because he's suspects you have the nerve to be attracted to him.

He's looking at me now with his eyebrows lifted, the tips of his thin, pale fingers tented together. It's time for me to go; there's nothing more he can do.

I glance at the stiff paper rectangle he has handed me. It's an appointment card, imprinted with his name, inviting me to return on Monday at three p.m. to receive my check. *Sean Owens. Financial Aid Specialist.* Who is now calling my bluff. Will I stand up, raise my voice, demand that he find me someone else to talk to, thereby demonstrating that I'm the vulgar prole he thinks I am, or will I slink meekly away, letting him have a victory that means nothing to him but means a great deal to me?

The check he is holding but won't let me have will cover the check I wrote several hours ago for my rent. By Monday afternoon, there's a good chance my rent check will bounce, which isn't how I'd prefer to have things go with my landlord, who doesn't know me very well and isn't happy that I've been late with the rent for the last few months. The longest it was ever late was three days, but it might as well have been three years. "You know, we write the late-charge clause into the lease for a reason," he said today, as I held my check out to him.

"I know," I say, "and I'm sorry. You should go ahead and charge me if you need to." I'm holding the piece of paper hopefully between my thumb and forefinger, and he still hasn't taken his hands out of his pockets.

"No," he says, "no, I don't want to do that." He sighs like he's doing me the biggest favor in the world over twenty-five fucking bucks. "But please just try to get the rent here on time, okay?"

"Sure," I say. He sighs again, drags one hand out of his Dockers, folds my check in half without looking at it, and slips it into his pocket along with his fist.

After all that, having the check bounce would be ... inconvenient. Plus my landlord would definitely insist on the late penalty, and his bank and mine will both want their bounced-check charges.

The queen sitting across from me is about to cost me eighty bucks easy, which is more than a week's food budget. I could tell him this; maybe he'd even relent. But my stubbornness is blossoming. Why should I give him the satisfaction of hearing me explain my life? What right does he have, with his slinky, thousand-dollar Movado watch, to know that I'm broke? No doubt he collects such information, not because any individual piece of it is valuable, but because the accumulated mass of it is a physical souvenir, like an ear, that he can carry in a pouch above the cinder of his heart.

I stare at the floor. My Keds knockoffs are worn and pretty putrid, even for me—the tip of the right one is nearly black with grease from where I catch it, at least once a day, in my bike chain, which is coming loose around the derailleur. Both shoes are frilled with semi-dry mud: an afternoon downpour drenched the campus as I was leaving the house, and I'd taken a short cut to the Financial Aid building, riding through the soccer field and an unpaved parking lot next to the dorms in order to arrive on time for my appointment. I slouch down in my chair.

"Look," I say, lifting my head slowly so that my brown eyes are dead-on level with his gray ones. "I know you think that being a fag gives you the right to act like an officious little Nazi, but things are going to go different for you today from how they usually do." As I'm speaking I swing my right leg up under the table between us and prop it on the edge of his chair, placing my heel carefully between his legs. He tries to push back, but I've been watching him move slowly toward the wall as we talked, and he doesn't have more than a couple of inches to spare.

"So now you have a choice," I say calmly. "I'm going to count to three, and on three, one of two things is going to happen. Either you're going to hand that check over to me, and we'll go on about our business, or I am going to grind my nasty, greasy, muddy foot right up into your crotch. I realize you may not feel much like giving me my check after that, but you don't feel much like giving it to me now, so I don't see how I lose anything. Besides, that'll be all right because then we'll be square. I'm going to ruin you a pair of nice, clean khakis, which cost you a lot more than it's going to cost me not to have that check when I leave here today, plus you'll have to go home looking like you had some kind of embarrassing accident, and you don't strike me as the kind of guy who enjoys that sort of thing. I really don't care which one it is."

The look on his face is just what I had hoped for. He isn't scared or even angry, just shocked. *This isn't how civilized people act*, his eyes are telling me. His eyes, and the slight gap that has opened between his thin, elegant lips. I slouch forward a bit more for emphasis. "ONE!" I begin.

Before I can get to two, he flips the check over, stabs at it with a rubber stamp, and shoves it across the desk.

"You still have to sign for it," he snarls. I pick up the check, then casually lift my foot down from the edge of his chair.

"You sign for me," I say. "And you remember something, too, you arrogant piece of crap. You remember that it was another faggot who did this to you. You be sure and understand that it was another queer cocksucking motherfucker who was here today so you don't make a mistake and try to tell people how you were almost *gay bashed* or some shit, because you never were. It was much worse than that." I stand and start to go.

"Trash," he sniffs. I don't turn around. Instead, I kick the base of his hollow-core door as hard as I can so that it flies back and slams into the wall outside, the knob digging a neat, round divot into the plaster. Secretaries in the outer office look up, alarmed looks on their faces, but nobody moves. At the bottom of his door, my filthy Keds leave a brown-and-black arc smeared across the institutional white paint. I know that probably won't be there for long. He'll be on the phone to maintenance as soon as I'm out of sight, screaming for somebody to come and wash it off.

As I walk out to the rack to unchain my bike, I imagine what the janitor might look like when he comes to deal with the stain on the door. I hope he's queer, and I hope he's handsome, and I hope he can sense the vibration left behind in that room from what went on there and decides that Mr. Sean Owens has not even come close to the end of being fucked with today.

MEN WITHOUT BLISS
Rigoberto González

For Richard Yañez

At his "good-bye and good luck" party, Andrés looks around at the faces of his coworkers and tries to remember when he has had an intimate conversation with any of them. He can't recall a single exchange that warrants their theatrical display of last-minute friendship. In the corner, the silver helium balloon has begun to flatten, and Andrés knows that the blue corn tortilla chips, staples at every function, come from a garbage-can-sized bag in the storage room. He takes pleasure, however, in watching people parade up to him to say their good-byes.

"You'll be missed," declares a tall, hefty redhead. Andrés had never been introduced to her until that afternoon. Her lipstick matches her blood-red nails. She retraces her steps to the center table for a second slice of chocolate cake. Andrés wants to watch her eat it but his view is blocked by another well-wisher.

"You'll be missed," he tells Andrés.

Andrés doesn't recognize the overweight white guy dressed in a white shirt and tie. "Why?" he asks him. The white guy titters uncertainly as he walks toward the punch bowl.

Thirty minutes after ushering everyone into the conference room, Mary Ann, the supervisor, announces that it's time to get back to work. The French, Spanish, German, and Italian tutors shuffle obediently out the door. Only a few of them walk up to Andrés to shake his hand or to give him a European kiss on both cheeks. The hefty redhead sways forward again and tilts her head to the left. Teary-eyed, she declares: "What's the Italian group going to do without you?" She's out the door before Andrés can tell her he tutored Spanish.

Only the ill-humored secretary—Program Associate according to the nameplate on her desk—stays behind to clean up. She mumbles under her breath as she wipes the conference tables and empties the uneaten chips into a trash bin.

Mary Ann returns with an envelope in her hand. "You'll need this," she says. "A letter of rec. Accrued sick days will be included in your final paycheck."

Andrés takes the envelope.

"I'm sure you'll do better in your next place of employment," Mary Ann says. She's shorter than Andrés, but in her high heels and with the tone of reprehension in her voice she seems taller.

"I'll certainly try," Andrés says.

"Professionalism cannot be compromised," Mary Ann adds as she shakes her head. "I'm sure you've learned your lesson here." Andrés taught individual and group tutoring sessions for a year at the language center, never once canceling an appointment or showing up late. And then they fired him.

"I don't think I've done anything wrong," Andrés mumbles. In the background, he sees the Program Associate roll her eyes. His teaching evaluations were generally noncommittal, but every other month one or another of his female students launched a harassment complaint. Not even Mary Ann, who was a stickler for policy and procedure, could clearly articulate what he was doing wrong.

"We've discussed this, Andrés," Mary Ann says. "With you we're risking a lawsuit that we can't afford." She'd said the same thing when she gave him his notice two weeks ago.

"But I've never done or said anything that was inappropriate."

"The complaints read the same: you make the women students feel uncomfortable when you look at them. That's enough for us to take action," she says.

None of the male students had complained, though it was true that he sometimes looked at them in a way someone might call funny. But they preferred to make their appointments with the female Spanish tutors, so he hardly saw them. "Maybe that's their problem," Andrés says.

Mary Ann shakes her head in disbelief. "If you want to file an unlawful termination of employment form, you can speak with someone in resources." She storms off to her office.

The Program Associate closes the cake box and wipes the knife with a paper towel. "I'd appreciate it if you emptied your desk out before four o'clock," she says. "I don't want to put in overtime setting up your cubicle for the new Spanish teacher. Do you want to take the rest of this cake home?"

Andrés walks out of the building with the cake box and the helium balloon. The bag over his shoulder holds a few blank pages of good, cream-colored paper he'll use for his résumé, three used Agatha Christie paperbacks, and a recycled manila folder to seal the damaged screen in his father's bedroom window. He's well aware that he's dragging the deflated balloon behind him like an empty dog collar, but he has no choice because the string is tightly bound to the cake box and he didn't want to ask the edgy Program Associate for the scissors. He throws everything into the back seat and drives off, taking one last look at the language tutorial center. He can't recall why he ended up teaching Spanish in the first place. His training that one semester at the community college was in psychology.

When he gets home he finds his father slumped on the couch. A janitor at the elementary school, he hasn't changed out of his dark blue work shirt. The name stitched above the left hand pocket reads "Rapael."

"They tried to spell Rafael the gringo way," his father explained when he first brought home the three regulation shirts he had been issued. "And then they left out the h. I really don't give a shit. They never call me by my name anyhow."

Andrés sets the cake box and newspaper on the table; the deflated balloon hangs over the edge like a silver placenta trailing its umbilical cord.

"Pop," he says to his father. "Do you want a piece of cake?"

"With my diabetes and high blood pressure?" his father answers. "I'll take two pieces. Is it my birthday or yours?"

"I lost my job," Andrés said. He rummages through the cupboards for a plate.

"Oh," his father says, uninterested. "What kind of cake is it?"

Andrés cuts a large piece for his father. "The store-bought kind," he says.

"I like those," his father says, twisting his pinky in his ear. "They don't skimp on the frosting."

As Andrés looks over the classifieds in the newspaper later that evening, his father watches television on the couch. He hasn't changed out of his work shirt. In fact he hasn't changed position all afternoon.

Andrés is fascinated by the exotic items in the "for sale" listings. "Do you want to buy a ferret, Pop?" Andrés calls out.

"A parrot? No, they stink," his father says.

"A ferret," Andrés says. "It's like a weasel."

"They stink," his father says. "How about another piece of that cake?"

After giving his father another helping of cake, Andrés circles potential jobs. Delivery Driver. Dental Assistant. Healthcare Provider. Housekeeper. Teaching Assistant. All of them minimum wage, but that doesn't matter. Healthcare doesn't ask for any previous experience, so he makes a note of the address.

"You know what this cake reminds me of?" his father says. He waves the fork in the air, dropping a few crumbs on his lap. "The day you were born."

"You had cake on the day I was born?" says Andrés.

"It's a birthday cake, ain't it," his father says, exasperated.

Andrés circles an ad for proofreader, though he isn't a good speller. But he figures he can run the documents through the computer's spell check.

"So what about the day I was born, Pop?" Andrés says.

"On the day you were born I went to see a movie," his father says. "Since you took your damn time popping out of your mother's oven." He laughs at his own joke and coughs a few times.

"Don't choke on your funny, Pop," Andrés says.

"Fuck you," his father says. He continues talking with cake in his mouth, spitting out crumbs. "Anyway, the hospital waiting room was making me sick, so I took a long walk and ended up at this movie theater. A few hours of distraction is what I needed so I bought a ticket. You were born halfway through the movie. I could feel it in the way my body relaxed. But I decided to stay and watch the other half. Your mother was pissed, God rest her soul."

Andrés suddenly looks up from the newspaper. He turns to look at his father.

"What movie did you see?" he asks.

"I don't remember," his father says.

"You don't remember the movie you were watching while I was being born?"

"That was like forty years ago," his father says.

"Thirty-eight," Andrés corrects him.

"Whatever, it's still a lifetime ago. Last millennium as a matter of fact."

"Don't you even remember what it was about?"

"Nope," his father says.

Andrés turns to the sheets of newspaper again.

That night Andrés tosses in bed. He can hear his father wheezing in his sleep in the next bedroom. He tries to guess what sort of movie his father had been watching and how it might have marked his own fate. Knowing his father, he'd probably walked into a porn theater, which is why he didn't want to say the name of the movie. Andrés tries not to think of his father sitting in a smelly dark room as the projector tosses out images of a naked woman taking it from behind, her breasts knocking against each other like water balloons.

Andrés overdresses for the visit to the group home though he's only going in to drop off his résumé. On the porch, a cluster of old guys in faded clothes blow smoke into each other's faces. Cigarette butts are scattered on the porch, and Andrés pictures the shreds of paper left behind after a string of firecrackers explodes.

As he walks in, a musty odor invades his nose. His father's room smells the same.

"The title is residential counselor," the young female administrator says. She's wearing an ankle-length dress with a slit going down the side that exposes her calf when she crosses her legs. She looks closely over his résumé.

"Looks like you've got plenty of work experience," she says.

Andrés counts the piercings on her face: one nose stud, one eyebrow ring, two lip rings, six earrings on the left ear.

"We only have graveyard shift available at the moment," she says. "The hours are eleven p.m. to nine a.m."

"I'm interested," Andrés says. "What are the duties required?"

"Primarily that you be awake and aware at all hours in case of an emergency. You'll need to get your first-aid and CPR certification. Secondly, you'll need to fetch anyone for meds if they haven't taken their bedtime pills."

Andrés pictures himself whistling from the front porch and the residents running up to him like trained dogs.

"And thirdly," she says. "Make them breakfast by seven a.m., plus start handing out the morning meds to anyone who's awake. Usually only half of them are. You have to log into the record book for each resident as you dispense meds. But it's super easy."

"How many residents?" Andrés asks.

"Twenty-five. Twenty of them are males. These are all developmentally disabled adults," she adds. "Pretty low-maintenance. They do everything for themselves except they can't cook and they can't manage their own meds. They're very low-key. Nice people."

Andrés is suddenly aware that she's trying to sell him the position.

"So you'll let me know if I need to come in for an interview?" he asks.

"Oh, I thought this was it," she says, flustered. "I mean, you seem very capable and you're our strongest candidate. It's yours if you want it."

Andrés is suspicious but just as desperate as she is. So he accepts the position: full-time graveyard shift Sunday through Wednesday. Health and dental included. He'll start the next day. They give him thirty days to get his CPR certificate. He hopes no one needs CPR before then.

At home, Andrés opens up a can of minestrone soup for dinner. When his father arrives, he carries a bag of toilet paper, the partially dispensed rolls in varying thicknesses, and a stack of paper towels from a bathroom dispenser.

"Soup's on," Andrés says.

"What kind of soup is it?"

"Vegetable," Andrés says.

"Any more of that cake left?"

Later that evening Andrés stares at his father as he dozes on the couch. At his feet, the untouched bowl of soup. On his lap, a small dish with crumbs. The fork dangles from his left hand.

"I found a new job," Andrés says.

"What?" his father responds in a sleepy tone.

"I found a new job. I'll be working nights, Sunday through Wednesday."

"That's good, son," his father says and falls asleep again.

In the morning Andrés fries eggs and sausages for breakfast. He also makes toast, oatmeal, and fresh juice, which pleases his father.

"Smells good," his father says.

"I'm practicing for my new job at the group home," Andrés says. "I'll be making breakfast for a dozen people every morning at work. Try the sausages."

"What kind of people are these? Retards?"

"They're developmentally disabled adults,"

"Retards," his father says.

The young female administrator, Cassie was her name, said that most of the residents were paranoid schizophrenics. "But they're harmless," she was quick to add.

"You know, I think I remember a little more about that theater I went to the day you were born," his father says.

Andrés' ears perk up. "What do you remember?"

"A woman in a red hat," his father says.

"There was a woman in a red hat in the movie?"

"I didn't say anything about the movie," his father corrects him. "I said I remembered something about the theater."

"You met a woman with a red hat in the theater?"

"No, stupid, let me finish," his father snaps. He takes a long gulp of his orange juice and then continues. "There was a movie poster at the theater showing a woman in a red hat. That's why I bought a ticket in the first place. The poster looked interesting. You couldn't see the woman's face because the hat was tilted forward. You could catch a glimpse of her chin. And I think her fingers were resting on the brim of the hat like she was pulling it down to hide her face. Her nails were as red as the hat. That's it. Draw your own conclusions."

"And you're sure there was no woman in a red hat in the movie?"

"I don't remember," his father says. "The orange juice could use a little sugar."

Andrés tries to nap during the day, but ends up reading through the pages of *The Body in the Library* without much interest. He finishes the murder mystery before his father returns from work but he can't remember who done it. He resolves to reread the ending at work since there will be nothing else to do in the pre-dawn hours.

At ten p.m. he drives to work early. His father is already wheezing away in his room.

Every light in the group home is on. The same cluster of residents smoke on the porch and a new cluster has gathered in the garden to smoke as well. They puff away without talking like a row of strangers at a bus stop.

"Are you the new guy?" one of the residents asks. He has a long beard and a pair of wide blue eyes that look as if they are being crushed open by his glasses.

"I sure am," Andrés says. "I'm Andy. Good to meet you."

The old guy shakes his hand.

"That's disgusting, man," another resident says. He has a large tattoo of a bird on his forearm. "He was picking his nose all afternoon." The other residents laugh.

Andrés walks into the hall and then into the small office where he was interviewed. The swing shift person is surprised to see him. She's sitting on the chair with her feet up on the desk, a bag of yarn on her lap.

"Hello, there," she says, setting her knitting needles down. "Welcome. I'm Louise. You're Andy?"

"Yes," he says. "The graveyard shift."

"That's nice," she says. "The rest of us were taking turns with that shift. I told Cassie she better hire someone quick or she'd have a group full of disgruntled employees in her hands."

"Well, I'm here to relieve you," he says, attempting a smile.

"You sure are," Louise says. She stuffs her knitting in a plastic bag and rushes out of the office before Andrés can remind her that his shift doesn't start for another twenty minutes. He had been hoping to chat with her.

Andrés follows the instructions Cassie provided: he checks the record book—all of the residents have received their evening meds; he goes down to the storage room to bring up breakfast supplies—milk, coffee, eggs, sausage; he makes sure any lights not in use are off; he makes his rounds through the top floor, where residents watch television in their private rooms; he sweeps the dining area where a few residents watch television at no volume.

"It doesn't work," one of the residents says to him when he suggests turning up the sound. He leaves them staring into the screen.

He sits down at the desk with his book in his hand and by midnight he falls asleep. He's awakened numerous times during the night by the shuffling of bodies around the halls. Each time he thinks it is his father sneaking into the kitchen for a midnight snack.

One of the residents walks into the office. "Hey," he says. "You got any smokes, buddy?"

"I don't smoke," Andrés answers with a yawn.

"Then you're not going to be very popular around here," the resident warns. He's a large man in suspenders that stretch precariously across his belly. He's about to leave when he suddenly turns around and adds, "Well I hope you last longer than the other guy."

"What happened to the other guy?" Andrés asks, curiously.

"Heart attack," the resident says. "I dialed 911 myself, but they didn't get here in time."

"Oh," Andrés says.

"I kept dialing the wrong number," he says, breaking into chuckles as he walks off.

Before dawn Andrés drags himself into the kitchen and gets the stove going to prepare breakfast. A few residents knock on the kitchen door demanding their morning meds and Andrés maneuvers between the two tasks.

"What's your name?" he asks them as he runs his finger across the row of Medikits.

"Brunswick," one of the residents answers, annoyed. "Haven't you learned my name yet?"

"I'm sorry, sir," Andrés says. "But this is my first day."

"It is?" Mr. Brunswick says in surprise. "Aren't you the guy who had the heart attack?"

Andrés finished cooking and logs in Mr. Brunswick, Mr. Shepley, Ms. Calloway, Mr. Newman, and Mr. Harrison-Boyd. All of them have helpings of scrambled eggs and toast, spooning jam from a container the size of a coffee can. When it's clear no one else is coming down for breakfast, Andrés helps himself to a plate of eggs. They taste bland.

"Hey, buddy," the large man in suspenders says. Mr. Velasco, Andrés has learned.

"Ready for some breakfast?" Andrés says. "

"You got any smokes?" Mr. Velasco asks.

"Sorry, Mr. Velasco," Andrés says. "I don't smoke. Would you like some eggs?"

"Shove the eggs up your ass," Mr. Velasco says before storming off.

When the morning shift comes, Andrés hands over the keys to the office and walks sleepily to his car. Once in bed he sleeps all day until his father gets home from work. The noise from the television wakes Andrés up.

"How was your new job?" his father asks. He has his hand stuffed inside a yellow box of breakfast cereal.

Andrés makes circles with his head, stretching out his neck. "I need to get used to staying awake all night," he says. "How was your day?"

"Nothing exciting. Except some kid brought a gun to school."

"Did he shoot anybody?"

"For show and tell," his father says. "Made one of the girls piss in her panties. They called me to clean it up. The kid didn't know any better. Say, do any of those retards take Lipitor?"

"They're not retards."

"Departmentally handicapped adults or whatever. They take Lipitor?"

"Some do," Andrés says. "Why? You want me to bring you some?"

"I'm running out," his father says.

"No problem," Andrés says.

He opens another can of soup and serves his father a bowl with crackers he brought home from the kitchen at work.

"Have you given any more thought to the woman in the red hat?" Andrés asks.

"Not as much as you apparently," says his father. He dips each cracker into the soup until it gets soggy before he pops it into his mouth. "I told you I don't remember anything else beside the red hat and the weird writing on the poster."

"What writing?" Andrés says.

"I thought I told you about that," his father says. "They had this weird-looking title above the red hat. Like those letters in the Chinese menus. But they were American letters made to look like Chinese letters."

"And?"

"And nothing. That's all I remember," his father says. "I thought that was the movie I was walking into but nope. The movie had no Chinese letters or woman in a red hat to speak of."

"Interesting," Andrés mumbles.

"I'm sure they're also taking Depakote," says his father.

"Say what?" Andrés says.

"Your people," his father says. "Check if they're also taking Depakote. Big pink pills."

"Oh," says Andrés. "Sure."

That night at work he has to track down Ms. Ryan to give her her meds. She won't open the door to her room.

"I've got keys, Ms. Ryan," Andrés says. "Either you open up or I do."

"Go to hell!" she screams. "I told them I wasn't taking any more meds. Been taking meds for thirty years and I'm losing my eyesight because of it."

"Is everything all right in there?" he asks.

"I'm not even decent so you better not open that door!"

He walks back into the office and marks the medication log: R for refusal.

"Hey, buddy," Mr. Velasco says. "You got any smokes?"

Andrés looks up at the old man in suspenders. "I just ran out," he says. "Mr. Shepley took my last one."

"That goddamn Shepley," Mr. Velasco says, and walks away.

Andrés checks the resident records, pulls out the Medikits that have Lipitor in the small plastic compartments, and fishes out a few pills. Since the residents take up to half a dozen different pills, one less isn't noticeable. In the shelf marked refills, he finds entire bottles of Depakote. He stuffs the one labeled for Mr. Velasco into his coat and resolves to bring him some cigarettes the following week. For the rest of the night he simply presses his fists to his mouth as he leans on the desk with his elbows and thinks about the woman in the red hat.

"Say," one of the residents interrupts. He holds a large sheet of paper in his hands.

"What is it, sir," says Andrés. "Mr.—"

"Guilman," the man says. "Can I show you my drawing?"

"Sure," says Andrés. "What did you draw?"

Mr. Guilman turns the paper over. "A ship."

The drawing has been made exclusively with straight lines.

"Is that the *Titanic*?" Andrés asks.

Mr. Guilman chuckles. "Not quite. I have many more in my room if you care to see them."

"Why not?" Andrés says, and he follows Mr. Guilman into his room down the hall.

The room is small with an unmade bed on one side, a chair with an old suitcase on it. The wall opposite the bed displays a small gallery of drawings—ships, helicopters, cars—all of them drawn with ink and a straight edge. Andrés notices a picture of a space ship in the center of the drawings.

"That's interesting," Andrés says as he leans in closer to inspect it. "Is that like the Star Trek *Enterprise*?"

After a brief silence Mr. Guilman speaks up. "That's the mother ship," he says in a serious tone. "She's hovering up in space looking out for us."

"Well, thank you for sharing your drawings, Mr. Guilman," Andrés says as he slowly creeps out. "I need to get back into my office."

Mr. Guilman places one hand on Andrés' shoulder. "You understand, don't you?" he asks.

Andrés nods. "I do," he says.

The rest of the night goes by without incident.

The next afternoon, after waking up, Andrés goes into the bookstore at the mall. As usual, Helen J waits behind the counter.

"Hi, Andrés," she says, waving him over. Andrés makes his way to her reluctantly.

She leans over to kiss him on the cheek and Andrés complies, slightly embarrassed. Helen J's hair feels coarse where it rubs against his skin; her own skin feels cold and slightly clammy.

"Haven't seen you in a while," she says. "Here to buy some more mysteries?"

"Not exactly," he says. "I came to buy a movie guide."

"Are you looking for video recommendations?" she asks excitedly. "I've seen some great ones lately."

"No, Helen J," he says. "I'm looking for a book that will tell me about the movies that were out in the sixties."

"Oooh, the classics," Helen J whispers in an attempt to sound impressed. "I love those old movies."

"Well, does such a book exist, Helen J?"

Helen J smirks as she walks around the counter and leads him to the reference section. She pulls a thick book from the shelf.

Andrés takes it from her hands and leafs through it.

"Is this what you're looking for?" Helen J asks.

Andrés turns his back on her and begins to browse through the glossy reproductions of movie posters. There are so many. It will be a painstaking process, but he has the time, hours on end of time, at his new job.

"I'll take it," he says when he looks up finally, but Helen J has returned to the counter to ring up another customer.

His father is already on the couch when Andrés walks into the house. The empty cake box sits on the floor beside him.

"Where were you?" his father says. "I had important news."

"About what, Pop?" Andrés says. He sets the bookstore bag on the table.

"About the woman in the red hat," his father says.

"Really?" Andrés says, holding back his excitement.

"She was using her left hand to pull down the brim of her hat," he announces.

"Oh," Andrés says, disappointed. "Why is that important?"

"You should know, stupid," his father says. "Left-handed people always notice other left-handed people. You're left-handed. So am I. So was your mother. One houseful of goddamn left-handers."

"My mother was left-handed?" Andrés says.

"Jesus Christ," his father says. "I can't believe you. You only knew her for about eighteen years."

Andrés remembers the day his mother died. His father wasn't home from work yet. His mother was in the bedroom and wouldn't come out. Andrés knocked and knocked but got no response, so he pushed the door open only to find her slumped over on the floor. The zipper on the back of her dress was wide open. He was shocked to see her freckled back and the pink strap of the bra. She'd had a stroke while changing clothes so she could be dressed nicely when she gave Andrés and his father their supper. Andrés zipped her up before his father came through the door.

While his father watches television for the rest of the evening, Andrés sketches a picture of the woman in the red hat with her left hand pulling down the brim.

Andrés decides to hold off on his search for the woman in the red hat until Sunday night. He uses the three days of rest to sleep and clean up the house, which is susceptible to ants. His father's couch floats like a small island surrounded by an atoll of crumbs and spilled food, and Andrés circles it a number of times with the vacuum cleaner.

On Saturday afternoon he and his father take their usual outing to the bar at the end of town. When his mother was still alive she wouldn't allow alcohol in the house and his father had to drop in at the bar for a beer after work on Friday evenings. When Andrés came of age his father invited him for a drink, and since Andrés' twenty-first birthday fell on a Saturday, his father changed his weekly outings to Saturdays. Andrés was surprised to learn that his father drank alone all those years and made no friends at the bar, except for Pirata, the one-eyed bartender. But Pirata had died ten years ago. His son, who took over tending bar, had invited them to funeral, but Andrés' father didn't want to attend. The next time they came into the bar, Pirata's son didn't ask why they didn't go, but after that he never made any effort to be friendly with them. Not even after ten years.

"The usual," his father says to Pirata's son as they hop onto the bar stools.

"Right," Pirata's son says, and brings them two bottles of Corona.

They chug their beers in silence while the jukebox plays the same tunes it played the Saturday before.

"What do you think of that new margarita-mixing machine?" Pirata's son asks.

Andrés' father glares at it. He takes out his glasses and places them on his face. After taking another swig of beer, he says, "What's the point?"

"Saves time, I guess," Andrés says helpfully.

His father looks around at the near-empty bar. "To do what?" he asks.

They chuckle into their beers. Pirata's son throws an annoyed look in their direction.

"Another round?" he asks.

"If you're not too busy," Andrés says, and they burst into laughter again.

On Sunday, nothing unusual happens at the group home, except that the television has been repaired and now the residents keep it on at full volume. Before she left, Louise warned him, "Good luck trying to get them to turn that down."

The dining room is cold. Andrés turns the television down and leaves. As soon as he's out the door, he hears the volume go up again. The pattern repeats itself twice before Andrés goes to the basement and shuts off the breaker to that part of the house.

"The lights went out," a voice comes to inform him at the office. Andrés flashes a flashlight on his face.

"I'm sorry about that, Mr. Shepley," he says. "We're on it. We'll get them back on as soon as we can."

He turns the flashlight on his video book and makes his way slowly down the columns of photographs as he searches in the semi-darkness for the woman in the red hat.

By the time he turns the breaker back on, it's past two in the morning. A few residents are still smoking on the front porch. He looks through the medication record book. Five residents haven't taken their evening meds, so Andrés pulls out their Medikits and drops the pills into the garbage can, logging in each evening dose as if it's been taken.

The next morning he serves the same breakfast as always, eggs and sausage. He stuffs the automatic dishwasher with dirty dishes and then hands the keys over to the morning shift before heading home. As he drives into his neighborhood he realizes that he's forgotten the video book in the office, but it will be safe there.

Andrés sleeps seven hours, waking at five p.m. When he walks out to the living room, his father greets him from the couch.

"I've got some more news for you," his father says.

"About?" Andrés yawns.

"About the woman in the red hat," his father says.

"Do tell," Andrés says. He opens the refrigerator to rummage for a soda. He finds two cans left in the door, both half-consumed and abandoned by his father. He takes one and sips the flat, cool liquid.

"She wasn't Chinese at all," his father says.

"How do you know?" Andrés says. "Her face was covered by the red hat, remember?"

"Yes, I know," his father says. "But her hand wasn't a Chinawoman's hand."

"What's a Chinawoman's hand?"

"You know," his father says. "Yellow."

"That's actually a misconception about Asian people. They aren't really yellow. Just like black people aren't really black."

"Well, what I meant was that I remember it was a Latina hand."

"You mean her hand was brown?"

"Oh, so brown people really are brown?" his father snaps.

Andrés takes another sip of soda. "Go on," he says.

"There's nothing more to it. I knew it was a Latina, so I thought maybe I was walking into one of those artsy foreign films."

"I think you're making it up," Andrés says.

"Why should I make it up? You're the one who wants to know what goddamn film I watched while you were being born. What the fuck does it matter anyway?"

Andrés pulls out a chair and sits down. He feels a slight tension at the temples.

"You know what, forget I said anything about any movie or any woman in a white fucking hat. I don't remember shit!"

Andrés says softly, "The woman's hat is red."

"Shut up with that," his father demands, turning up the volume on the television.

Andrés' headache worsens. He decides to lie down for a while longer. He still has a few hours before work. In bed he presses his fists to his eyes and somehow manages to fall asleep.

When he awakes his heart is pounding. The sound of the television carries into his room. He didn't set his alarm clock because he didn't think he would sleep this long, but it's close to nine o'clock.

On his way to the shower he calls to his father, "Turn that down, Pop." When he comes out again, one towel wrapped around his waist, another hanging over his shoulders, the television is just as loud. He's annoyed but decides to leave his father alone. He dresses, thinking he'll show up for work early again so he can make himself something to eat in the kitchen. The Sysco cheese is stocked in bulk, the odor pungent but appetizing.

As he makes his way down the hall he notices his father's left hand dangling over the arm of his chair. Andrés walks around him to turn the television off. He lifts his father's arm to drop it into his lap, the way his father usually falls asleep. His father's arm is cold.

Andrés bites his lip and his foot taps uncontrollably against the floor. Pressing his hands against his mouth he releases a muffled wail. He squats, taking a few deep breaths, calming himself down. The need to cry surges and he grabs his face with both hands, piecing together an image of his father through the openings between his fingers.

And then suddenly the grief lifts, as if those few moments of panic were all he had to offer. He's uncertain what to do next. He looks around the room. Nothing seems different. Even his father's body on the couch is a familiar sight. It's as if he's sleeping.

After a few minutes on the floor he checks his watch. There are twenty-five people expecting him at the group home. Someone has to check to make sure they've taken their bedtime meds. In the morning, half of them will want their eggs and sausage. He turns off the living room lights and walks out to his car.

In his office, there is a woman in a red hat, waiting.

MIDDLE-CLASS DRAG: A PERFORMANCE PIECE
Renny Christopher

I had an idyllic working-class boyhood, dressing in cowboy clothes, playing with my toy Winchester rifle, my bow and arrow, my GI Joe. I played with toy tools my dad gave me until he taught me to use the real ones, and then I worked construction with him from the time I was eleven or twelve until I left for college at seventeen.

There were only two problems with this working-class boyhood: first, I wasn't actually a boy, anatomically speaking, and second, for every hour I spent playing with guns and tools, I spent three or four hours with my nose "stuck in a book," as my mother called it, working on becoming a nerdy intellectual, which was not an appropriate activity for a good working-class boy (or girl, for that matter). Thus I always felt divided and different, and my internal feeling was reinforced by how people responded to me.

My mother was the first person to tell me I was gay, long before I had any idea, and she was also the first person to tell me I should go to college, long before I had any idea of going. She'd known many gay people, and if I were gay, that was no big problem for her. But she'd never known a college graduate, and she had no idea what a problem that would become, as I became more and more of an alien to my family through my pursuit of higher education.

My mother's cousin Elaine was brilliant, far smarter than anyone else my mother ever knew, and she was a lesbian. My mother's explanation for Elaine's lesbianism was that she could never find a man smart enough for her and that explanation made perfect sense to my mother. It wasn't until I was in my forties that I realized what a low opinion my heterosexual mother had of men.

One of the traumatic events in my mother's life was Elaine's suicide—she put the stock of a shotgun on the floor, put her head on the end of the barrel and pulled the trigger with her toe. When I was maybe twelve or thirteen, my mother started telling me, "And you're just like her." I now realize that what she was saying was, "You're really smart, I'm afraid you'll kill yourself, and I think you're a lesbian." My family never spoke directly about anything abstract, anything involving emotions or ways of being or how we thought about issues or ideas. When we did try to speak about anything abstract, we did it through indirection. So I now understand that my mother was telling me that she already knew I was gay, and that she wasn't going to have a fit about it. She was also the first person who ever told me I was going to college.

May 4, 1970

In my first year of high school
my friends already talked
of marriage and children.
When they did
I put my hands over my ears.
A teacher told me
I'd never get a husband
if I didn't stop answering
all the questions in class.

My friends talked of work.
I had no talent, like my mom,
for fixing hair.
And I was
too clumsy for a waitress
too sarcastic for a store clerk
too selfish for a nurse
too impatient for a factory line.
I was smart,
so I could be a secretary.
But restlessness ran in my veins—
I crossed my arms, clamped my jaw
and refused to learn how to type.

I didn't know what to dream of,
so I watched the news,
looking for a clue.

I wanted to see those places far from here
where there were wars.
I yearned for the rifle in my hands
but had to settle for shooting BBs
at popsicle sticks in the creek
while dreaming of being a boy
joining the marines.

The TV seemed the only window
out of the living room walls.
My mother walked back and forth
while cooking dinner.
She paused
her worn hand resting
on the back of my chair
while Huntley and Brinkley
gave us the news.

We heard their voices explain while
we saw on the screen the face of a long-haired girl
shouting and raising a fist.
The camera bobbled, moved,
focused on a boy lying face down,
moved again to students

screaming at soldiers whose guns pointed
at the camera. This time the war
not overseas, but in Ohio.

"I hope this trouble's over,"
my mother said
"before you go off to college."

She had never said
I could go to college—
Kids from my town became the soldiers,
never the students.

What she said made my heart beat faster

but I never turned away
from the guns on the TV.
As I stared I thought
yes, yes.

On the screen I saw a way out.
The shooting and the panic
matched the anger in my hands,
matched the silent screams ringing in my ears,
screaming no against
those possible futures that I knew
screaming yes
for the unimaginable.

I watched the distant college campus
on the little screen
and I longed fervently
for revolution.

Until I was in graduate school, I never had a name for my gender identity. I was just a girl who acted like a boy and never worried about what that was called or what it meant. I didn't need a name for my sexual orientation, either. I wasn't exactly a lesbian, as my mom thought, nor was I exactly straight. And I certainly didn't have a name for my class background. I thought everybody was like us until I started meeting middle-class people, who were so different they seemed to come from a foreign country. But let's begin at the beginning.

When my mother was pregnant with me, she was so sure she was having a boy that she and my dad picked out a boy's name—Renny—and didn't bother to pick one out for a girl. When I turned out to be a girl, they gave me the boy's name anyway.

I don't know if I simply followed my own inclinations in preferring to be a boy, or if I was influenced by their expectation that I *would be one*, but I was perfectly happy. My mother thought she wouldn't have any more kids. My little brother, four years younger, was a surprise. My dad, I think, had no idea what to do with a daughter, so he just carried on as if I were his son, which was fine with me. Shortly after I got my PhD my mother told me, "You've always been your dad's oldest son." That was the best thing she ever said to me.

I wanted to be exactly like my dad in every way when I was a little kid. I wore my jeans low on my hips, like he did. I had a tool belt that was a miniature copy of his. My brother and I each had beautiful toolboxes dad made us with our names inlaid in them, and wooden wagons he made for us, which we dragged around like they were hotrods, pushing each other downhill like daredevils. But although I lived a boy's life at home, I wasn't allowed to do so at school, so my life was split in two.

I got my first public lesson in gender when I was in kindergarten. There were two play areas in my classroom—a workshop and a kitchen, enforcing the class and gender expectations of my working-class neighborhood school. I headed directly to the workshop, because that's the kind of play I knew from home. The teacher dragged me out of there by the ear and tossed me unceremoniously into the kitchen to the snickers of the students who had already, obviously, been thoroughly and "properly" gendered. Marked instantly as a misfit, I stood in the corner of that kitchen feeling isolated, exposed, and vulnerable. That feeling lasted through all my elementary and primary school years. I filled that emptiness with books, which made me academically successful, but took me further and further away from the working-class boyhood I'd been enjoying at home. [*Takes off the hat.*]

Although I went to public schools, the dress code required that girls wear skirts. My mother colluded with me in subverting this. She made all my school clothes, and she always made matching shorts to wear under my dresses and skirts, so I could hang upside-down on the monkey bars, and so I managed to feel like I wasn't really wearing a skirt at all. Nonetheless as soon as I got home every day the skirts came off and my jeans and boots went on. That pattern continued throughout high school. Was I a boy in drag at school, or a girl in drag at home? I was a spiritual hermaphrodite, bi-gendered from the beginning.

Being Both Things

When I think
of my body I feel my chest
flat and muscular, my thighs hard and hairy.

When I look
at my body I see breasts bursting
and soft full thighs.

I want to cut my hair real short
put on red lipstick and a man's pinstripe suit,
walk down the street
like I was headed somewhere.

When I was a teenager, working for my dad doing construction, I had great fun masquerading as a boy. I had very short hair, and until I was sixteen or so, had a fairly boyish body. Once, when I was hammering together the framing for a house on a new construction site, a delivery truck from a lumber yard pulled up and the driver jumped out and headed in my direction. I'd been facing away from him, and when I turned around, he did a literal double-take as he realized I wasn't a boy. In those days it was unusual to see women working construction, so that kind of double-take happened to me often. I loved it. I loved both parts—the initial perception of me as a boy, then the recognition that I wasn't, but that I was still working the job. It made me feel rebellious, defiant, and strong.

Carpenter

What my hands did was good—
using screwdrivers, wrenches, hammer, nail gun,
putting pieces together to make wholeness
fastening, tightening, joining, smoothing—
dimpling nails in sheetrock just so
making a mosaic of hardwood floor boards
another one of fence lattice.

But, too often, I worked with an audience.
Guys looking over my shoulder,
surprised when my screw gun
ran the screw in instead of out,
surprised when I drilled through the post,
and not through my own hand.

Surprised when I lifted sheets of wood,
chunks of steel I-beam
surprised when I drove the forklift.
Surprised when, with sure strokes of the putty knife
I patched a hole, rather than making it bigger.
Surprised when my hammer hit the nail
instead of the wall beside it.

"Gee," they'd say, "I guess you really do know
how to do it, after all."
They didn't know how dangerous it was
to say that to a woman
with a hammer in her hand.

My dad never betrayed me. He never tried to make me into a girl. He never once told me not to do something physical. Rather, he'd teach me the best way to do it. My mother went along with that until I hit puberty, then her attitude toward me changed. She started warning me not to hurt myself. I've always wondered what that means, when adults tell girl children not to do something because they'll "hurt" themselves. Does it mean if you climb a tree your uterus will fall out?

Mom tried to teach me to walk in high heels when I was sixteen or seventeen. I can't remember why I ever cooperated with that project—to humor her, I guess. She soon gave up, telling me that no matter what I did, I still looked like I was "clomping around" in cowboy boots. I took that as a major compliment.

Meanwhile, my own bookishness continued to exert itself as an influence that felt contradictory to my boyishness. I had the distinct feeling that books, poetry in particular, which I wanted to write, were effeminate. I felt distinctly uncomfortable doing anything effeminate, since I always modeled myself in everything other than bookishness after my dad. But the pull of books was too strong for me to resist. In the afternoons and on Saturdays and Sundays I'd climb up into the treehouse that my brother and I had built with my dad's help. I'd take a book up there and read for hours. I was consciously hiding my reading, as if it were a vice. It turned out to be not so much a vice, as the road away from the world I grew up in.

I got pretty tired of always being alone and having no friends. In the way many girls do, I discovered that one way to get attention was through sex. I had no interest in sex itself, no feelings of physical attraction for anyone, male or female, although I had plenty of intellectual curiosity about it, which arose through my reading. I read a lot of books with rather oblique references to sex, but was picking up some of the details through more explicit works like *The Godfather* and *The Last Picture Show*. I first learned about the existence of (male) homosexuality from Mary Renault's books about Alexander the Great, although I was still pretty unclear on how the physical details might work in practice.

I learned the heterosexual details when I acquired a motorcycle-riding, drug-dealing, leather-jacket-wearing dropout boyfriend, with whom I had sex for the first time when I was fifteen. It neither thrilled me nor repelled me. I stayed in that state until I wound up in bed with one of my high school teachers. And his wife. They were a hippie couple who'd recently moved to my small town, and were different (by a mile!) from anyone I'd met before. When she found out that her husband was having an affair, her response was to make it a threesome. My response was to discover that I was far more attracted to her than I was to him.

Somehow, I just didn't see my attraction to her as a problem, or as extraordinary in any way. (There's something to be said for ignorance and pigheadedness.) A bit later I fell head, feet, heart, and mind in love with a recently-divorced woman who was, at best, ambivalent about her feelings toward me. We never once used the word "lesbian" until the day she told me we had no future. She said she couldn't live a lesbian life while she was raising her children. In my twenties, while I was having relationships with men and with women, I never heard, thought of, or needed, the word "bisexual." I never thought about what I might be—I just was "it," whatever "it" was. Another term for it would have to be just plain promiscuous. It was the late 70s and early 80s, that magic time in human history when there was easily available birth-control, cures for syphilis and other STDs, and HIV/AIDS was not yet on the horizon of cultural awareness. The way I looked at myself then, had I been forced to articulate it, might have been reflected by Margaret Cho's line from *I'm the One That I Want*: "I'm not gay or straight—I'm just slutty. Where's my parade?"

Meanwhile, back to my other education. I won a scholarship to Mills College, a private liberal arts women's college in Oakland, California, and fell off the edge of the world into major culture shock. I struggled academically, socially, and psychologically for a year and a half. Then I dropped out.

I did blue-collar jobs for the next few years, working a printing press and a typesetting machine, until I went back to college four years later. I was working my way through college in print shops, working swing shift and going to school days. Despite having to work thirty or forty hours a week, I had become a much, much better student. I had read a lot of books in the four years I was a dropout, and made up a lot of the deficiencies I had entered college with. I had also learned to write, by doing a lot of it, mostly short stories and poems.

When I got my BA I still didn't have the terms working-class, bisexual, or cross-dressing in my lexicon. I still simply felt myself to be an outsider, increasingly alienated by my academic interests from my family and world of origin, but not finding a place I wanted to be. In that slightly lost state, I went into a master's program. I also went back to work for my dad. During the year I attended graduate school and worked on a construction site, I straddled worlds of class and gender in a more obvious fashion than at any other time in my life. Dad was working on a major commercial remodel job. [*Ties a bandana around her head.*]

I went to work with him in the morning, dressed in work boots, jeans or painter's pants, a T-shirt, and a rolled-up bandanna around my forehead. I did a lot of demolition and work with wallboard and joint compound. In the afternoons I took off for two and a half hours and went to class at San Jose State. My change of clothes consisted of taking the bandana off and sticking it in my pocket. [*Removes bandana.*] So there I was, a worker in men's clothes with a woman's body sitting in a classroom of higher education. My fellow students were very ambivalent toward me. I was getting the highest grades in class, and I studied with a group of students who appreciated my help, but it had taken quite a while before they invited me to join their study group. Eventually one of them told me that most of the other students were afraid of me, because I seemed so "tough."

Then I took the first step into crossing over altogether into the white-collar world when I got a job as a substitute high school teacher. I never wore what I call "work clothes"—blue collar clothes—to class again. (And I've never learned to call a button-down shirt and slacks "work clothes," even though I've been working in them since leaving that last blue-collar job). I have been teaching, in one form or another, ever since then, never again earning a living in a blue-collar job. [*Takes off the nametag.*]

During my first year in the MA program I met and became lovers with Gary, a bisexual man who first started giving me terminology. He gave me a birthday card with a picture of a person who was dressed on the left side in men's clothing and the right side in women's clothing. The caption read, "Both of us wish you a happy birthday." It was the first image I ever saw in which someone represented both male and female. Gary also gave me a button that said "Working-Class Dyke." I still have it. When he gave it to me, it was the first time anyone had ever applied either of those terms to me. I knew what a dyke was, but though I was struck by the term "working class," I didn't yet know what it meant.

In my twenties I was physically very strong, and the thinnest I have ever been in my life. I had taken up distance running and I ran about fifty miles a week. I lifted weights with a partner who was an amateur bodybuilding champion. I was fit, strong, and muscular, and cocky about my physical abilities. With short hair and bulging biceps, I felt positioned comfortably between genders. But then I went back for more miseducation.

In the PhD program I entered at thirty, I learned all the terms for classes and genders and sexual orientations, all the meanings of the terms, and all the strengths and the restrictions that went with the terms. I was cocky going into the program. I wasn't so cocky any more coming out five years later.

At first I felt utterly, completely lost. Eventually I learned to name that sense of being lost as being a first-generation college student, as being a working-class academic. Forming, defining, and claiming that identity took a lot of work and a lot of pain. I count it as the true subject matter and methodology I learned in graduate school, more than the disciplinary knowledge I was supposed to be learning.

However, one of the aspects of that dislocation I never looked at until years later was how the process knocked the hell out of my gender identity, as well as my class identity.

I had always been a cross-dresser by preference, wearing either gender-neutral or explicitly masculine clothes. I'd worn skirts when I had to, but had always worn them as a costume. I'd had very little consciousness concerning these practices. They were just the way I was. In graduate school I lost a great deal of my masculinity. It took me years to regain it. I knew how to be a working-class man. I had no idea how to be a middle-class man. Anyway, middle-class men looked pretty feminine to me.

When I started meeting a number of academic men of middle-class origin, I initially thought most of them were gay. I took their mannerisms, habits of speech, and attention to the details of dress as signs that they were effeminate, because the masculinity that they performed was so different from the working-class masculinity I'd grown up emulating. I thought, how cool this university is—everybody here is gay! Eventually I understood my error. They were displaying their masculinity, their power, through modalities that were completely alien to me, such as having elevated vocabularies, being able to quote literary sources, knowing which wine went with which food, and which glass to put the wine in and which fork to eat the food with.

One of my problems in graduate school was that my fellow students, as well as my professors, usually classified me as too loud, as rude, as taking up too much space, as obnoxious. I was simply behaving as I had always behaved while I was wearing work boots and work pants, behavior which didn't fit in the rarefied atmosphere of a research institution.

Large Woman

I don't like things to be nice or sweet.
I like them to be breathtaking and wild.
I like to walk on the rough side, with a swagger.
I have no patience with the trivial and small,
with the everyday grind, with stopping and smelling the flowers.
I'd rather sail, I'd rather soar, bet it all on a single roll
of the dice, walk away with a smile and a wave—win or lose.
I am a woman of large passions, which means
in this world, I am hardly a woman at all.

I started softening myself, so people wouldn't physically pull back from me when I moved or spoke. Because I didn't "get" middle-class masculinity, it felt like what I was doing was feminizing myself. I started wearing skirts. Voluntarily. I had read a magazine article that gave advice about job interviews. The article said that women in skirts were perceived as less aggressive than women wearing slacks. I took that to heart. I also grew my hair out. The long hair and less-butch clothing I adopted had a profound effect on me, and on those perceiving me. I was transforming myself from a working-class man into [*puts on a scarf*] a professional middle-class woman. While I was going about the class transformation consciously and deliberately, the gender transformation was largely invisible to me while it was happening.

In the late 80s in the town of Santa Cruz, as well as on the University campus, an intense lesbian feminist movement was demanding a voice and a physical space for lesbians on campus and in the gay and lesbian community center downtown, which had been dominated by men. It was a time when a small but very vocal demand was being mounted by bisexual women for their inclusion in these spaces. I knew many of the women fighting these culture wars, but I largely steered clear, without even realizing that I was doing so. I felt disenfranchised from claiming a bisexual identity too loudly, because I was living with a man, and among the lesbians I knew there was a great deal of animosity toward bisexuals who, they said, "just hadn't made up their minds yet."

Santa Cruz was very politicized about sexual orientation, but not yet about gender identity. And there were plenty of people around ready to tell me that I wasn't really gay if I were bisexual, and I couldn't take too many additional iterations of being told what I wasn't and should be—I was getting enough of those comments related to being a working-class person in a professional middle-class milieu. So while I was unconsciously being transformed into a sort of professional-middle-class femininity, I was (mostly) consciously *not* proclaiming my queer identity. "Queer" was not yet a term and a definition fully available to me at that point in the development of the idea and of my own education. The need for definition and scholarly legitimation of every aspect of my identity was, ironically, eroding my longtime-unconsciously held identity. I was lost in more ways than I even knew I was lost.

I made it through graduate school, which was a breeze intellectually, if not emotionally. I didn't really know who I was any more. [*Puts on a hat.*] I had been an unhappy working-class boy, yearning for a world of books and ideas. Now I found myself a professional-middle-class woman, better educated but not any wiser, lost between worlds. [*Takes off the hat.*]

I found a tenure-track job at Cal State Stanislaus in the Central Valley, a part of California that might as well be Idaho, or the bible belt. I spent several years writing about class identity, trying to sort that out, after my difficult years in graduate school. And I sort of forgot about gender identity. I typically wore black jeans and a silk shirt to work, and used so many "big words" in my everyday speech that my family was afraid to talk to me anymore. The look was not gender-neutral: the silk shirts were feminine and my speech was not that of the working-class boy I had once been. I had clearly lost myself, in terms of my class identity and my gender identity. Until the homophobia of the area I was in drew me into becoming a gay rights activist on campus. Quiet as I'd been in Santa Cruz, I now became very outspoken.

And I tried on middle-class drag for the first time. When I was named director of the new Women's Center on campus, I wore a jacket, shirt, and tie to the opening. [*Takes off the scarf and puts on a tie.*] My hair was still long, and I parted and combed it to look sort of like Marlene Dietrich or Greta Garbo in one of their drag performances. I wanted to be shocking. It worked. And it was the first unwitting step into the next stage of my evolution: from working-class boy/girl to middle class woman to middle class woman/man.

After seven hard years at Stanislaus, I moved to a new job at a startup campus of the California State University system, Channel Islands in coastal Southern California. I thought, OK, a new campus with an explicit commitment to diversity. This is going to be all right; this is going to be like being back in Santa Cruz. So, at the new faculty orientation I introduced myself by saying, "I'm really glad to be here because Stanislaus was a very hard place to be a bisexual socialist atheist poet." I had been very wrong in my assessment of the place. Just about everybody in the room was shocked by my characterization of myself. Some were shocked by my sexual orientation, some by my socialism, and, I suppose some by my atheism, although nobody ever said anything about that to me. I heard about all the other aspects of myself I had named, though.

I decided there was work to be done. I was, after spending a year proving that I'm a hard and efficient worker, elected Chair of the Academic Senate. That gave me a platform to do a little more educating. So at the initial all-faculty meeting of the fall semester, I wore a suit and tie. [*Puts on a jacket.*] In my remarks, I said, "Please don't address me as Madam Chair. I'd prefer to be addressed as Mr. Chair." That got a laugh, although a bit of a nervous one. From then on, I put on middle-class drag for real. I started wearing a shirt and tie and men's slacks on any occasion that required me to get out of my usual black jeans. So, finally, I got my cockiness back.

Costume

I finish the knot in my tie,
slide the clip into place,
check out the effect in the mirror.
I look like a little girl playing dress-up
in her father's clothes. Except, my father
never wore clothes like these—fine-woven
shirt, silk jacket, slacks and wingtips.
My dad wore blue jeans or painter's pants,
a cap with "Ford" embroidered on the front.
For dress-up, his shirts had snaps instead of buttons.
I dressed in miniature imitation of him when I was small,
learned to stand like him, walk like him, cock my head the way he did,
gestures that don't fit in this jacket and tie
any better than my female body does.
But somehow, I did fit into his kind of clothes,
his kind of boots, and my hands were roughened and strong
like his those years I worked for him, before
I got a different kind of education, a "Dr." in front of my name
helping to hide not only my sex, but all the truth
of my origin. These clothes I'm wearing today
would be a costume for him as much as they are for me.

He taught me, with love and care, how to wear his boots.
There is no one to teach me how to wear these soft expensive shoes
that I have chosen.

I used to just unconsciously be who I was when I was a working-class boy/girl. Now, because of my education, I spend a lot of time thinking about who I am and about how to account for it and explain it. Performing class is a type of drag for me, as much as performing gender is drag. Putting on women's middle-class clothes is a drag performance. Putting on male-middle-class clothes is double drag.

I have a very nice wool men's cardigan that I had to get used to wearing because, in the context I grew up in, no man would ever have worn cardigan sweaters. In my working-class eyes, a cardigan is distinctly effeminate, something only a "fairy" would wear. Although that makes it very appropriate for me, it just doesn't feel right with my working-class masculine identity. Middle-class men wear cardigans, not the guys I grew up with, from whom I learned how to be a man. If

I'm a drag king in terms of gender, am I a "drag doctor" in terms of class and education?

Straddling identities is not always easy. I feel like a visitor in the professional middle class, and always will, but I can't go back to the working class. And whereas once, in my ignorant youth, my boyishness just felt normal and fine and I had no need to name it, now my attempts to claim it again in the clothes of another class make me feel like a double imposter. [*Puts on the scarf.*]

Performance Art

If I were rich I'd buy a Mapplethorpe print
and hang it on my wall. No, not one of the ones
you might expect me to choose, just to shock everybody,
an image of transgression,
of leather or S&M or male-on-male miscegenation.
No, I'd choose one of his flowers, those silent,
formal shapes, so still, so strange; and then I'd buy
a Georgia O'Keefe painting of an orchid, one of the flowing
anemones of petals, about to leap off the canvas
and into your face. And I'd hang it on another wall.
And I'd say to visitors, like a gallery docent,
"between these walls somewhere, that's where I am,
that's who I am. See if you can find me."

I'm really not either-or, in sexual orientation, gender identity, or class orientation. I move back and forth. I see myself now as an adventurer, not as a woman. I do "Gender Studies" and started a "Gender Studies" program at my university, rather than a "Women's Studies" program, because just thinking about the idea of being a woman gives me the willies, so to speak.

One reason I've never called myself a lesbian, even when it might have been more convenient than insisting on my bisexuality, is that lesbians, in my mind, are women. My girlfriend might (or might not) be a lesbian, but I could never be.

Yet I'm not a man, nor do I think of myself as a man. I'm not really transgender or transsexual. I'm something else. Just genderqueer, like I'm class-queer. If gender is a means of social control, well, I've spent my life resisting or eluding social control.

Riki Wilchins writes that "gender is the new frontier: the place to rebel, to create new individuality and uniqueness, to defy old, tired outdated social norms."[1]

So I'm genderqueer and classqueer. I live in layers of gender and sexual identity: I grew up wanting to be a working-class man, but became a middle-class woman trying to invent a gendered and classed identity that spans boundaries.

So Arrest Me

In the old days in the bars
the butches could be arrested if they weren't wearing
three pieces of women's clothing.

What, exactly, is "women's clothing," anyway?
Frilly panties? A push-up bra to make your little boobs look bigger?
A skirt? In Carolyn Gage's play about Joan of Arc,
(executed for the crime of wearing men's clothes)
the prison guards strip Joan of her shirt and trousers and put her
in a dress. Then they come into her cell and rape her.

In the butch-femme test the question is:
Do you feel more powerful in a skirt or in pants?

In a skirt I feel like a little girl
playing dress-up in her mother's clothes.
No, I feel like a gay man in drag, who might be arrested,
thrown in a cell, beaten up and raped.
I feel like Joan of Arc stripped of her power
before she's burned. So go ahead and arrest me

because I'm not wearing three pieces of "women's clothing."
[*Removes the scarf.*]

I'm wearing shoes I can run in,
pants I can stand and fight in,
and a shirt that conceals my true heart, just like every man.

---

[1] Nestle, Joan, Howell, Clare, and Wilchins, Riki (Eds.) (2002). *GenderQueer: Voices From Beyond the Sexual Binary.* New York, NY: Alyson Books: 13.

ANYWAY, IT'S NOT LIKE THINGS COULD GET MUCH WORSE
Andrej Longo
Translated by Wendell Ricketts

Me, if I could, I'd take a Kalashnikov and I'd shoot every last person I know. Plus a couple of hand grenades and a bazooka. That'd be the end of them going around acting like a bunch of hot shits and that'd be the last anyone heard of them busting people's balls. But since I can't do that, I came all the way up here to the top floor of the Hotel Riviera. I never seen Naples like this. In fact, looking across the city from up here, it seems like a different place all together: the ocean, the Castel dell'Ovo, the Maschio Angioino, the Capodimonte museum, the cars that look like so many ants and the people ... them you can't even see.

Seems like a different place all together.

"So, ma'am. How'd you get this idea in your head, anyway?" This fireman was sticking his head through the window and that's what he says to me.

"And what fucking difference does it make to you, *sir*?"

"Personally, none. But this is my job, and I'm trying to do it the best I can."

"Mister, you are wasting your time."

"So you definitely made up your mind?"

"You can take that all the way to the bank."

"What happened? Love affair go wrong?"

"I really seem that dizzy to you?"

"No, no. I don't mean that."

"That I'd throw myself off the top of a building because some man let me down?"

"Okay," he said, "then I'm wrong."

"In my case, it's my whole life that's let me down."

"Sounds rough."

"And if life has let you down...." I nodded toward the street below.

"Sure."

"How about you just leave me alone, then? It's better all the way around."

"Ma'am, if you could just explain to me first why you want to jump."

"Damn, you're stubborn."

"I know."

"Why so pushy?"

"Because, ma'am. If you really wanted to jump, you'd of done it already."

"No, sir. You got that all wrong. I do really want to jump. I just can't work up the nerve."

"That the only reason?"

"Plus, when you look at things from up here they seem different. The shit is still the same shit, but you get a nice feeling sitting up here and I wanted to enjoy it a little while before I jump. You understand?"

"No."

"Forget it."

He didn't talk for a while, then he pulled out a pack of Marlboros.

"Cigarette?"

"No, I gotta jump soon anyway."

"Smoke a cigarette, ma'am, and then you can jump."

I smiled and took a cigarette.

"Need a light?"

"I got a lighter, thanks."

I sat down with my legs hanging out in space and I lit the cigarette. He started smoking, too.

"What's your name?" he asked.

"Samantha."

"That's exotic," he said.

"It's perfect for a whore like me," I answered.

"Oh," he said. "So that's it."

"That's what?"

"No, I just mean: that's why."

"What do you know about anything?"

"You have to explain it to me better, then."

"You're interested even if I am a whore, Mr. Fireman?"

"You're still a person."

Life is definitely strange. For twenty years you meet nothing but lowlifes and scumbags and then, just when you've finally decided to end it all, a decent person comes along.

"Okay," I said. "Before I die I guess I better tell the story to someone."

"Sounds like a good idea," he said.

"First off, I'm not a woman."

"What do you mean you're not a woman?"

"Oh come on. You don't get it, for real?"

"No."

"I'm a trans. I'm a trans even though I didn't choose to be one. But, really, that's not the problem, either.

"When I was five or six, I was a regular boy, it was just that I had this real smooth skin and big, soft eyes and these long legs like a girl. So they started giving me hormones and pills and shit so I'd start growing breasts, and my mother made me play with dolls, and she used to put makeup on my face and tell me I was the prettiest little girl of all.

"At five or six you can say anything you want to a kid, he'll believe you. You can tell him about the boogey man, Santa Claus or little green men from outer space, and he's gonna think they exist. So if you tell a little boy he's really a little girl, it's not like he knows any different.

"Why'd they do it? For the money, of course. Because then when you're twelve, thirteen, you can start turning tricks.

"They get you to believe that's normal, too. And the men are hot for you. Mister, you'd never believe how much they want it. We got more customers than a regular whore, we got lines all the way down the street waiting for us and the money's coming in like it was raining cash. You find that hard to believe? You shouldn't. It happens. People raise hens because they lay eggs and they raise us like we are so we can do what we do.

"When you finally figure things out, it's too late because by then you can't tell anymore what you really are: a woman, a man, some other breed entirely, you got no idea.

"But I'm saying, a girl, once she gets to be eighteen, she could figure out on her own what she'd do if she had a little money, or at least decide what she wants to do with her life: be a whore or a hairdresser, or maybe start studying and get her a diploma, am I right?

"Nosiree. No chance in hell of that. No chance because that douche-bag of a mother who brought you into this world and who's a bigger whore than you are, she sold you out. So now you belong to some piece-a-shit boss who doesn't give a fuck about you and uses you however and whenever he feels like.

"Just like some laying chicken.

"But I was sick and tired of being a chicken, so I ran off to Rome 'cuz I thought I'd find some way to get myself out of this prison camp. But they found me and they took me back to Naples again, and the next mistake I make, it's bye-bye Samantha."

The fireman was looking at me sort of pop-eyed, because you could tell he'd never heard nothing like this in his whole life.

"But, ma'am, can't you go to the police?" he asked.

"Yeah, right, the police. You got no idea what the police are like, right?" I said.

"So what are you going to do?" he asked.

"So I'm going to jump and then I won't have to worry about it no more," I said, and I stood up.

"No, no, it can't end like this," he said. "It's not right."

"What are you gonna do," I said, "that's life." I was getting ready to jump but then the fireman climbed out onto the ledge with me.

He goes, "If you jump, then I'm going to jump, too."

I could tell he wasn't joking around, but what I couldn't figure out was how he got such a messed-up idea in his head.

"What's wrong with you?" I said. "You lose your mind?"

"Maybe."

"You got a wife, haven't you, sir?"

"She left me this morning."

"But you got kids, right?"

"Two."

"Then go back inside and stop acting like you're on crack."

"You have to come back in, too," he said.

It's getting so a girl can't even kill herself in peace these days, you know?

"What's your name?"

"Francesco."

"Francesco, now you listen up, okay? If I jump it doesn't have nothing in the world to do with you."

"I know that. But if you jump, ma'am, so help me I'm jumping, too."

"Sure you are," I said.

"Sure I am."

This guy was really going to do it.

I could of let him. I could of decided I didn't give a flying fuck who decided to jump off a ledge right next to me. Who was this guy sposed to be, anyway? It's not like I knew him.

But in my whole life, he was the only kind person I ever met.

Maybe he was doing it because his wife left him, maybe his brain was fried from the heat, or maybe it had something to do with all those firemen who died in America trying to save people and he felt he needed to play the hero a little. You try and figure it out.

In the end, I decided to let it slide.

Anyway, If I wanted, I could jump the next day. What difference did it make to me? None, that's what. But for him to jump—that wasn't right. He'd go home that evening, take a shower, hug his kids, and forget all this madness.

When we were both back inside, he goes, "Thank you, ma'am, for not jumping."

"Thank you, sir," I said.

I said it like that because I wanted to say something nice, but then I started thinking that maybe the thing with the fireman was some kind of sign, that if I looked hard enough, there might still be a chance.

Maybe all I had to do was buy me a train ticket to Paris or Madrid.

I'd get on the train and my life would change.

I could try, like I was giving myself some kind of gift, yeah, exactly like I was giving myself permission to have a dream. My whole life, I been giving other people their dreams. Who knows, for once maybe things might could even go the other way.

HEAVEN
Royston Tester

A month before I was due to leave for Blanchland House, I started to fool around again. Nicking stuff. Don't ask me why.

It kept me going while I waited for the court-imposed sentence to begin.

Worked on me like a coke rush. Easy pickings all round. On Sunday nights.

My stepfather Graham was in the pub—the Jolly Fitter across from St. John the Baptist. And ma—Vera—was at home wailing along to "Songs of Praise" on the BBC. Once her piety was over for the Day of Rest—holy communion at 8:30 of a Sunday morning, family service at 11—she could resume what she'd been doing with Graham every Friday and Saturday night since we'd arrived in Longbridge, spitting distance from Birmingham's sprawling Austin Motor Company: at the bar until closing, "never more than a rum and orange."

To make herself feel holier, she'd enrolled me in the church choir.

St. John the Baptist was a stripped-down place—heavily polished lily-white pine work and bleached walls. The building smelled of honey and the elbow grease Mrs. Fidgeon and Mrs. Hawkesford worked off on its maintenance and "floral improvements." To my nose it was tooty-fruity.

There, every Sunday morning, I churned out hymns and ma would appraise the congregation. She never missed a trick: attended coffee mornings, socials, jumble sales, scout and cub bazaars, the works. Girl Guide and Brownie bingo nights. Christian Fellowship of England club. You couldn't fault her for trying to blend in. But ma had all the regulars down pat. According to her, no one passed the rinse cycle.

With their dowdy slip-ons and cheap velvet hats, the women of St. John's were, according to her, "gormless to a bunion—sooner they climb into their litter boxes the better." Men didn't count at all—"most of 'em are women, anyway," she'd say.

And yet ma spent more time with the harridans—those, grim God-fearing ladies—than with anyone in her life, even Graham. She detested the parishioners—men, women alike—no matter how kindly they behaved.

But I don't believe ma ever troubled to ask herself why. What was so wrong? Did we look so different? Was it our accents from a canalside, country area only thirty miles away near Bloxwich? Were we gypsies selling clothes pegs? Or had someone, once too often, put her down? Found her girlish, deferential, social ways too stagy? Who knows why newcomers didn't fit in. Ma sold football pools for *our* living. Graham was on the dole. *They* were all bricklayers', plumbers', and carpenters' wives. And Austin car people. *Skilled.*

Ma wanted out, that's my guess, but didn't know where else was better. So Vera and Graham went on being the cheeriest outcasts in all Longbridge, doors closed all around. She ingratiated herself, never inviting a parish soul into our home. Nor they us into one of theirs. Ever. Except Nelly Barton next door—and she was heathen.

But church was like living in our council house in Edenhurst Grove, too. Infiltrators, each one of us. Fear hovering beneath every confident gesture. Upbeat pass-bys on the stairs and in the cramped hallway. Thin cheeriness. Masks. None of us daring to speak honestly about our lives, what we really felt. Questions we yearned to ask. No wonder my philosophy had blossomed at wanking and leveling war veterans for the life savings hidden in their squirrel teapots (hence the magistrate's sentence). What the hell did it take to turn my family circus off? Find some tenderness in our eyes? An honest word?

Wrongness loomed large over Edenhurst Grove, like David and Goliath entwined. One face ignoring the other. Not surprisingly, I was ready to explode.

I'd been at St. John's since 1970. Two years chanting and prattling my adolescence away. But after the business with the magistrate, ma discreetly asked the vicar if I could join the senior choristers for weddings and funerals, held on Saturdays, as well as for the two Sunday services and Evensong at 6:30. A weekend of blistering Protestant devotion, not to mention the choir practices of a Monday and Wednesday night. Shrouded in her guilt over my criminal lapse, I was heading for a bishopric. A spiritual high for the damnation that was surely to follow at Blanchland House.

The Reverend Langston Garnett from Bradford via Bloxwich—"a meddling wog and the oddest you'll ever meet," as ma liked to put it behind his back—had not hesitated. Or so she said. They always needed a good alto. Moreover, he'd offered to counsel her "delinquent Enoch" if I had *need*. Reverend Garnett would pray for my soul. And, of course, the circumstances would be safe with him. Not a word to anyone about reform school or Borstal. "This is Longbridge, Mrs. Jones," he had said—meaning a cut above any place you've known to date and compassionate about its fallen (although he didn't say that bit). He would expect me for three Sunday services. No monies paid. And would enroll me in the Catechism Group for Young Britons. It would help me on that yellow brick road to enlightenment, if not to Damascus.

And there went Tuesday and Thursday nights! Up in more chants and responses. Nothing like a script and routine to purify the damned, I thought. The whole enterprise stank of abuse. You should have seen the other devotees around the table: blubberbods, spinsters, a cub mistress for scouts-in-waiting and an alcoholic factory worker who saw existence in terms of gear-cutting. Some hippy freak from Northfield Lending Library. I was drowning in righteousness.

The real knives came out over the matter of Sunday at 6:30, however: Evensong at St. John's.

Nobody in the choir—except the old timers—enjoyed this hour-long excruciation of canticles and psalms. With a congregation of five or six widowed pensioners and the occasional refugee from the Jolly Fitter, this was the low point of St. John's week, illuminated solely by candles that trembled from many a draught in the hold—and from the merciless gaze of a certain Mr. Ketland, the new and exemplary church warden, who seemed especially devoted to the pearl-faced boy choristers.

Even Reverend Garnett appeared downcast by it all—or was this *faith*?—especially as he declined to allow heating until December ("the numbers don't warrant"). And Mr. Swithin, organist and choirmaster, who used the nocturnal occasion to rehearse his frenzied Bach before and after the actual service, scratching his buttock between the thunderous seizures of music. Melancholy Mr. Swithin, he lived for religious abandonment. And for conducting his sopranos. Pick, swerve, pluck. They broke his heart—which explained the twitch on him; and on all of us at his practices.

Evensong was purgatory. I was opting out.

On the third Sunday in September, I left the house at six o'clock as usual to walk up Longbridge Lane to Calvary. I stopped by Windeatt's for some Polo mints and then, bowels stirring with mischievousness, I ducked behind some trees on a patch of wasteland across from St. John's.

Waiting and watching in the darkness. Drizzle. Until Evensong resurrected itself for yet another spine-tingling week. If God only knew what people put themselves through in His name.

Someone should write a letter.

From between the branches, I could see the maneuvers commence: Mr. Ketland—alongside a table of prayer books at the rear of the church—his head bowed but one eye kept on his favorites among the teenaged angels; the skeleton choir, led by Reverend Garnett, making its way through a congregation that had survived to see another day. After five minutes or so I hurried across Longbridge Lane to the church's side entrance, past the choir vestiary on the right and into the men's washroom.

And there they were. The Apostles. Three of them, all flush for the reaping.

It took seconds. There was always some spare change, cigarettes and, the previous Sunday, a wallet with fifty quid. Overcoats in a welcoming row.

As I was clearing out the third set of pockets, I heard the distant squeak of a St. John's door.

I rushed to a urinal, unzipped and desperately tried to splash onto the fragrant porcelain.

The washroom door eased open. In walked Mr. Ketland, a dusty-faced, straitened Welshman—anywhere between thirty and sixty—with a brusque manner and polished shoes. Recently promoted from assembly-line Austin worker to foreman, he was therefore newly converted to Tory politics as well as to spiritual rigor. And neckties. A factory menopause like no other. He stood and observed me as a hysterectomy might the immaculate conception. No go there.

"Evening, Mr. Ketland," I said. "Damp night."

He nodded and put his hands in his pockets as though seeking guidance. How do you supervise a parish lavatory, O Lord?

I smiled and looked away. Had he noticed my three absences from Evensong? Had ma been informed? Reverend Garnett? I'd never considered that my last week's harvest might have led to *complaints* and *investigations*.

My ears felt hot.

"Arrived late for choir," I told him, shaking my dick of non-existent pee. "Better get off home."

Mr. Ketland was looking stern. I was in for it. On top of the Blanchland fuss. It'd be jail next: Wormwood Scrubs—skinned alive. Maybe I should invite Foreman Ketland to the Catechism Group?

Desperate measures, Enoch.

So instead of slipping my cock back into its jeans, I let it flop out, turning around slowly so that he could see the uncut length. He stared at it, his chest rising and falling beneath the phony regimental tie.

I spat into my fingers and began massaging the head like I was soaping in the shower. With finger and thumb I pulled the foreskin back and forth: see it stretch and have a nice day. Happy teatime marshmallow rising from the flames, Mr. Ketland?

I offered him a lick.

Cheeks stained red, he murmured something foreman-like but walked toward me, breathing rapidly.

Hit me or fuck me, I thought patting the shaft of my dick left and right.

As he approached, I reached deftly for his groin and there, beneath his neatly pressed twill trousers, lay the stiffness of redemption.

Slipping his cock out from beneath layers of flannel, I began jacking him.

"You're bad news, Enoch Jones," he said hoarsely, pulling me against his Norfolk jacket. He smelled of Old Spice.

"Aren't I," I replied, adjusting my grip.

He knelt down heavily and sucked for a minute or two as I rested my hand on his Brylcreemed head.

Eventually he struggled back to his feet. "Sooner you're in reform school, the better for us all."

"First line of a hymn, Mr. Ketland?"

He started kissing me on the lips. I felt sick to my socks but liked the taste of skin. Even his. How did he know about Blanchland House?

"Minute you and that Vera Jones walked in here...," he began, throat straining, "... trouble."

I yanked the Austin prick harder and harder.

He buried his face in my shoulder.

"Oh Jesus," he moaned, thrusting for eternity and God himself.

Almost there.

"Jesus, yeah," I whispered encouragingly, steadying myself against a urinal.

"The lot of you," he gasped, beginning a lengthy choking sound as he reached for my ass, "not from around here...."

"That's it, man."

"Trash," he managed to say, trembling from tip to toe.

And he came—or rather, sputtered—over my anorak sleeve.

"You were right then, Mr. Ketland," I said, squirting jism onto the tiled floor. Something simultaneous to remember me by.

"Caravan runts," he said, still gripping my elbow.

"Yeah," I agreed, fastening my jeans. "Not your sort at all."

"Next time, you'll be reported," he added, zipping up and checking himself in the mirror.

"For bringing you off, like?" I replied, hurrying toward the line of coats.

"You know what for," he said, turning off a tap. With wet hands, straightening his tie.

"Thanks, Mr. Ketland."

"Hop it before I change my mind, lad."

Before you could say Jack Robinson I was out on Turves Green, taking the back route home by the Carisbrooke flats so I wouldn't bump into ma on Longbridge Lane. She of a Sunday night. Imbued with holy spirit, serenading the pub for a wee dram more.

Loose change and cigarettes in my pocket. "God, I love Evensong!" I yelled out loud. Benediction felt sticky in my Y fronts as I started to catch on. Ma, Graham and me, we really weren't from around here. And it showed. Trailer trash. Caravan runts: love 'em, fuck 'em, or hate 'em; it's all the same.

Christ, I'm dim.

It's truly eye-opening what you learn when you're in communion with everything you're not supposed to see. Maybe my family was not so out of the ordinary, keeping everything that mattered under wraps. We'd fit right in if the locals let us. Still, it isn't pretty when grown-ups—well, mothers and fathers and church wardens, so far—will do anything to keep you in the shadows, fingers, and thumbs in front of your face.

But I had Mr. Ketland to thank for letting me see beneath a pair of Longbridge trousers. The way you discover things about yourself—Nancy-boy? Trash? Bog whore?—is when you're not expecting to. Even the worst sounding places—and people—can turn you right around.

If I'd had a breakthrough that rainy Sunday night, it was downright confusing. Nothing seemed to mesh except for one small thing: the taste of someone's lips, the solid heft of him in my hand. And the way it could end with you back on the street and no harm done, wanting to yell to the sleeping houses from something like happiness.

The Word made flesh.

No St. Paul, me, but finally, at one of St. John's blessed services—albeit in the wrong room—I'd had a fearful glimpse of heaven.

At seventeen, more than most would wish to see.

I was growing more optimistic about reform school.

AUSTIN
Robby Nadler

The first driver mosey in round 10 even though they got guys
stretchin' and pullin' frozen about 4 in the morning. Senior
comes in at 10 cause that way he gets dibs on the catering.
Which is where you bury big treasure tips in Austin. Never
hardly a thing to take that early, but every blue day on 6th some
hung-over bartender wakes with another tat and wants a BLT.
Don't matter—those guys usually tip you good like with a 5 note
and a shot of Patron and it makes the shift helluva faster when
sloshed 'cause the heat don't creep down as hard.

Quarter 'til the other boys ride in tired 'cause they kept that
bartender company at Darwin's. All 'sposed to flash by 11, but
stragglers get going which the manager bitches for, but aint no
need since nothing kicks in the phones 'til-nother half-past. Let
the pretty boys sleep in I say.

The Capitol sits six blocks north like an old bird that draws
in the day. Everything gets near it so all them buses and
important commuters take over the district like fleas. Too many
people in their shifts to delivery nothing in a decent time. The
best parking you gonna find if any is gonna charge you 10 bucks
a slot. So many peeps in suits who can't leave their desks and i-
berries to grab a bite willing to pay more than a shoe to cough
lunch. This is the answer for all the bike deliveries 'cause they
weave the cars pretty good and you park anywhere with a metal
neck to chain.

Pull in third mostly. Sometimes second and on last days when
senior trips I steal first. I don't got any seniority over the guys, but
they work hours 'til sleep so they don't throw a word since I
grabbed sole shift unless to cover. Same guys play hello over the
classic and the sun goes down but the heat don't in Texas, so I'd

only brush with a signal since the sweat's already rolling quarters. In the back with the bleach and TP there's aprons to grab if in-shop, but the boys change and hang their shit from an open rack or toss it on the grate if there's not. Some of the others mix up the uniform, but I kept it khaki and short in the summer. Don't know the idiot in Chi-Town that thought up black, but it was prolly Jimmy himself. Like the sun don't shine up in Urbana. So it's important to keep a hand of beaters to change out less you want that sweat riding your back.

I got a helmet too cause the store says something about hats and I didn't need no hat with a helmet. Shit. If you wanna gamble head with the SOBs out there take your shot, but I wouldn't risk the bill for appearance sake. My mind we already looked full moron in the getup so didn't matter none too much for a bit of flare.

We got called lazy 'cause we are in lots of ways. The drivers get it. Aint no money in-shop and no money in salary. Tips is cracking. The smart ones drive 'cause they see the money. Didn't start as one, but worked myself up. Doubled dipped my change bank on spot. But we get paid to drive, which we do well. But you can't deliver what isn't there to take. We stand and wait ourselves on clock to the red eyes of management until in-shop opens mouths like you can pine the indie bands all you want 'til Mona Moans Mother Truckers and the Swedish chick on violin takes on at Mohawks at 8 like that ride east the fuck fly-by-through before Neches cuts you off in a police tape of punk lesbians pissed drunk Elysium aint gay night tonight. Still, there's a point we could do shit like sweep, but we don't.

But we got paid to drive, which we do well. Delivery takes less than eight minutes from door to door and aint no one say "Subs so fast you'll freak!" like us. Take it this way. Grid useta be Chavez by Eleventh, Guadaloop to Red River. 816 opened not long before and we found ourselves half as big. Up to south of 8th. All in all we like it. None too much big order come up that ways to begin with. Save us the trip and fitty-cent tip. Second we sees ourselves a weird order we knows who gets it. Show us any ten deliveries and we'll route 'em faster than you can check 'em.

Perks of the job is I got my bike all day. Leave Hyde Park at 10 where all us drivers lived 'cause we're smart enough to settle north of the drag with pools. Ride 'til 3 for the latest for cash, then ride back home some time before 5 with stops to grub. It's nice that way. Plenty of air to make thoughts and no one to bother you a word. Walk in and chat for few then out the door.

Then you can take all that huff and puff air into your muscles and show up to the glitter bars on 4th Saturday nights like AIDS never happened. Them boys that offer to buy you drinks can be nothing more than the same ones that barley never sign a dollar to your delivery when you shuttle them lunch. Under strobe lights ask you what you do to stay so hard in the pecs. Wouldn't even break them in ten pieces if they put two and two to sauce and recognized even a gorilla can put on a mortgage shirt, spit his hair down the middle, and dance the dance dance dropped my heart o'swear it to me with eggs in the morning. One of the first rules of driving is never give your digits to a tie-man if he isn't kind to you with the uniform on.

But that aint gonna change that water runs downhill, traffic one way on 9th, so all 'paticos and Latins and Schemats 9-5ers listen like the dude who flew from the thirteenth floor forgetting the sky is painted in the other direction; the best rides are heading to Los Angeles and somehow everything else is out of the delivery area, but trust me, when you get 200 west you better pray 1980 is the floor a sweet-potato-pancake Janis Joplin choked Rick Perry's cock on and now answers the telephone with "Hello, Kim's outback riding god into Moonshine and Magnolia, but there's tip" like powdered donut dust facializing the veins in your Labradors on leash for hands, and to tell me that this aint about music.

Purty though with the job I mean. Going into the buildings for every floor every office and no one sees the city like you. Meets all kinds of people. Lots nicer than the ones who can't. It's the occasional prick with a log in his ass that treats you like the JC dropout he thinks you are. Side from that, folks treat ya well. Nice anyone pulls over for directions and you tell 'em all, if you want to. And that's 'cause there's outsiders and sometimes we don't. One thing here cause you gotta know my boys chase away San Jac cause they say it right and the second you Antonian mosey on it flashing big Tex talk of Salt Lick and jahlapenoh jam we're gonna slam Kerby Lane gingerbread down your throat and make you buy us a Mexican martini cause you god swearing hicks of the way east are Mondays apart from Louisiana and don't let no Luby's Luanne platter with side o'grits convince you otherwise.

I get misty for my boys back at the shop. Worry about 'em too. I got out when I did 'cause you can only spend so much daylight on the job before the decades catch up. Said to myself degree is happening now. Ride the hurricane economy out.

Delivery sandwiches by bike can be a funny gig though. Didn't think no bread and ham could mean a damn 'cept to pay the way for grad apps, but it does. Alls I did back then was ride and talk and even my biggest problems were the best ones one could have. Looking back is water.

But I seen them after last Christmas on a visit to scout the pad and there was a party in my name. Real low key, but genuine Texan beer to boot props of the host. Spoke to each one and they seemed happy. Started calling me "college boy" though most did college too, just not grad. Smart too. Like you wouldn't know. Spin shit on Orwell or photography and you'd think you was speaking to a teach minus the tats, chains, and tight jeans.

They kept asking if I was happy up north with the snow, balls frozen. Said yeah, that the place was the jump-off. That seemed to make 'em smile, and they were happy for me, which is such a rare thing to get these day, much less from other people. Truth is that wasn't no truth. My whole life I've spent moving, leaving people like boxes behind because it's what I do. Picked up words here and there and got to be local now and then. Not much to me more than I can write about it now. But this was different. They could tell by the way I spat talk outside the shop, something we never did. It was always "Yes" and "Good morning" when the helmets came off. Our own world for a bit, you know? Even when I said goodbye to them all I took salute and call. That's 'cause I knew when the door came clocked I'd be "college boy" again and lose the language that bound us in more than just how we flipped the customers. Honestly, I had never been as happy.

HOOTERS, TOOTERS, AND THE BIG DOG
Timothy Anderson

I spent last night with a fugitive
Tonight with a saint
Tomorrow with a drag queen
Who isn't as bent

Don't know where I'm going
Don't know who I've been
Don't know if I'm doing good
But I'd do it all again

The eyes just weren't cooperating. It was morning, and although I'd gotten three hours of sleep the night before, they refused to stay open in the spring morning sun. Running westbound on I-40 between Amarillo and nowhere, I was just east of New Mexico. The last of the Texas plains were a memory, and the rough country of New Mexico loomed ahead. I hightailed it into the San Jon rest area and grabbed an hour of shuteye. The fertilizer wasn't in a hurry and neither was I. Dallas was home recovering from surgery for an old rodeo injury, so it was just me and my big red truck, Little Red Ride 'Em Good.

I awoke an hour or so later. Groggy but ready to roll. The truck eased out of the parking lot nice and slow. Not much weight but enough to make each gear work. Eighteen gears and a dozen poses as we smoothly profiled our way out of the large vehicle parking area, past RV coaches and lost tourists and other sleeping drivers. On the road again.

The CB was active. I merged onto the freeway and heard some lady driver in the background. She was going by the handle "In Between" and, although she sounded like Bodacious, I was relieved to hear she wasn't. Unless Bodacious had changed her handle. The last time I'd met up with Bodacious and her chicken truck on I-40, she'd goaded me into racing her from just outside Barstow, California, almost all the way to Kingman, Arizona. She taunted me, and I'd gotten my ego involved. Chicken haulers, as a breed, aren't known for lolly gaggin', and I was proud of myself for beating her fair and square, but my partner, Dallas, was plenty skeptical when I tried to explain how a thirty-two-year-old grown man had gotten involved in a pissing contest with a nutcase of an outlaw hauler. The thought of restarting a race with Bodacious and her chicken truck was intriguing, but it would be hell on the fuel mileage. I was looking forward to a 6.5 average. If Bodacious was around, that number would plummet like an express elevator.

Hitting the top gear, I set the cruise control and sat back. In the background, Brad Pitt was reading Cormac McCarthy's *All the Pretty Horses*. The speakers echoed with each inflection, and the sun got hotter, and the story fell headlong into starkness and strife. Pitt was the perfect reader for the story. In his quiet voice, descriptions rolled off the tongue. Words became the tales of New Mexico meeting Mexico and cultures clashing and youth slung shot out of the passivity of protection and into reality.

In Between was gaining on me. She was in a green W-900 KW coming up fast in the hammer lane—definitely not Bodacious. Momentarily distracted by a hill, she seemed to pause. Behind her a Blue Classic Freightliner pulling a freight wagon was hot on her tail. From the CB I gathered his handle was "Big Dog." In Between and Big Dog were making miles. Running hard.

She wasn't pulling a chicken wagon but had a load of beef. Kansas style. Fresh from the packing plant and late before she started, In Between rolled into the sun. Chrome sparkled and clean paint caught the light. Behind her, Big Dog was the definition of likewise.

Caught up on the hill behind me, In Between groaned when I pulled out in front of her to get around a slow JB Hunt truck. Then I knocked off a couple of U.S. Express trucks and a Werner. The Who's Who of those not making miles with their governed, castrated, wanna be "large cars." Been there, done that. Crawled up those hills in what seemed to be a cruel version of reverse. I waved at the drivers and they waved back.

"Look at that, Big Dog," whined In Between. "A freight hauler just pulled in front of us. We are gonna have to slow waaaayyyy down." She was referring to me.

"No way. Damn freight haulers," commented Big Dog. Neither he nor In Between could see around my back doors to take in the fact that this company trailer was not pulled by a company driver in the standard issue, gutless company truck. I stroked it over the hill and left the two of them scrambling and struggling behind me.

"You see that, Big Dog?" In Between asked.

"Yep. That truck has either got a load of sailboat fuel on or it ain't no company truck," he said.

"We'll get 'em," she said.

I pulled out Brad Pitt and *All the Pretty Horses*, shut down the radio, and started concentrating on the 525 horses I was running. It was decision time. Be good, get passed, and get the going over from In Between and Big Dog, or make a hard run for it. The way they were pulling I could easily lose them in just a few hills, and it would be Albuquerque before they even thought of catching me again. Fuel mileage would go to shit but I could hear the rest of my cassette without any further interruptions. True, the CB could be shut off, but that was asking for rude surprises if I lost a tire or the road got shut down ahead and I missed the news.

Up ahead, a Winnebago passed an Airstream and made the decision for me. Two sets of grandparents proudly displaying "We're Spending our Children's Inheritance" bumper stickers clogged up the works as traffic bottlenecked and everything slowed to ten miles under the posted limit. Big Dog and In Between cussed. I was boxed in and found myself staring into In Between's cab as she came up next to me. She had a rider. A pretty young lady. In Between was older but not bad herself. Almost a Reba McIntyre look-a-like. She had some miles on her, and a person could tell that innocent wasn't exactly in her vocabulary.

"Big Dog, you should see the pretty truck I am passing. That ain't no ordinary freight hauler. It's a large car. Driver's kinda cute. Hey, what's your handle there sweetie?"

"I can't tell you," I told her.

"Sure you can. I'm harmless," she said.

"Nope. Can't. And I already know you are anything but harmless," I told her.

"How's it that you know so much?" she asked.

"Just do. I can tell. My handle, it would trouble you. So I can't."

"Yes, you can. It must be a good one. Talk real quiet so just I can hear it and I won't never tell no one. Swear." She was looking at me then looking at the road then back at me. Her rider was trying her best not to get involved. Yet every once in a while she'd look over too.

"Nope. Can't." I kept on keeping on. Traffic was rolling again in the hammer lane, and she could have rolled ahead of me but she stayed steady next to me instead. I was boxed in. All I could see on my horizon was an aluminum monstrosity with Airstream plastered all over it.

Big Dog was getting impatient. "In Between, what are you doing up there?"

"Looking," she said.

"At what?" he asked.

"This purty little thing running next to me in the High Mountain truck. I got to get me one of him. I ain't budging until he talks. He's hiding something and I can smell it. He won't tell me his handle but I'll get it out a' him. I'm good." She talked in that famous Kentucky Fried Chicken Hauler voice. Low, scratchy, and sexy. She had the looks to match the voice. Her rider, on closer view, was much younger and a different definition of pretty. She didn't look old enough to be In Between's co-driver. She glanced over at me and rolled her eyes.

"C'mon, In Between. Let's get it going. We're making a mess back here. Hell, even JB caught back up." Big Dog was getting impatient.

"Nope. Not 'til he talks. I want to get a handle on his handle." She looked over at me. Red tangles of teased hair dangled across her forehead, just this side of mall hair. A cigarette hung suspended between long, painted nails. Every once in a while, she flicked it out the open window. She was grinning at me, and her rider was trying to pretend she was anywhere but in that truck.

"Listen, In Between. You and me, we got to get one thing straight. I ain't telling you my handle. I can't. I won't. No matter what. You JUST ain't getting it. It's JUST the way things are supposed to be. And I know it's JUST killing you and it's JUST killing me that it's killing you but we both JUST gonna have to deal with it or JUST roll over and die. Because that is what's gonna have to happen before I tell you my handle. Now I'm sure y'all got much more important things to be fretting about and my handle sure ain't one of 'em." The last thing she needed to know was that I was known as Northern Exposure on the highway. I gave her my best "catch me if you can" grin. Luckily for my ass, that Airstream finally pulled off at the bottom of a good hill, and I powered down into it.

Pulling away from Big Dog and In Between, I left them struggling in the hammer lane to get over that whoop-dee-do of a hill. Behind them, both lanes were a mass of traffic.

"In Between?" I asked.

"Yes?" she came back.

"You look mighty foolish sitting there holding up all that traffic. I just want you to know that it was a pleasure running with you." It was arrogant of me to say such a thing. I knew it just added fuel to her fire. I suppose it even made me a Male Chauvinist Pig, but damn, if it didn't feel good just to walk over that hill and put a half mile on her and Big Dog in no more than a few.

"Big Dog?" In Between asked.

"What?" he responded. He almost sounded irritated.

"We got to catch that High Mountain truck. I'm gonna get that handle." She sounded determined.

"Oh for Chrissakes, In Between, just leave it be. You ain't ever gonna catch that boy. You just gotta put it out of your mind. Forget about it." Big Dog was frustrated.

"Can't," she responded.

Big Dog groaned.

I stayed out of traffic bottlenecks and made good time. Big Dog and In Between got smaller and smaller in my mirrors. Soon enough it seemed they were on to other topics. Forgotten, I listened in amazement at the goings-on behind me.

"I am a full Irish redhead," In Between was saying. "It's all real. Ain't no dye on this head. I got me red on my head and a snatch to match."

Big Dog was intrigued. "Let me see," he begged.

Apparently she stuck her head out of the window as he passed her.

"Look, In Between, I already seen your head. I want to see the other," he pleaded.

"Uh uh," she said.

"Please...," he begged.

"Nope, I can't. But if you slow down I'll show you something else." I instantly recognized that tone in her voice. I hadn't known her for even an hour but I knew. It meant mayhem. Trouble. I turned my CB up.

Things were quiet for a minute.

"Damn, In Between ... that is a fine set of hooters you got. Mighty fine." Big Dog was impressed.

"Why, thank you, Big Dog. I'm rather fond of them myself." She sounded tickled.

I wondered what the hell was going on back there. So did every other driver within ear shot. Both Eastbound and Westbound.

"Where's the hooters?" driver after driver asked. Mile markers were exchanged. Locations given. The suspect's vehicle was identified. Chaos reigned.

Big Dog wanted to see the hooters of In Between's rider next. She wasn't cooperating. I watched in my mirrors as the blue Freightliner came around on the passenger side of the green KW. Big Dog was pleading with her. "Please show me your hooters, darling ... I'll make it worth your while, I promise."

I wondered what Big Dog had to offer that would be worth her exposing her breasts to a leering, middle-aged driver. In Between answered my question.

"Damn, Big Dog! You are one BIG DOG. You better put that away before someone gets in an accident!" In Between exclaimed.

"No. I'm gonna leave it out until that purty rider of yours plays, too," he said.

They went on rolling down the highway, and I heard Big Dog tell everyone listening that In Between had entirely removed both her blouse and her bra and was now driving down the road completely topless. Big Dog continued to expose himself and continued to plead with In Between's uncooperative passenger.

Then it happened. Without warning. I saw the two trucks, running side by side behind me, do a strange dance. The radio went silent. The commotion only lasted a few seconds. But when it was over there were several pregnant seconds of silence while everyone regrouped. Big Dog was now trailing In Between by several truck lengths. In the meantime, she seemed to have regained possession of her lane.

"Sorry 'bout that, Big Dog," In Between finally exclaimed breathlessly.

"You better be. What the hell happened?" Big Dog responded. They both sounded like they'd seen a ghost.

"I dropped my cigarette. Burned my hooter. I missed it and the damn thing fell into my lap. Burned my tooter, too." She was stunned.

"No shit?" asked The Big Dog. "You OK?"

"No shit," she responded. "And, yeah I'm OK. It burns a bit ... but my hooters'll be OK. Don't know 'bout the other."

"Well, I almost lost Little Big Dog in the steering wheel trying to stay out of your way. You don't know what a scare like that does to a man." He was still shaken.

"You don't know what a cigarette out a control does to a woman either." Her voice wasn't quite the same as it had been before.

"Damn, In Between ... you gotta be more careful," he commanded,

"OK, OK. I will. Still ain't putting my hooters away though," she replied.

"And we wouldn't want you to," another driver responded.

Chaos returned to the radio as drivers tried to figure out where Big Dog and In Between were. The terrain was flatter now. As we flew by the junipers and cedars on the plateau west of Santa Rosa, the radio was a constant hum of speculation about the whereabouts of the runaway hooters.

Company drivers cussed their predicament, frustrated at governed company tractors that wouldn't allow them to tag along or get a long enough glimpse as the two truckers flew by. Still other drivers did manage to catch up and joined the procession led by a proudly topless redhead.

Another couple somewhere ahead of us seemed bent on adding more topless hooters to the mix. A woman named "Go Figure" proudly announced that her husband was convinced she had a finer set. He wanted Go Figure to compare her set with In Between's. They weren't sure where we were. In Between asked them for a mile marker and to identify their truck, which Go Figure's husband proudly did.

They were in a red freightliner. I realized, as they announced it, that I was in the process of passing the very same truck. I looked over into the cab and the husband smiled at me. I also saw his wife, Go Figure, who hadn't realized that another driver was passing them and suddenly scrambled for something to cover herself. She belted her husband for not warning her and then grabbed the CB mike.

"Did you see 'em, High Mountain?" Go Figure asked.

"Yeah, I saw 'em," I answered.

"What did you think?" she asked. "Who has the better hooters?"

"Well ma'am, I can't rightly tell you. I ain't seen In Between's Hooters. I have only seen yours. They're nice though. You ain't got nothin' to be ashamed of."

I could appreciate the artistic merits of mammary gland form. It was all academic. A pursuit of the highest standards of excellence. I shared my vision of Go Figure's hooters with everyone who was listening, and I felt no misrepresentation. In fact, my credentials as judge were unquestionable. I pondered my grandfather's well known love for all things hooter and used his finely tuned skills and criteria (which he had often shared with me) to make my call. She had a fine set.

In fact, right up until just before grandpa died, he had continued to refine his judgment in this area. In Spokane there is a quaint little franchised club where he used to hang out with his buddies.

For "lunch."

Known as Déjà Vu, the home of ninety-nine beautiful girls and three ugly ones, it was also the home of the Texas Couch Dance. It wasn't until late one evening several years ago, when Dallas's and my pickup truck broke down outside this establishment, that we found ourselves inside the place my grandfather had so frequently and fondly spoken of to my grandmother as having the "finest food in town."

We sat down at the bar and waited for the menu. A beautiful woman approached and asked what she could do for us. Although it was obviously a strip joint, we were still under the impression that they had a full menu. Imagine the surprise on our faces when we learned they didn't serve any food. Never had. Never would. They only served beverages. Suddenly my grandfather's curious development of diabetes was explained. It wasn't grandma's cooking but all those years of going without a midday meal so he could have "lunch" with the boys at Déjà Vu. Imagine day after twelve-hour day of hard work without a bite to eat.

He got caught several years later. Ill with terminal cancer, he sat across from a hospice worker who explained to him the progression of his disease. My grandmother and I sat with them in the living room, taking it all in as he asked many questions of the pretty young woman. After a long silence, grandpa finally asked the hospice woman if he could continue to have lunch with my uncles at the Déjà Vu. The stunned and blushing hospice worker looked at my grandfather in amazement. Frail with cancer and worn from the treatments, he still wanted to go to the Déjà Vu. She finally laughed and told him, "Orin, you know they don't serve food there."

My grandmother shot me an alarmed look, and I quickly interjected, "Oh, yes they do serve food. I've been there." Grandma was looking at me now, puzzled.

"Damn right," Grandpa interjected. The hospice worker gave us one of those condescending smiles that women sometimes give men who are in cahoots together. It said, "Well, aren't you two just a fine work in progress." Thankfully she didn't pursue it any further. And, my grandmother, horrified that the subject had been brought up to begin with, was content to let the matter drop. I think she knew all along what my grandfather and my uncles were up to. Montana women are just plain smart that way.

Still, my grandfather would have approved of the compliments I'd directed toward Go Figure.

Go Figure responded enthusiastically, "Why thank you High...."

Go Figure was cut off by In Between's booming voice. "High Mountain? Is that you? I'm gonna catch you so you can see mine. Why won't you run with me?"

I responded, "Because I know you are trouble, In Between."

"How do you know that?" she asked.

"What color is your hair?" I asked.

"Red. Naturally red." She said.

"See, that's how I know you are trouble and that if I run with you, you will get me into trouble. I have a lot of experience with redheads. They only lead to trouble. I've been down this road before." I was determined to stay out of this one. I didn't want to see In Between's hooters. I didn't want to get Big Dog pissed at me for moving in on whatever he thought he had going with In Between. And I didn't want to be forced to judge who had the nicest set. The irony of the situation was not lost on me. I knew there were far better judges than me in the very near vicinity.

In Between's green KW was now running next to Go Figure's red Freightliner. I wondered if Big Dog was just beside himself that there wasn't a third lane. I knew right where he'd be if he could. In the middle.

Over the next few miles there was a lively roundtable discussion over who had the best set. The old timers were voting for In Between because she had "Class and the Sass to Match." The other drivers were inclined to vote for Go Figure because she was from the "Show Me" state and had promised never to drop a cigarette anywhere that might "alter the mood." I wondered what her husband was thinking about the competition. I considered that things might be getting just a little bit out of control. Looking in my mirrors I figured there were at least twenty trucks bunched up behind me in the hooter procession.

Unfortunately, In Between tired of the competition and once again focused her sizable attention on me. "High Mountain?" she asked.

Oh no, I thought. *What now?* I'd stayed close enough to keep tabs on their goings on but far enough ahead to be out of harm's way if In Between dropped another cigarette. Big Dog was silent.

"Yes," I responded.

"I have to go pot-tay," In Between announced, using the Arkansas French pronunciation for piss.

"OOOOhhhkkaaaayyy," I answered.

"Why don't you stop with us at Clines Corners? I can use the ladies room and I'll buy ya' a cup a' coffee. Then we can keep running together. Where you heading?" she asked.

"California."

"Me, too," she said.

I groaned to myself. "I can't stop, In Between. I gotta keep going." It was a lie but it was necessary. I could imagine the convention that would descend on Clines Corners when she stopped. I already knew who the keynote speaker would be.

"You are no fun," she responded. "You won't tell me your handle. You won't look at my hooters. And you won't run with me. I think you are hurtin' my feelings. You don't want to piss off a redhead now do you?"

I felt the jaws of strife descending on me. "No, ma'am. I certainly would never want to piss you off. You are way too pretty to be walking around pissed off or with a frown on your face. Just look at all those nice drivers who are willing to escort you across the 40. Now why would you want to hang out with an inexperienced hand like me when you can be surrounded by people who know how to do right by a fine woman like you? I just can't fill those shoes. But I appreciate the offer and hell, if I told you my handle, it would just upset you no end so I am gonna keep it to myself, 'cause I can't do that to a lady such as yourself."

I hated myself. I had no pride. Big Dog confirmed it. "That was smoother than Slick Willy, In Between. You gonna let him get away with shinin' you on like that?"

"Yeah, it was smooth wasn't it? I liked it, though. He knows how to talk. He claims to be sweet and innocent, but that boy knows something. He ain't worried about me getting him into trouble. Nope, that boy is worried about him getting me into trouble. I know it. And as soon as I go pot-tay I am gonna catch him. That's some trouble I gotta find out about."

We said our goodbyes and I started wondering where I was going to hide out for twelve hours while she got ahead of me. I finally settled on the Ranch in Albuquerque. Behind me, I watched as the whole pack of trucks exited off the freeway. Clines Corners would never be the same.

In my mirrors, I also noticed one lone truck that hadn't exited with the other hounds. A red, long-nosed, "Pete" pulling a bull wagon. A truck I hadn't passed. I wondered how long it had been there, sneaking up on our back door. Listening.

The truck was immaculate, with a big chrome Texas bumper and painted in the kind of red that glows in all-type weather. I watched the truck quickly catch me and was surprised when it moved out into the hammer lane and then slowed as it came up next to me. The truck was piloted by a cowboy with a big, dark, bushy mustache and a straw Stetson hat. He wasn't wearing a shirt and I could see he hadn't been eating a lot of chicken-fried steak. He studied me for a minute, then extended a muscular arm across the passenger seat. He threw me a big smile and gave me a thumbs up. And then he was off.

I took out after him toward the looming Sangre de Cristo mountains. He was running hard and after a minute he came over the radio in a low voice that was quiet and calm. "High Mountain, you know she won't rest until she finds you."

"Yeah, I 'spose you're right," I answered, sullen.

We rode in silence though Moriarty. Then he spoke again. "So how about it. You fixin' to tell me your handle or am I gonna be chasin' ya, too?"

I thought for a minute. Considered my options.

"Well?" he said. "I only ask once, then...." He got quiet, like he was also considering options.

I told him to take it to another channel. Here was a hand I'd have no problem sharing my name with.

FRAGMENTS FROM AN AUTOBIOGRAPHY
John Gilgun

I

My mother Bea's mantra was: "You were born to get up every morning and go to work. That's it."

She and May, my father's Wicked Stepmother, agreed on this. May's mantra: "Someone's got to get that milk to our customers even if it kills them."

My father would say about me, "What's he going to do? How's he going to earn a living? He's got no friends and he can't get along with the guys. Who's going to support me in my old age?" Not very subtle code for "What are we going to do with this useless queer?"

His brother, my Uncle Charles, wrote to me, "After your father finished the eighth grade, May yanked him out of school and made him do coolie labor at a dollar a day for Gilgun's Milk."

Years later, at a working-class studies conference that I attended in Youngstown, Ohio, I delivered a paper on work, and I used this statement from Charles's letter in my speech. A hand shot up in the audience and a thin, narrow-faced woman said, "You can't use the word *coolie!*"

I said, "It's in a direct quotation taken from a letter from my uncle."

"You can't use it," this idiot said again. "You can't use that word." Then she wrapped herself in her Political Correctness shawl and looked superior in a solidly middle-class way, like Carrie Nation hacking up a bar room in Kansas with her hatchet circa 1919.

I continued on and finished my talk.

But it *was* coolie labor, up at four every morning, into the milk room, onto the truck, a dollar a day, six dollars a week. Charles was put to the same coolie labor. That milk had to be on the doorstep that day. "It was for a customer!" The word "customer" was right up there with God, Jesus, the Virgin Mary, and Sister Ernestina at the Cattle-Smash School every Gilgun child was sent to. (Except me who went to public school.)

"Why did God make you?" This was the first question in the Baltimore Catechism.

Answer, because God never lies: "To work your ass off at coolie labor for a dollar a day, six days a week. Sunday you have off so you can spend it in church with me."

My father broke from Gilgun's Milk when he went to work for H.P. Hood, a rival milk company.

Charles, knowing that he, too, had to escape Gilgun's Milk or perish, took classes at a business school.

The Big Exam came up and Charles had to pass it to escape from Overseer Simon LeMay. May saw her labor force slipping away. Charles was studying his aching ass off in the dining room. That is when May decided she needed to vacuum the rug in there. ("Raise your feet, move your chair!") She also had to wash the windows, clean up the table on which his papers and books were laid out, clean out the bird cage, rearrange the photographs on the wall, dust the couch, repaint the ceiling, varnish the floor, water the mother-in-law's tongue in its glazed pot....

Uncle Charles told me he said to May, "*If—you—don't—get—out—of—this—room—I—will—kill—you!*"

He said it with absolute determination. May left the room and didn't come back. Charles would have broken her scrawny chicken's neck and she knew it.

People who have never worked for a "family business" can be sentimental about "the days of free enterprise and the good old family business." Those who have worked for one know better.

Charles passed the exam & "escaped" to California. He still had to work in California but at least he earned a living wage.

II

The facts of existence for a gay child are unbearable. If he's going to survive, he twists the facts around until they are corkscrews & makes them funny. I saw the paradox at an early age & began to make up stories for my sister in our crowded bedroom. I began my nightly stories for her at the age of seven.

These were stories about people we knew in Malden, mostly her friends. For instance, my sister had a friend named Linda

Bagnall. I changed her name to Linda Bagnose—the girl born with a bag on her face instead of a nose—& gave her a hot air balloon so she could fly around in the sky all night. The balloon always ended up impaled on the clock on top of the elementary school so that the principal of the school—who was called Herbert the Sherbert—had to crawl up there & try to get the balloon loose so it could fly away again.

I was always a storyteller, the potential writer of stories that I wanted to be, that I did become and which I still am. I still am, as I am writing my autobiography here. Every time you laugh at something I write here, I get a day off in Purgatory.

First there is the official series of lies from the straights— gays can't fall in love, gays can't spit or whistle, gays are men with female souls, etc.—which are such obvious lies that they beg to be twisted around & turned into paradoxes. All my non- sexual relationships with females were copies of my friendship with my sister. I could make them laugh by turning things into total absurdities. I was a stand-up comedian from the beginning. When TV came in, with all those Yiddish stand-up acts ("Take my wife ... please!") I recognized myself in the comedians. Later this became my secret of success as a teacher. Many students wrote on their evaluations: "He tells great stories."

My father, sitting in the kitchen reading the horse & dog racing news in the Hearst paper, the *Record American* (he went to the races) hated, hated, hated, hated the chit-chattering & the laughter coming from our bedroom. He'd come in screaming, "Stop your god-damned foolishness!"

Then he'd beat the shit out of me. Much later, he insisted my sister sleep on a day bed in the dining room to stop the laughter. The foolishness went on, however, during the daylight hours. I developed entire comic routines. I invented words my father couldn't understand. I had to do something to ease the pain & the "foolishness" was my gay answer. If you could turn the dreadful "truth" into weirdness & laugh you could kill the pain. I killed the pain for my sister as a gift to her.

This is the origin of camp—this foolishness—as Susan Sontag pointed out later. First the straight lie then the twist & the transformation which made it funny. I made it funny.

My father's mother died in childbirth when my father was ten years old. My father was born in 1910, so that means his mother died in 1920.

My father's father was named Pat, Grandpaw Pat.

With no wife and three boys to raise—my father, my Uncle Charles & my gay Uncle James—Grandpaw Pat had to have live-in help, a series of women who dealt with the three children and kept the house clean. It may have been the best house in Malden. No one called it a mansion, but that's what it was. It was located at 63 Granite Street—four houses from where my father's family (my mother, myself, my sister Janet & my brother Bob) finally came to earth, 43 and then 41 Granite when we displaced Crazy Old Granny Campbell & her daughter Olive & moved into the downstairs flat.

You could walk to the Gilgun mansion from our flat in three minutes. It consisted not only of this magnificent mansion but the family business itself, *Gilgun's Milk From 1895*. Grandpaw Pat had established the business & it was a financial success. Along with the business—the milk room, etc.—there was a henhouse with an upper story for pigeons, a barn for the horse who hauled the milk wagon, a garage for the black Oldsmobile, a hen-run with ducks, a grape arbor, fruit trees, you name it. Pat was rich during the Depression & got steadily richer during World War II.

But also, with no wife, Grandpaw Pat had only the housekeepers as sexual outlets. Pat bedded the housekeepers. This meant he could never keep them. In that Irish-Catholic ghetto, this anti-sex pit, with Hell a few feet underground & God on his cloud over the park across the street, the housekeepers quit in droves.

My Uncle Charles told me that one of the housekeepers took to sleeping with James, who was a little boy then, a sickly little boy & already a gay sis, because she knew Pat, my randy grandpaw, wouldn't try to bed her with James sleeping beside her. She didn't last anyway. If Pat bedded them, they quit. If they refused to be fucked, Pat fired them.

Finally, Grandpaw Pat hired May who stayed. May was shanty Irish, living somewhere in a shack without a toilet. Then she woke in this mansion. She must have figured she had only one choice. She waited breathlessly for her fertile period & let my grandfather fuck her. She immediately got preggie, which meant he had to marry her. The infant, Margaret, was born three & a half months after the wedding.

"They hadda," my sister told me, many, many years later. "Hadda" is a Boston word which, when translated into standard English, means "They *had to* get married." May got pregnant deliberately, according to Uncle Charles.

It didn't take shanty-Irish May long to transform herself into a duchess: food from S.S. Pierce, etc., which provided gourmet food in cans to the real Mayflower duchesses on Beacon Hill. Upper class, upper middle class: May had made it. She put on airs the way the rest of us put on our socks. "The Duchess of Granite Street." When May signed on as housekeeper to Grandpaw Pat she didn't have a pot to piss in, as they say. Afterward, in the mansion, she had several of them.

As Charles said, "As soon as you moved to Granite Street, May moved right in. She got the house & the family business & kept Pat around as caretaker."

My mother Bea had left my father by that time. She was hiding out with friends in another city. My father told my maternal grandfather, "I don't care if she never comes back." But she came back.

Not ten years after my father left Gilgun's Milk, May hired his wife to do the job he had done. My father had signed up to work for Hood's Milk, a rival to Gilgun's Milk, which may have been the only independent act of his life & now his wife was working for his Wicked Stepmother. For my mother, this proved she could "do a man's work," best my father at it & get others to raise her kids. My father wanted a traditional wife who stayed home & took care of her kids. My mother refused.

This came close to ending my father's marriage. But of course the Cattle-Smash Church did not permit divorce. Besides, there was a war on & my mother's brothers were in the Pacific & my mother's father came to my father & asked him not to divorce his daughter because he didn't want them going into battle with the disgrace (divorce was a disgrace in 1942) of their sister's failed marriage on their minds.

What May saw in my mother was labor. May saw a strong woman who could drive the horse & wagon & later the Divco truck. She saw a Charles Atlas of a woman who could get out on that milk route & rattle them milk bottles. May hired her to work for Gilgun's Milk. It was as if May were buying an ox & my mother was the ox. My mother loved this.

With May, Grandpaw Pat had not only Margaret but Alice, Jean & Buddy. That meant my father, Charles & gay James at one time lived in the mansion with four other children. May stuffed her three stepsons in the attic to live. As soon as they attained their majority at fifteen, they were put to work in the milk room or delivering milk from the wagon at one dollar a day, six days a week, rain, blizzard, ice storm, heat wave, that milk had to be delivered to customers by six each morning. The boys became a vital part of May's labor force. Where was Karl Marx when everyone needed him?

I said to Uncle Charles once, "If Grandpaw Pat could have kept it in his pants all our lives would be different." Not necessarily better but different. As the oldest son, my father would have inherited the house, the money, and the family business when Pat died in 1944. Assuming I was born as me, as who I am, I'd have been put to work by my father at the age of fifteen.

As I said to Charles, who told me that the abuse I received from my father meant I had the worst childhood he'd ever seen, "Had I been put to work at fifteen with my father as my boss, it would have been World War III on Granite Street, because I would never never never have submitted."

My mother used to say of me, as my father was beating me, "You'll never break his spirit!"

Had my father inherited that business & put me to work as cheap labor at fifteen years of age, it would have made the murder of Laius by Oedipus look like the Teddy Bear's picnic. Patricide! I'd have killed the son of a bitch. Or he'd have killed me. There would have been blood in that spotless mansion right there on the gleaming, polished kitchen floor.

III

May got her children to go to our house, three minutes up the street, "to raise Bea's kids." So I was raised by Margaret, Alice, and Buddy. I wasn't raised by Jean because she was too young.

Uncle Charles was still furious the last time I talked to him about this because "All those step-kids sacrificed their childhoods to take care of your mother's kids, all except Jean. Your mother walked out on you kids. My step-sisters & brother were sacrificed to bring up kids your mother didn't want to take care of."

But Uncle Charles hated May, and he didn't think it through. For me, by getting pregnant & shaming Grandpaw Pat into marrying her, May gave me a life. Charles called her "evil." "She was evil, evil!" To me she was a blue fairy out of Disney's *Pinocchio*.

Alice

Alice & her younger sister Jean were playing at being nuns in the cellar of the "mansion." To imitate the habits of the nuns at school they had wrapped themselves in curtains which were not flame-retardant. They were carrying burning candles which is what the nuns carry in church. Suddenly Alice was wrapped in flames. The curtains caught on fire from the candles.

My grandfather Pat happened to come into the cellar at that moment. There was a rolled-up carpet next to the door. Pat grabbed the carpet & wrapped Alice in it, snuffing out the flames. Otherwise she'd have burned to death. She carried scars from those flames all her life, from her left hip down to her left knee. She still carries them in the old folk's home in Malden where she is now confined with dementia.

Jean

In her 40s Jean began to have "black fits." She'd collapse & go into a coma. This happened several times before May took her to a doctor. The doctor took an X-Ray of Jean's skull and reported to May: "I found hairline cracks in her skull which seem to have been there since her infancy before her skull hardened, probably as a result of being hit on the head with an object like a broom handle."

Of course no one else would have hit Jean on the head with a broom handle in her infancy except May.

The "black fits" wiped out parts of Jean's memory.

Buddy

Buddy had gone into the bathroom to take a piss. A few minutes later May opened the bathroom door & saw him rolling on the tile floor screaming in agony with his dick hanging out of his pants. She called one of her brothers who came over and he examined Buddy, who had developed phimosis. This is a congenital narrowing of the opening of the foreskin so that it cannot be retracted. The brother took Buddy to the hospital where the doctor circumcised him. If you can't retract the foreskin you can't piss through it. Result: agony.

My mother asked May why she didn't deal with Buddy's problem earlier. May answered, "We don't talk about such problems here." Children who are not "cut" are usually taught to retract the foreskin frequently & wash the glans. Pat was too busy or too exhausted to do his fatherly duty. Everyone else in the mansion was female & "We don't talk about such things here."

Buddy got seriously sick when he was seventeen. My mother not only worked for May delivering milk, she was her driver in the big black Oldsmobile either because May hadn't learned to drive or because she couldn't deal with Boston traffic which was & perhaps still is the worst in the country. I can remember sitting in the back seat with my mother at the wheel and May sitting beside her in the front seat going into Boston to visit Buddy in the hospital.

Buddy had what the doctors diagnosed as "mucus colitis," now called "ulcerative colitis." It is "a persistent inflammation of the lining of the colon; small ulcers form & eventually may affect the entire colonic surface. Episodes of painful, bloody diarrhea occur."—*Symptoms & Remedies*, p. 389.

In the summer of 1945, Buddy came to visit us at Martin's Pond. The first morning of his visit I took him out in the rowboat. I probably wanted to show him I knew how to row. Somewhere out there on the pond, he lowered his pants, put his ass over the side of the boat & poured out what seemed to me to be several gallons of bloody diarrhea. I had never seen anything like this & I was horrified. I remember shouting, "What is the matter with you!" I rowed him back to shore & that afternoon someone drove him back to Malden. There were no doctors or hospitals at the pond, of course.

Uncle Charles told me much later that in the middle of a New England winter the sister of his biological mother (who died in childbirth in 1920 when my father was ten years old) stopped by for a visit & found Buddy, who was sick with colitis at the time, working, doing heavy lifting in the milk room. This woman told May, "The child is sick. He should be in bed. He should not be out here working." May replied something like, "We're short-handed & somebody has to do the work."

A month after Buddy's visit to us at the pond, he died of colitis. He was 18.

When I talked about his death many years later with Uncle Charles, Charles said, "Buddy was well enough out of it."

Charles is usually right: Buddy was well enough out of it. Still, I have always thought he deserved a life. But not the life he was living the year before he died.

IV

During the summer of 1959 I was in Boston. It was the worst summer of my life. I borrowed fifty dollars from my gay Uncle James in order to fly back to Iowa City where I'd lived with my first boyfriend. He'd thrown me out in May, but I told James I needed to go back to Iowa City to be with him. But he wasn't in Iowa City; he'd moved to San Francisco. Still, I told Uncle James I had to connect with my friend in Iowa City. I was desperate to get out of Malden, so I lied.

James & I were as OUT to each other as we'd ever been in our lives at that moment, which was never at all before that moment. But James responded to my lie by telling me that he himself had had a "friend."

Uncle James told me that this friend had come to the mansion, 63 Granite Street, looking for him & been turned away. Who turned him away? May, the Wicked Stepmother? Any one of a dozen of her relatives who happened to be at 63 Granite Street when the friend turned up? Anyway this gay friend rang the doorbell & when someone opened the door, he explained that he was a friend of James & wanted to see him. The friend was told to get off the property. "Go & darken our door no more!"

Other years, other times, decades passed. In the summer of 1974 I moved to a studio apartment in Sunnyvale, California, with the purpose of consulting with Uncle Charles who lived a few blocks away. I wanted to find out what I could about what really happened in Malden, Massachusetts, as I was growing up there. Charles was already an adult at the time & knew what happened. I'd been a boy & as a boy everyone in the Gilgun family lied to me or were totally silent, the silence of the deepest, darkest closet. All closets for Gilguns rattle with the chattering bones of gay skeletons.

I told Uncle Charles & his wife Agnes that I was gay. It couldn't have come as any surprised to Charles that I was gay. But the lies were still going on. Charles had never in thirty years of marriage told his wife Agnes that his brother, James, was gay. The same shit goes on, generation after generation after generation. I told Charles & Agnes that I knew James had a gay friend.

Uncle Charles immediately got angry & started shouting, odd behavior for a man who was very careful never to get angry or to show any emotion at all. Charles, angry, said, "Yes, the friend came to the house & we turned him away, told him to get off our property, said we'd get the police on him if he came back. So what?"

"Maybe he loved James," I said. "Had you let him inside the house perhaps Uncle James's life might have better."

V

Doesn't there have to be a body before a case can be constructed? I have no evidence that Uncle Charles ever had a boyfriend. I do have evidence that James had a boyfriend, yes. But no evidence that Charles did.

Agnes, Charles's wife, told me & I quote, "Charles was a virgin when he married me & he might have been gay." Then she denied ever telling me this.

Uncle Charles said of my father, "He never had a friend." He had a lot of drinking buddies but no friend. No gay friend. No straight friend either. He too was a virgin when he married but at the time that was expected, at least in Irish-Catholic Boston. Both my parents were virgins at marriage. But so was my sister a generation later.

This is "social" & "cultural." It is not an indication of closeted homosexuality. You cannot believe the amount of sexual repression that existed in the "culture" of working-class Irish-Catholic Boston in the '30s, '40s & '50s. There was no break from this until the birth control pill became available in the late '60s.

My brother said once that my father was a real stud. But my brother was mentally deficient. It's true my father had many affairs with many women. It enhanced his sense of masculinity. He, like Charles & James, was effeminate but I have read that this comes in under "gender." Being effeminate is not the same as being gay, or so they tell me, so they say.

How many gay boys think their fathers are gay? Has a survey ever been done? I thought my father was deeply closeted & gay because of the intensity of his alcoholism. I could see that he was trying to destroy his brain. So I wondered what "terrible secret" lay in that brain that led to nightly blackouts on alcohol during which he would lie on the floor in a coma.

He did end by destroying his brain with alcohol & ended his life a state mental hospital in Massachusetts. He was put in there because he couldn't be left on the streets. He had "wet brain," which means the total destruction of memory. Funny but I just finished gathering material on "Wet Brain" so that if I ever get to this topic in my autobiography I'm aware of what it is. There is a connection in Wet Brain between violence, my father's bipolar mood swings & his alcoholism. My brother was also an alcoholic & was also diagnosed as bipolar before he died. I have not had any alcohol in the past thirty years.

But then, I love my brain & what I can do with it, but my father hated his brain, his mind, his memories. My father was so intent on destroying thought in himself that he destroyed his brain with alcohol. Of course his father, my Grandpaw Pat, was also an alcoholic & probably every male Gilgun was an alcoholic from the time of Brian Boru.

Which is why I drink no alcohol. I'm friends with my thoughts. My father hated & feared thought. Inside himself my father was terrified of something & destroyed his brain rather than think about it.

Why he did that is anyone's guess. But he fucked women with volcanic intensity & crowed about his conquests to enhance his sense of masculinity. In Malden in my childhood, that made him straight. Being a drunk also "made him straight." Real men drank. That's what alcohol was for, according to the Malden ethic of fifty years ago. Alcohol separated the men from the boys, etc. So drinks on the house, me hearties! Chug the glug down! (Burp!)

Sometimes when I think about the bullshit I was brought up with I laugh. Other times I just want to throw up.

VI

I have only a single memory of my father's father, Pat, at the Gilgun "mansion." I didn't spend much time there.

Grandpaw Pat was sitting at the kitchen table, like the airless Graf Zeppelin crumpled up on the ground and burning in New Jersey & he almost never spoke. He simply sat there, waiting for one of his three daughters by the Wicked Stepmother to serve him his daily plate of mashed potato with Gilgun's Milk butter melting on it. Of course Gilgun's Milk sold butter as well as milk. Even when butter was rationed in World War II, we Gilguns had plenty of butter melting on our daily mashed potato.

Very large hemp bags filled with Maine potatoes weighed down the platform of the railroad station on Broadway in

Malden because, as Irish-Americans, we ate potatoes every day, just as we did before the Great Potato Famine that brought us to Boston between 1844 & 1850.

Each October, "the man of the house" bought hemp bags of potatoes to see us through the winter. They sprouted in the hemp bags "down cellar" & generations of hapless daughters spent the precious moments of their youth peeling them, washing them & cooking them.

In the classy kitchen at Grandpaw Pat Gilgun's they had a Dutch oven to cook them in. Three minutes up the street, at 43 & then 41 Granite, they were boiled in water in a pan on a stove older than Saint Patrick's grandmother. If the potatoes were lumpy & hard for a kid to swallow... "Shad op & eat it! You're lucky t' git any!"

"Shad op" is Bostonese for "Shut up."

But here's my single memory of my paternal grandfather, Pat: I was in the kitchen, four years old. Pat sat at the table deflated but still cruel & dangerous. He said, "I want y' t' go to Brennan's store next door t' buy me a can of pipe tobacco. Here's a quarter. Keep the change."

At the age of four I did what I was told. I went to the store & bought Grandpaw Pat his can of pipe tobacco.

The change was one penny.

I went back to the kitchen with the can & the penny. Even at the age of four I knew I couldn't buy much with a penny. I told Grandpaw Pat so. "What can I buy with a penny!"

He began to cackle like a turkey—clack clack clack. "Much obliged fer gittin' me the tobacco," he cackled. "This'll teach yuh to ask how much change your gonna git before you do the errand. Much obliged—clack!"

When Grandpaw Pat died in 1944 the word on the street was he had a quarter of a million dollars in the bank. But all I recall about him is he screwed me as a four year old into going to the store for him for the reward of a single penny.

This story is so Irish-American I've turned green as a shamrock while writing it. Grandpaw Pat—tight as a duck's ass, Irish as Paddy's pig.

As for living on potatoes, think of Van Gogh's *The Potato Eaters*. The Dutch existed on them also. Poor starvin' bastards.

LOWEST OF THE LOW
Keith Banner

Hell I don't know. Barney's gone. I just heard his car door slam. I stick a frozen pizza in, I go out on the patio, smoke while it nukes. There's that March sky with cottage-cheese for clouds and bony trees around the half-frozen field and beyond that the backs of a McDonald's and a Walgreen's and the United Dairy Farmers where I work.

Barney's Tercel is stopped at the stoplight by the bank.

It doesn't matter. He told me upfront he wasn't into me, and I kind of liked that. It took the pressure off, and when I needed him, he was there, bored and glassy-eyed, embarrassed by how much I felt.

The other day he said his wife wanted him back.

"So you're not queer anymore?" I said.

"I guess not." He laughed. "She said she's pregnant."

I laughed too.

This is one of those deluxe frozen pizzas. Not bad. I eat half the thing and I smoke some more on the patio, with the TV on in my living room. I can hear the wheel of fortune and the overemotional audience. This apartment has some pretty nice amenities for being so crappy—a fireplace I don't use, brand new wall-to-wall carpet, this patio with sliding glass doors and vertical blinds. A washer-dryer combo in the bathroom. Too bad it doesn't work.

There's a knock on my door while I'm peeing. I yell that I'll be there in a sec. And of course as I finish, I whip up a whole new fantasy of Barney's Tercel doing a U-turn. Barney out there in the foyer next to the row of rusty robot-looking mailboxes.

I open it, and there's Tiffany, the teenage girl from upstairs.

"I'm sorry," she says. She wears a midriff, Britney-looking thing and thick mascara, purple streaks in her hair. You can kind of tell that she's looking for something more out of life.

"Sorry for what?" I ask.

We don't talk that much. One time I helped her carry groceries in, and her and her mom's place was decorated with all kinds of funky shit, like a big cream-colored vinyl sectional sofa and ostrich feathers and an abstract painting with sparkling lights embedded in it they told me they got on vacation.

"I have a favor to ask."

"Come on in."

I am not in the mood, but there you go. My boyfriend of three months just left me. I am a forty-two-year-old homosexual who day-manages a convenience-store. I have a major bald spot. I bite the crap out of my fingernails.

Tiffany and I sit down in the living room with *Entertainment Tonight* on.

"I need a lift over to my boyfriend's place. Mom's gone, and I don't have money for a cab, and it's just I really need to see him. He's been weird all day, calling me and begging me to come over, and I really think he's completely depressed, you know? I'm afraid of what he might do." She smiles, like it's a joke but it's not.

I do know "depressed." Hell I know it intimately. I look right at her and I can feel tears starting in my own eyes, just because she asked me, and I notice how she has a gut on her, poking out from the bright orange T-shirt she's chopped in two to make herself look like a star. That white little belly breaks my heart.

"Let me get my keys."

She smiles great big. I've seen that boy before. Skinny as a rail with a wiry goatee and always in the same black T-shirt and pants hanging down so you can see the Old Navy label on his underwear.

"You really are nice," she says.

I don't answer. I saran my pizza, I get my keys, and we are off. It's dark, and the little town is dead all around us, except for the drive-thrus. I look in at the convenience store I manage, and there's Monique, that one woman I can't stand, running register, frowning like a mental patient, which she happens to be sometimes I bet.

One time, Monique comes up to me at the change of shift and she says, "I saw that sticker on your car." Her expression was so serious as to be comical.

"What sticker?"

"That gay sticker." Monique frowned like a spy. She wasn't a Bible-thumper either. Just pissed and on the prowl for a target.

"Yeah," I said. It was a rainbow bumper-sticker Barney and me got when we went to Key West the month before.

"Aren't you afraid you'll get your brains bashed in? My cousin's gay, and he lives in Indianapolis and he got beat up last year. Him and his little boyfriend. I told him you can't be holding hands no matter what's on TV, *Will and Grace* or not, people can't take it."

The pitch in her voice was going higher. There's a certain kind of pleasure certain kind of people take in letting other people know how dangerous it is for them to be alive. Monique had that going on big-time.

"I'd peel that thing off if I was you. I mean. Come on."

I let it pass. I laughed nervously, like I really was scared, and secretly I hoped she had a prescription in her purse for Zoloft. Which is what I used to be on, and I'll probably go back on now.

Barney and me in fact met at the UDF. He was taking a second job to pay off credit-card bills, and that day he first came on I trained him. I didn't hire him, the night manager did, but I always ended up having to train people. He came in dressed in a pair of khakis and a short-sleeved shirt and a wrinkled clip-on necktie and scuffed-up Nikes.

"Am I late?" he said.

"No," I said, and right off I knew he was what I wanted. I saw his short dark hair, and the wrinkles in his tie, and the wetness of his sleepy eyes and I knew.

I tried not to show it at first. I showed him how to change the register tape and how to do inventories in back, where the mop sinks were. He followed along, real tired, you could tell, and after about two hours of training he said, "Can you smoke in here?"

I was pulling night-shifts back then. I just got the day-management position two months back. So I had slept all day. I was okay.

"No. But you can go outside there and smoke if you need to. I'll watch the register. I'm a smoker too."

I grinned at him, and he nodded his head, went outside, lit up. I watched him from beside the Slurpee machine. He smoked like a little lost nobody, looking out at the parking lot as though he were staring out at his own future and just seeing litter and oil-stains.

He came back in, and he said, "So where's the caffeine pills?"

"How about some extra strong black coffee?"

"Sure."

So we drank French Roast and I showed him how to cut deli meats and how to arrange the donuts that came in and how to make sure you check inventory and the bank deposit, all that, and then it was time to go home. His wife had fallen asleep, though, and they only had one car and he called her five times to no avail.

"She sleeps like a corpse," he said, ringing out the mop. He looked down at the floor as he mopped. There was a tiny piece of a candy wrapper floating in the mop water.

"I'll take you home."

Suddenly his face was full of hope—like an insomniac just discovering there are sleeping pills in a desk drawer.

At the stoplight just outside his apartment complex, Barney said he didn't want to go home.

"You wanna go get something to eat?" he asked. It was 5 a.m.

"I guess."

"I really just don't want to see her," he said over scrambled eggs at that one pancake house that used to be a Ponderosa, pig plaques and daisies on the wall.

I was drinking more coffee. I wouldn't sleep a wink I knew and yet I felt him pulling me into his orbit just by being what he was: some sad-sack loser in a bad marriage having to work a second job to keep out of bankruptcy court. All his misery was giving him over to me.

"Where do you want to go?"

"I don't know," he said and he coughed, got his cigarettes out.

"So what's so bad about home?"

"Everything." He laughed and then his eyes were right on me.

"I have a couch," I said.

But of course that night he slept in my bed with me, and I remember feeling like I had died and gone to some alternate universe, not heaven, but close—a place where I got what I wanted without a lot of struggle, and it wasn't a perfect world but it was somehow fair. Love got reciprocated right away in this universe. Love got love. He was what I wanted and he didn't pay a lot of attention to me while we did it, and when he got off it was like one single sad little pop and then he was unconscious beside me. I watched him breath for a long time. My eyes got hot while I watched.

Hell I think I actually cried from happiness.

Barney moved in with me a few days later, and every day my life got easier because he was there, blank and willing to be the object of my desire. I didn't have to pretend that I could make it anymore. I realized what my main problem was, what had kept me in turmoil: just plain old run-of-the-mill loneliness. Of course, that realization would end up fucking me over in the end.

We're inside this condo over by I-275, on a cul-de-sac of beat-up-looking townhouses and condos with toys in the grass and bags of garbage waiting to be picked up. This condo we're in is completely gutted, no furniture or nothing, boxes on boxes, and part of the living room wall has been karate-kicked in.

Beside the biggest hole, on the floor, is Tiffany's boyfriend, whose name is Kyle. Kyle has not had a good day either. He's in sweatpants with no shirt and has the whitest skin like he was born and raised in a basement in the light of Nintendo games. He has a tattoo of a demonic sun on his back, big black combat boots on his feet with no socks, strings untied. He just sits there, Indian-style, with his eyes focused on the paperclip he has untangled, trying to clean out his one-hitter so he can smoke more pot.

"His brother moved out last week," Tiffany whispers.

"Hey you okay?" I say. We just came in, the door being half open and a cat meowing beside the porch. The cat was in now, roaming the empty condo, smelling for its litter-box.

Kyle throws the used paperclip into the kicked-in hole in the wall. The hole is about the size of an open mouth on a billboard. That took a lot of karate kicks to do that. His goatee beard has grown into a long strand spilling out of his chin. When he looks up, his eyes are a glittery fake gold.

"I'm fine. I mean I'm getting fucking evicted tomorrow, but I am so goddamn fine." He laughs a messed-up-boy-on-a-soap-opera laugh then lights the one-hitter and inhales like he is inhaling the Smoke of God.

Tiffany says, "Did you do that to the walls?"

"No," he says, and he laughs again that way, and he looks her right in the eye, "Keanu Reeves did." His fake gold eyes are contacts. They have to be.

Tiffany laughs too and goes over to him and sits down and he packs her a hit in the one-hitter and she does it and looks up to me.

"He's gonna be homeless, Dwayne." She smiles with tears starting.

"I'm sorry."

Kyle stands and hands the one-hitter back to Tiffany. The only unboxed thing in the room is a boom-box on the floor, and he goes and turns it on. Hard rock with a whiny singing boy comes out. Kyle stands up and feels his left nipple, looks up at me.

"I get pissed off all the time. I can't keep a job." He stares down at the floor.

Tiffany says, "When he goes low, you know, like from bipolar, you know? I mean when he goes low he is the lowest of the low." She stands up and sways a little. It looks like she's proud of Kyle's low status in a way.

I keep on smiling. I'm thinking of Barney. What he's doing. Are they ordering a welcome-home pizza from Papa John's? Are they talking about redecorating a room in their little house to turn into a nursery? Kyle steps closer and I can smell his bipolar body heat like an oven that's been on too long without anything in it. He blows a wind past me and then turns into the Karate Kid, connecting with a part of the wall that's not been demolished yet, his combat-booted foot going all the way through until half his body is in the adjacent kitchen and the rest of him is still with us. He lays there in the rubble.

Tiffany goes over to him, high as a kite now, but not laughing.

"Are you dead?" she says.

"No," he says. "Help me up."

He gets up, breathing real hard. The bottom part of him is covered in drywall dust. His chest is bleeding little red stars.

"I hate my landlord," he says to me, like that might make me understand the whole thing, and I do for a second. And it happens right then of course that feeling of love busting out of its container, like 2% milk turning into a thundercloud. For a second I look at Tiff and feel sorry for her and sorry for me and just plain sorry for the whole damn world.

"You need a place to stay?" I ask.

He dusts off his sweatpants' legs, stands up, smiles.

"Thank you Dwayne," Tiffany says. She comes over and I smell that burnt-poinsettia smell of pot.

"Yeah," Kyle says. "Thank you Dwayne."

Kyle and me and Tiffany share three weeks together.

When she gets time, Tiffany's mom comes down to get Tiff. She's a skinny lady with hardly any hair in a pair of jeans and a Grateful Dead T-shirt, glasses on a chain. She makes a lot of noise thumping down the stairs. She knocks on the door and yells Tiff's name, me and Tiff and Kyle usually in the dark living room watching DVDs we rent. It's almost like we're a family in a way, we're so quiet and disenchanted, and Kyle laughing too hard at Jim Carrey. We eat whatever we want to. Neapolitan ice cream and circus peanuts and beef jerky and Chinese food from a can, etc. At work I whip up decadent ideas in my head about what we'll be eating and watching every night. It's sick and yet it's also like hope.

And so tonight, three weeks in, there's the thunder of Tiff's mom stomping down the stairs, and Tiff's mom pounds on the door. We're in the middle of *The Sixth Sense*, some very scary stuff.

"Tiffany," her mom yells. "You are coming home."

Tiffany yells back, "Mom! We're watching a movie!"

She pounds more. This time it's like she's had it. I am about to get up to face the music, when Kyle pushes me back down, stands up, stops by the DVD player and puts it on pause, then half-stumbles to the door. He is in his underwear and nothing else. He opens the door.

"Why don't you fucking stop this shit?" He's yelling like he's on a reality TV show, like there's cameras everywhere and he has to put on some kind of act or get booted off.

I see him yell and I can see parts of Tiff's mom out in the corridor—this time it's cutoffs and her uniform top from Target. I'm thinking I should disappear off the face of the earth. Her face is pale and tired and irate. She's not ready for a fight. She does not even know if it's worth it saving her daughter you can tell, but then again that's all she's been doing lately so it's become sort of second-nature.

"Get some clothes on right now," she says.

She tries to come into the apartment. Kyle won't let her though. I look over at Tiff and she looks halfway between wanting to protect her mother and wanting to go back to the movie.

Tiffany looks at me and slumps her shoulders. "This is weird," she whispers. "I love them both. It's like a tug of war for my heart."

Kyle keeps blocking the door like a goalie.

"Let me in. She's my daughter goddammit," Tiff's mom grunts and growls almost. She goes from one side of the doorway to the other, but he's fast and he keeps her out. Finally she gets down on all fours and crawls through, knocking him back with her head. She's in and runs toward us. It's dark except for the TV, so I turn on the lamp. Tiff's mom is breathing real hard, standing beside the La-Z-Boy.

"I can't believe this," she says.

Kyle comes over to her and grabs her and slams into the chair.

"I am so sick of you," he says.

"You're crazy!" she screams.

He hovers over her like he has trapped her with his secret powers and she will never be free. I slowly get up.

"Hey you guys come on," I say.

Kyle does not have his colored contacts in. His eyes are very brown, so brown as to be black and in his white Old Navy underwear he resembles a refugee from a nighttime tornado. He won't take his eyes off Tiff's mom. He has her targeted.

Tiff is standing up now.

"We just wanted to finish the movie Mom!" she screams.

Tiff is not in her underwear, but she might as well be—a halter-top-thing, skin-tight jeans. I'm in my sweats. I must look sixty years old by now, all the bad food and no-sleep for the past three weeks, that feeling of being held captive by Kyle because he never leaves the house even though he keeps telling me his brother is coming back to get him and they are going to pick up Tiffany at school and escape to Arizona.

Tiff's mom is looking at me.

"You ought to be ashamed," she says.

Kyle comes to my defense, "He's a kind and gentle person." He says that like it's so true it's downright embarrassing. Hell I love him but I can't love him too.

I've fallen in love with the both of them in a way. It's like they have come into my head and nested there, replacing normal life with their junk food comfort and pot-head slumber and always asking me to buy them beer and I do and we drink it and get drunk and they go into my bedroom and have their sex and I half-sleep out here and wake up and quietly get ready for work the next day, Tiff having slipped off upstairs after they did it and Kyle snoring like a cowboy with sleep apnea.

"Kind and gentle my ass," Tiff's mom says.

Kyle's nostrils flare. "I will hit you, okay? I will fucking hit you you pick on Dwayne!"

Tiff's mom looks away. "I just want my daughter."

Tiff runs over to her mom, bawling now.

"I'm sorry Mom! He's bipolar."

Kyle starts crying too then. He goes over to the wall, and he makes a fist and he punches a hole right next to the TV. This is the first time he's done that in here. The wall gives in like a piece of nothing.

"Time out," I say. I go over to Tiff and her mom, and I say, "Tiff you go home with your mom. It's time to take a break."

Tiffany nods and gets up. Her mom stands up, looking all hateful at me. "I ought to call Children's Services and the goddamn cops."

She knows what I am, but I'm not that. I don't love them like that. The love I do have for them is lazy and good-for-nothing, even possibly illegal. But it is not that.

"I'm not a pervert," I tell her.

She and Tiffany just walk out. Kyle is on the floor, not crying, just staring into space.

"Why don't you go to bed?" I ask him.

"I took my meds, swear to God," he says, still staring into space.

"I know you did. I'm the one that went and got them for you."

I walk over to the couch and lay down. Eventually he gets up and comes over to me.

"That stuff about my brother?" he says in the dark.

"Yes." I close my eyes.

"He never calls me. I made that thing up about Arizona. I'd like to go though. Maybe me and you and Tiff?"

Even with my eyes closed I can feel his smile. It's got the sticky warmth of not being able to live right. He wants me to take that smile in like a pervert would, use it to make myself happier than I ever should be.

When he bends down and kisses me, I just let my lips fold into my mouth, and then I open my eyes.

"Go on to bed," I say.

He stands there for a second or two, swaying.

"Whatever you say," he whispers.

Monique comes in at the end of my shift that next day. She gives me the evil eye.

"You don't look so good," she says. She's got the biggest ass in the tri-state area, wearing baggy sweatpants and a big smock to cover.

It's close to 3:30 PM. While I am at work I try to do my job very well thank you. But my clothes are not clean. I haven't gone to the laundromat in these three past weeks. Basically I rinse out stuff in the kitchen sink and then hang it out on the balcony to dry.

My shift is almost over, and there's the smell of dirty bleach coming up from the floor I just sloppily mopped, the fake-butter in the popcorn machine, the waxy vapor of candy bars washed in sunlight.

"I feel okay," I lie.

"Are you sick?" she says, smiling.

"No."

"Well you look sick." She stops smiling and she goes over to the mop bucket where I left it in front of the milk coolers.

"Is this the water you used to mop with?" she asks, pissy and judgmental.

"Yeah."

"It looks like sewage water." She laughs really loud.

Fuck you, I want to say. *Fuck this whole fucking world.*

He wasn't who he is now, Barney, back when we went to Key West. We went there together a month into the relationship. I paid for everything. I paid for the plane tickets and I paid for the Super 8 Motel and I paid for the convertible we rode around in that one night, top down, humid as all get out. Barney and me drove next to the Gulf of Mexico, a beautiful storm riding in the orange sky like a jellyfish coming in for a smooch. It was so damn hot. We were drunk from going to some fancy place (all of this on my Visa remember). Shrimp and baked potatoes and white wine.

The wind whipped back Barney's straight dark hair. He had a tan from earlier that day at the beach. He looked like what I wanted him to look like.

"Damn," he'd said in the motel room right before we went out to eat that night, right after I sucked him off. "That was good. That was really good."

I knew he loved me. I was electric inside, all my fuses exploding in secret. I tried to make it seem like nothing. I did not want to scare him too much.

So I stop by Barney's house after work. He is out getting his mail. I sit in my car watching, half-camouflaged by the other cars and the sun light splashing through tree-limbs. But I get out. He's opening some letter and smiling. He looks up. Their little house is cute in a way, painted yellow, in a so-so neighborhood.

"Hey," I say.

His eyes go cold, and I go in closer. I must be smiling. Yes I took a few "magnums." That's what Kyle calls his speed pills. I took a few around one o'clock because I was about to go into a coma, and this is what love can do to you, I think right now, walking up to Barney, walking very slowly and my mouth hurts from how much I love him and now that he is gone it doesn't hurt as much as burn all the time and yet I know how he can just leave without one thought about me and pick up where he left off.

"What are you doing here?"

"I don't know."

"Come on, Dwayne. Don't go Glenn Close on my ass." He laughs, but he's nervous you can tell. "You look a little tired," he says.

"I'm very tired," I say, and I laugh too, but then I get choked up and I stop.

"Come on," Barney says. "Leave us alone."

I stand there on the sidewalk, and when he turns to go into the house I still don't move. He stops and looks back at me. He gets a little pissed.

"Go home," he says. "Go on."

"I can't," I say.

This is embarrassing to report to you, I know, me standing there in the sunshine on the sidewalk outside his yellow cottage and him in some uniform-type outfit, maybe UPS, I don't know. I can't move. There's a kind of hypnosis that you can do to yourself when you're so miserable you can barely stand it. It pushes you into the center of the freeze-ray, stubbornness sets in. You can do anything if you come to the understanding that you'll never get your way.

"It's over. Okay?" he is whispering, and he pulls my arm toward my car but I won't move. There is just no goddamn way.

I shake him off. I walk backwards.

"Go on," he says. "Get the hell out of here before someone sees you freak."

Barney kind of laughs then, not a real laugh, a cover-up. He looks both hurt and pissed, like he just can't understand this behavior of mine and it's that look that only blows my heart up into the size of that ocean storm, that look that he doesn't care but has let me love him, that look.

"Have some fucking self-respect," he says. Then he looks down the street both ways. "I mean come on."

When I get home the door is wide open. And inside furniture has been turned over, the walls are busted out all over the place, walls like Swiss cheese.

I get panicky and call out Kyle's name. There's no response. For a second, I think I might pass out. There's the familiar stomping down the stairs. When I turn around Tiff's mom is standing in the doorway. She looks like she wishes she had a gun.

"He did it," she says.

Right then I can't talk.

"He beat the living shit out of my daughter," she says. "I just took her to the hospital, buddy. Thank God I came home for lunch. She was beat to a pulp over some stupid movie they watched. She is in intensive care. I come back to get her some things."

I still can't talk. She shakes the bag of her daughter's things in my face.

"He's gone. That little fucker took off. I called the police. They know about you too buddy. What you were doing in there. It made me sick. Well he beat her good. I don't have anything against gays I don't, but I can't take a child molester. I cannot. I shouldn't have let it go on."

She keeps shaking that bag. It's clear plastic and inside it are a peach nightgown and some shampoo and socks and panties.

"I love Tiffany," I say.

"I am going to puke," she says, and glares at me like she would be the one at the front of the mob, the one who would start taking me apart limb by limb.

When Kyle comes back, he's all apologetic. He's coked up too I think. It's around 8:30, and the police haven't come yet. He has on his combat boots and sweat-pants and a suede jacket with fringes he told me his brother had got him. He stands in front of me in the kitchen.

"Write me a check," he says.

"I don't think so."

"Please," he says.

"No."

"Please God just write me a check!"

I shake my head no. I look him in the face.

"Let's go do laundry," I say.

His contacts are in. They glitter like gold fish. He looks like he doesn't understand.

"I don't have anything to wear to work tomorrow," I say.

"Everything I got smells," he says.

We go around the apartment, picking up dirty clothes. We get like seven big black garbage bags full of clothes. It's raining. The furniture is still overturned, the walls still botched. I don't want to notice anything then, and somehow Kyle is obedient, caught up in the need for clean clothes, like the boy he's supposed to be, vain and self-conscious. He carries four bags out to my car, and I carry the rest. I lock my door, and then we go by the Kroger's for some Tide and dryer sheets. We turn the radio on to his station. The rain is almost pretty on the windshield.

The Laundromat is just down the street. We run the clothes into the little place, in a strip-mall next to a bar and a Radio Shack. There's only one other person here tonight, and she's reading a Harry Potter book in front of the dryers. There's a hum and the smell of mildew and clean drying clothes. The chairs are orange and green plastic.

I give Kyle a five dollar bill and he gets change, standing in front of the machine like it's a slot machine. There's happiness on his face, and his eyes shielded with gold-drops. Maybe it's the lighting, but he doesn't look so ghoulish now. Like he has snapped out of something.

This needed to be done.

I sort and separate and Kyle puts quarters in. Pours detergent. We sit down after everything is loaded—five machines playing in unison like a country band. The woman with her book gets up and goes outside to smoke. The rain has stopped. The concrete and cars are glittery with it.

I turn toward Kyle, exhausted and for a second almost happy with this one accomplishment, all the machines going, the smell of detergent and hot water.

"Why did you hit her honey?" I ask him.

He doesn't say anything.

"Why?"

"I didn't hit anybody, Dwayne." His eyes are gold coins. He smiles. "Can I get a pop?"

I stand up and give him a dollar. He walks over to the pop machines and chooses Mountain Dew. The clock says 9:15 p.m. It's a Tuesday or a Wednesday. Hell I don't know.

BLEEDING TOY BOYS
Dean Durber

1.

The room was starting to look hazy. I noticed again the grey stains spread over walls whitewashed for the first and last time years back, long before my arrival. I wondered how many students had sat on this fraying chair, slept on this tiny bed, its mattress weary and sagging toward the floor.

This place was never built for the likes of me.

I stumped out a cigarette that I had smoked right down to the tip. My lungs breathed freely for a while as I twisted another cigarette in my fingers, staring down at it. I was enjoying relief after nearly a year of addiction to the inhalation of intoxicating infuriating fumes.

"I'm going to quit one day," I told myself. "I am."

I lit up and started to choke.

A pile of books balanced on my desk, closed now and resting beside an overflow of ash. Books I will never open again.

I stared out of the window and listened one last time to the shouts of summer rising up from the scorched patch of grass down below. I puffed out a circle of smoke and watched it climb to the ceiling.

I raise my feet and press the soles of my dirty shoes hard against the wall. I hold them there while I watch him. He jogs across the lawn, into the trees and into the distance. I notice how he wears a small white towel wrapped tightly around his neck.

I pull my feet away and smile desperately at the imprinted memories they have left. I know I should feel guilty about what I've done.

2.

"Where ya goin'?" my mother asks me, a half-smoked cigarette hanging from her lips.

I feign a cough as I wave the fumes away. I turn to offer an exaggerated stare at the boxes that I have packed so neatly into my car.

"University," I spit.

Her still face, dangling somewhere between puzzled and pleasure. I'm not sure. I notice only the depths of her wrinkles and the yellow of her crooked teeth.

"What, today?"

"Yes, today. Like now. I've packed my car. Didn't you even see me packing?"

The shared greyness of the houses around me makes this place seem so desolate. The streets are filled with the sounds of unwanted children running around in tattered clothes. They scream endlessly. Drunken old men stagger home to Sunday lunches covered in cold, solidified gravy.

"I thought you knew," I said.

"Maybe. Yes, maybe I did."

"I'm sure I told you."

She lets the cigarette fall to the ground and leaves it to burn. I use the sole of my new shoes to crush its embers. I lean down to pick up the extinguished butt and hold it tidily in my hand.

"I guess you just forgot then."

I think I catch a tear in her eye, but I try not to let her see me looking. She moves to hug me. She squeezes me too tightly. I can hardly breathe.

"Mum, I...."

"No, you go now, son. You go to your university and you make us proud."

She pulls out a crumpled green note from her pocket and pushes into the palm of my hand.

"I don't need this," I insist, thrusting it back toward her. "I'll find a job. I'll be fine."

She squeezes my palm closed.

"I know you will, son. You'll be fine now. I know that."

She turns away and wobbles back toward the house, a greying box squashed in the middle of squalor. I never want to come back here.

"And don't you ever come back here!" she shouts back.

"What?"

She doesn't turn.

"Don't you ever be coming back to this shitty life!"

She closes the gate. And suddenly I am filled with rage.

3.

His voice is what first grabbed my attention. That's what attracted me to him, I suppose. If attraction is the word. I don't know for sure, but I know that I listen intently to the way he speaks as if every word were important, e-v-e-r-y w-o-r-d meant something. There are no apostrophes in his life. No missing syllables.

"Joseph," he says to the girl beside him. "But most people call me Joe."

She smiles.

I can see the huge streams of dirty smoke rising from large chimneys way in the distance in a world outside of these windows. I hate their presence, their reminders.

"I'm from down south," I hear him say.

His voice is so soft, so clean.

"From just outside of London."

The girl smiles again. The anger won't leave me.

"In a place called Tunbridge. Tunbridge Wells to be exact. It's just outside of Tunbridge."

I sit through that lecture not caring what is said or if it will ever end. My notepad is filled only with rough scribbles of faceless mutated bodies and a sprawl of random dot-to-dot patterns that I piece together to form nothing. I know that I need to be paying more attention, but I can't. I can smell smoke. It's everywhere. It's in my clothes, clinging to my skin, on my breath. It will never leave me.

The sudden clatter of desks wakes me and I jump up. I hang at the end of the row of chairs where I have been sitting, fumbling with bits of paper in my hands, waiting. The girl beside him gets up to leave.

"Nice to meet you," the boy shouts out.

I step forward, forcing myself between them, following slowly behind her, feeling the slight breeze of his breath on the back of my neck as he moves closer. I step through the swinging door and push it backward, purposefully, harsh and hard. I hear the thud. The silence that follows. That moment stretches for an eternity of my joy. I can feel the ache of my smile.

"Fucking Jesus! Fucking Jesus Hell Christ!"

The corridor stills. People turn in slow motion while I grip the edge of the door with the very tips of my fingers and peel it back just enough to see his fallen body sprawled, his books scattered, his hands clinging to the side of his head where already a lump of flesh starts to thump and grow. His eyes are streaming with shameful tears. I squat down.

"I am so sorry," I say.

I reach out to touch his hurt.

"Are you all right?"

A hand flicks out and knocks my caring touch clear away. It takes all of my strength, all of my patience to resist forming my hand into a fist and smashing it down into his face. I know how badly I want to hurt him. I am not ashamed of that.

"Jesus fucking Christ!" he screams again.

People pass us by. They exit through other doors.

"It was totally my fault," I repeat. "I am so sorry."

Again my hand starts to move. This time it manages to come to rest on the top of his head where I stroke him.

"Maybe I should get you to a hospital."

He looks up, stares at me. His nose is dripping blood.

"I'm a total idiot. I just let the door go. I didn't even know you were there. I was miles away. I'm sorry."

Still he stares. Still my hand runs over his hair.

"I'll take you to the hospital." I stroke.

"I'll be fine," he whispers.

"But I feel so bad. Really. I feel so bad."

"It wasn't your fault. I'll be fine."

His eyes don't move.

I cup my hand beneath his elbow and help him to his feet. I can feel the flesh of his arm as I pinch it between my fingers.

"Can I at least buy you a drink? To say sorry."

He rubs fingers over the swelling, over the uncertain flesh of his elbow. He stares at me again, begins to smile.

"Yes. A drink would be fine."

I like watching him in the bar as he dabs himself clean, his blood soaking through onto my handkerchief.

4.

She tells me she's fine, things are fine, work is fine. I know she lies.

"How's the weather with you there?"

"Cold," I say. "Too cold."

"You keepin' warm then?"

"Yeah, yes, I'm keeping warm."

"I should try 'n' send ya some money, 'elp with ya bills a bit." She coughs, and then the sound of sucking as she inhales.

"I'm fine, really. It's warm. Not too cold at all."

"And your friends?"

"Yes, they're all fine."

"I bet you got some lovely friends there. It's good that you have some good friends. You'll need them."

I don't answer.

"Better than the likes of round here that's for sure."

She laughs, but I know she means it.

"They're not so bad," I lie.

"No, not too bad. But you can do better than the likes of us son. I'm proud of ya, ya knows that don't ya?"

"So you keep saying."

"Well I am. And I don't care 'ow many times I say it. Ain't nothing wrong with bein' proud o' me own son now is there? Not many folks round here got any son of theirs goin' to bloody university 'av they now?"

"Guess not."

"Too bloody right not. So I am proud of ya. I'm glad I got the chance to see ya makin' someat of yoursel'."

She coughs again.

"I could have 'ad them brains you know!"

She laughs. We are silent. I hear the click of a lighter.

"And you're talkin' right posh now and all."

"Am I?"

"So when ya comin' home to see us then?"

I leave the question to hang.

"Been well on three months by now."

"I know. But I have to study all the time. And then there's work. I can't really get time off work. I'd lose the job."

"Ai, I know luv. Happen if I had a bit more money...."

"You work hard enough. I'm fine."

"Thank Christ you'll never 'ave to do the kind o' work we does."

She coughs again and again, this time louder and harsher. It goes on forever.

"How are your hands?" I ask. "You still rubbing cream in every night?"

"Sometimes."

"You've got to do it every night to keep them soft."

"Listen to you there."

"You're a good 'un, you know that."

Silence.

"Well you take care son. You be good. And don't you worry about us now."

I hear the phone go click. Her voice is gone.

"You're a good 'un," I repeat into the silence.

And I cry.

5.

I didn't make it home for Christmas that year. Drove straight past my town and continued further south, heading to London, to Tunbridge, Tunbridge Wells to be exact. Here the doors of the houses open out onto scrubbed cobbled streets. There's a touch of frost in the air. It might snow. It should do.

"I understand, son," she sobs quietly, sniffling like it's only a cold. "You have your own life now. Don't wanna be spendin' all ya time here now."

I pull up outside Joe's house and grab my bag off the back seat. He is already standing at the open door, his face flushed red. I can't tell if he is cold or shamed, maybe neither. He smiles too much.

"Mom, this is Dan."

He looks at me, smiling.

"This is my best friend from university."

I reach out to shake her hand, feel its softness. I notice how her skin is so clean, so healthy, alive.

"You'd be bored comin' down 'ere anyways," she insists.

The coughing has grown worse.

"And besides, things aren't too happy round 'ere right now."

She wheezes. I know she's finding it harder to talk.

"It's very nice to meet you, Dan."

Soft, gentle hands.

"Joe has been telling us all so much about you."

Behind her, waiting on the kitchen table I notice a large lump of bread freshly baked. I can smell it. I see the unpacked butter. And a single silver knife, very sharp. Everything seems so tidy in here.

"Please make yourself at home," his mum says. His mom. "We are very happy to have you."

I imagine what it would be like to have my tiny infant mouth sucking on the nipple of this lady with silvery greying hair. I watch her slender body as she bends to pour juice into a small glass with not a drop spilled. She passes it to me, but all I can see are gleaming white teeth.

"So where are you from?" she asks me.

I give the name of some town that isn't mine but close enough.

"Oh yes. We have been there. A lovely part of the country."

"Yes, lovely."

"I thought you must have been from around that part of the country. I can hear it in your accent."

I stare at the knife.

"Come on, Dan. I'll show you to my room," Joe says.

"He can sleep in the spare room if he wants," his mother interrupts. "He might not want to sleep on the floor."

She looks at me, waits for an answer, but Joe pulls at my arm and drags me out of the room. He whispers to me as we climb up the tiny crooked stairs.

"The spare room is tiny. It's too cold. I thought you could sleep in my room."

"Look Joe...."

"It's so good to see you."

He goes to kiss me, lands on my cheek.

"Maybe I should just sleep in the spare room."

"Why?"

"Just because."

"But it's really small. The bed's tiny. We could just get you a mattress and put in on the floor in my...."

"It'll be fine!"

My hand stretches out. I push him away but during the night he comes back and rests his head sleepily on my chest.

"I'm so glad you're here," he tells me.

He starts to kiss at my naked flesh while I think of what it would feel like to slide that silver bread knife across the perfect smoothness of his cheek. How the blood would trickle down the curve of his neck.

"Do you ever think about cutting yourself?" I ask.

6.

I know I should have called to wish her Happy Christmas or Happy New Year at least, but time just ticked on by. We had turkey for lunch. Fresh potatoes with steamed vegetables. Christmas pudding and cream. I didn't want to make her cry.

"Hey, why don't we go out for a drink?" Joe says.

Too many. I tried to walk upright on the way back to the house but I pretend that I need his support so that I can drill my knuckles into the top of his head. I stumble forward and fall, pulling him down. I punch him hard on his nose, spraying blood on to the cobbled pavements of Tunbridge Wells. My heart races so fast. My hand grabs at his flesh through a torn T-shirt as I roll him on to the road and force him to dodge cars whose horns blast out. I feel my fist penetrate into the fleshy softness of his stomach. Joe pukes. I like how this feels.

My mother would have had chicken for lunch. Chicken and sausages wrapped in bacon. She would have sat at home listening to the sounds of screaming kids and drunken old men outside her window, and the sky would have stayed dark and grey. The cold of the house would have hurt. She would have closed her eyes and slept.

We stumbled home together, his body all sore and bleeding. Crusts of blood have already started to form to cover his wounds. I think I am sleeping when I suddenly hear his voice whisper beside me.

"I'm sorry."

I lie silent.

"I'm so sorry," he cries.

I open my eyes and turn him over onto his back, his face staring up at the empty ceiling. I have never noticed before the darkness of hair on his legs, the smoothness of his chest. I try not to look.

I sit on top of him, my legs stretched across his naked pelvis. My fingers pinch the razor blade that I use to slice gently across his chest. Blood trickles into tiny wrinkles in the skin of my fingers, under nails, seeping into my pores. I watch his face, his silence. I lower my face toward his wounds and touch his bleeding flesh with the tip of my tongue. For a moment I think I might puke. The taste of him slips down the back of my throat as I come.

My face stares down now into his open, pleading eyes. I lower my lips and kiss him where kisses between us should not go.

"Thank you," he cries, his eyes widened in shock.

7.

I throw my bag onto the backseat of my car and start the engine. It takes a while for the heat to show a hole through the mist on the windscreen. I sit shivering.

Through the cleared side window I can see him as he stands in the doorway, his mother stroking his hair. He kisses her and opens the door to sit beside me.

"Please take care of him, Dan. To think that this sort of attack could happen here." She touches his cheek.

"I know. Awful, isn't it?"

My hand rests caringly on his shoulder. "I'll look after him. Don't you worry. And thanks for a great Christmas."

When we are out of sight of his home, he dares to place his hand on my thigh. It stays there.

8.

"Hey, mom. It's me."

"Hello, son," she sighs.

"I just called to let you know I'm leaving university. I'm coming home."

"You make me so proud, you know that."

I speak through my tears. "I.... No.... You make me proud."

"Don't you be silly now."

"No, I'm serious. You do."

There's a silence while I wonder if she understands me.

"You don't know how much I love you," I cry. "It's like sometimes, when I'm here, I feel I'm in a completely different place and the people I meet are like, well, they're not like us. They.... Mum?"

I hear the phone click.

9.

I look down at the crumpled sheets and can still make out the stain. My cock throbs with pain.

It is dark outside. Streetlights flicker through the open window.

"Come on," I say as I take his hand and pull him to his feet.

His face is red, sore, hurting. His body is bruised.

"I think we should get you into the shower."

He nods his head and cries then, heavy sobs of passion while I think about hating him and all the reasons why. In that moment I love him, and I know all the reasons why.

"You and me, we don't belong together, you know that, don't you Joe?"

He cries and cries.

"We're from different worlds. Different times. We want different things. We don't even speak the same language for Christ's sake."

"But I love you."

I raise my fist, watch it hover above his head. My finger falls on his lips.

"I know you do, Joe."

I stand him in the shower and watch as warm water pours over his naked body. His hand moves backwards and forwards, gently rubbing between the cheeks of his arse as he stares out at me, his face smothered in dried tears.

"Does it hurt?" I ask.

"Not much. It's okay."

I want to hold him.

"I know what you're thinking," I add.

He waits.

"But you're wrong."

I glide the back of my hand over his shoulder and along the breadth of his arm.

"I don't want to be like you. I don't want to be the things you are. The way you talk. The house. Your mother. I thought I wanted all of that. But I don't. I want...."

I stop to kiss him gently, on the lips. His eyes widen with sadness and fear. But when he cries, I pull him tightly toward me. My lips rest on the softness of his cheek.

"I'm sorry," I whisper.

Through his tears he is silent. He tries to speak but can only splutter phlegm from the back of his throat. I can smell her now. I can feel her.

"It's okay," I whisper. "It's okay now."

10.

I haven't seen Joe for days. I have kept my door locked, holding my breath when I hear him knocking and knocking. After the knocking stops, I hold my breath for a while longer, counting the seconds. Seventy-two. Seventy-three. I find it hard to dare to breathe.

As I watch his body disappear into the trees, I feel lonely. Sitting in this room, my life packed into boxes. This space echoes with his presence. I smoke another cigarette.

Right then, smoking is such a joy, and I decide I will never quit. These burning embers remind me of her. It's her smell on my fingers, in my clothes, in the disease of my blackening lungs.

Uncontrollable tears suddenly begin to pour down the side of my face. My body spasms into a tiny ball. My legs crush up tightly against my aching chest. I cannot breathe. And I don't want to. I hold my breath and hope to turn blue. Ninety-two, ninety-three. I dare to breathe.

I place the last of the boxes in the boot and sit staring out the window. Joe's face appears in the mirror. I see a car driving down the road and I wonder what it would be like to have its metal body smash against our fragile ones and tear our flesh apart. To feel our heads crushed beneath the weight of its wheels as our bones crumble together into dust.

RED VS. BLUE
Tara Hardy

Written after the second election stolen by George W. Bush.

This is for the Red States....
Stupid.

My Uncle Melvin is stupid. He lives in Indiana—he voted for George Bush.

Hell, he voted for Bush, Senior. It went something like this: "Read my lips: no new taxes."

That time, like this time, the Democrats were not speaking a working people's language. Their candidates' arguments were all nuanced and complex, but what the hell does that mean to my Uncle Melvin? Whose parents sat him in front of a television since before he could walk.

Why? Because it's the option for exhausted laborers. People whose hands will never fully soften, no matter how much pumice they apply. Their skin grows that way. People keeping the bunion-pad companies in business from standing in bad shoes on assembly lines for lifetimes. People whose primary source of entertainment is—no stretch—the television. Because after a day on your feet, what a body needs is rest. Exercise is something people do who sit at computers all day.

It was from television that my Uncle Melvin learned to absorb information in highly emotional, oversimplified sound bites. So his very head works that way. But because he's stupid? No. Because he's brainwashed. Brainwashed and kept poor by underpaying his labor from the time he dropped out to support his sisters to today, when he can't even afford to buy his wife a proper set of teeth.

(I'm not kidding here and it isn't funny.) My Aunt Juanita has permanent sores in her mouth from her ill-fitting dentures—

which, by the way, without them she can't even go to the bathroom in the night for fear of someone seeing her. Shame comes standard in my family.

My Uncle Melvin is powerless to purchase his wife some relief. But we offer him a presidential "choice"—a guy with a fancy education or someone who sounds like a down-home boy promising no new taxes. No more bite out of his backbone that ain't gonna outlast the mortgage on the trailer.

(This is not fiction. The trailer is white, and they'd like to get a fence to keep the rabbits outa the pansies.)

Melvin is gonna vote his pocketbook because maybe Juanita can get some teeth.

Think about your own. Touch them with your tongue. Now imagine watching the person you love the most live without them. Face the world and try to feel beautiful or worthy.

Melvin's gonna vote for the guy who promises to put more power in his pocket. If the Democrats haven't learned this yet, then they're the dummies, not the people who didn't vote for them.

Have I mentioned that my Aunt Juanita can't read? I am a slim generation away from not being able to decipher my own ballot.

But yeah, Melvin responds to oversimplified, deep-fried versions of the truth. But why? Because it's been his diet for as long as he can remember.

"Have some turkey," he says to me at Thanksgiving. Then he covers the gap in his own smile with his palm. I slather my potatoes in Juanita's gravy and for shame will not interject my opinion when, at his table in front of his bounty, he asks me to bow my head and pray.

Why? Because what right do I have to judge their source of hope, really? During grace, I know that my Uncle's God is someone who hates me and my depraved, coastal ways. So once again, I'm torn, acutely aware of how far apart are both my homes. My hand in Melvin's, my cheek warms with cowardice over having left my whole family behind in search of my own freedom.

Just as quick, my other cheek cools with dread at the hate that is blooming in my new home. From stealth bias into full-bodied disgust, my liberal friends are condemning entire red regions as idiots, incapable of nourishing themselves out of the rickets that has rotted their brains.

Not new, certainly, but shocking as hell out of the mouths of people with whom I thought I shared values.

More than ever, I'm straddling two boats hell-bent on rowing in opposite directions. I wake up sweaty with the pressure to choose. And choking on the privilege it is to have the option in the first place.

Some days, I am side by side with my chosen if depraved queer family. Damn right I say, fuckin' homophobes.

I think about the last public hate crime to happen in my Midwest town and feel sick. Two gay men, sleeping, wake to find their house being painted with "Faggots Go Home!"

When I wonder about how this could happen, I remember who used to live there. The Geiger girls, whose father and uncle worked around silos all their lives but during the '80s farm crisis "accidentally" walked into one and were overcome by fumes. Each died in his brother's arms so the family might make it on the insurance money.

Which they did for about a decade—before Jim and Joseph, looking for weekend refuge from the city, bought the whole farm plus house for a screaming deal. As artists, they had plans to redecorate, and I quote: "Have these people ever heard of *paint?*"

Yeah, we have. And sometimes what gets called homophobia is a little more complicated than that.

Closer to home, I think about my Seattle neighborhood gone white in seven years. Not so when I moved in, but then again, white dykes are the first wave of gentrification. I sit with that in my pocket and look down at my rapidly separating feet, both boats spilling over with white people.

From this position, I have this to say to my queer peers: Gay marriage is something that privileged, specifically college-educated people can afford to long for. And it feels like a middle-class agenda. For me, given the choice, I'd sell out my wanna-get-married peers any day for equal pay for equal work. But not in the way the feminists thought of it—which by the way preserved the class order. But in a way that means an hour is an hour is an hour. I don't care if you're pushing a broom or paper, you oughta get paid the same.

If we mean what we say in this country—that all men are created equal—then it follows that we all have the same relationship to time, that it's precious, and giving it ought to be compensated.

So this is to say that I don't think we were defeated because of the middle-state homophobes. We were defeated because we haven't begun to address working people's needs let alone truly align ourselves with people of color.

We let the Right use us as a smokescreen for their real agendas: keeping the poor poor, and eroding the civil rights of people of color. If all queers devoted our lives full-time starting today to economic justice, I would not be surprised if we'd have our gay marriage sooner than Melvin and Juanita can get that fence.

And if all Democrats, starting today, devoted their party to an hour is an hour, I guarantee that every toothless bastard in Dumb Fuck, Everywhere would vote for that before you can say, "Read my lips: new class order."

ADVANCEDELVISCOURSE
CAConrad

1

Dear Elvis, I work in a gay and lesbian bookstore in Philadelphia. There's a six-and-a-half-foot lesbian who shops here. I told her she looks like a cross between you and Golda Meir; she said she was flattered by the comparison. She's invited me to play golf with her, she LIVES for golf! I think I'll go, just to see the old men react when she screams and bellows while swinging her club.

That's all for now.

P.S. Did you know there are no lesbian romance titles that begin with the letter R? Sometimes it makes me sad as a round dog caught in a tidal flush (as my Gramma used to say). But sometimes I'm elated for the possibilities of R in the realm of women who love women. If you were a woman, Elvis, you'd be a lesbian no doubt, and no doubt understand. Wish you had lived to do a duet with k.d. lang.

2

On board the Lisa Marie jet for a tour of what Elvis called his Graceland In The Sky, I couldn't help but think of my uncle who wanted to be a pilot for United Airlines. He always dreamed of flying one of those big jets from Cleveland to Hawai'i every day, ever since he saw Elvis in *Blue Hawai'i*. My uncle wound up driving a bus for Greyhound after failing pilot school. I used to imagine him driving a bus load of passengers from Cleveland to San Diego, pulling over at the coast, gazing out over the pacific, picturing Hawai'i thousands of miles away, beaches full of airline pilots reclining with piña coladas and cheeseburgers. San

Diego is about as close to Hawai'i as a Greyhound Bus could ever hope to get. My uncle died a sick, bitter man, having to drive from Cleveland to San Diego every week, the bus never lifting off the ground, no pretty stewardesses pacing up and down the aisles handing out peanuts and pillows. He would have loved the Lisa Marie jet. "Wow, this sure is classy," he'd have said, sitting down in the pilot's seat. "You know, those airline pilots all think they're such hot shit! I could've flown one of these things, no problem! Those fucking pilots are nothing more than glorified bus drivers if you ask me! I don't know who they think they're kidding?! Sons of bitches!"

3

My friend Ken and I could never feel Elvis the same. We'd be driving down the road listening to "It's Now Or Never." As soon as Elvis reached his peak in the song, Ken would turn the volume down a notch.

ME: Ken, you're doing it again.
KEN: What?
ME: Every time Elvis hits his peak, you dampen his flame.
KEN: I don't know, it just gets too loud.
ME: Ken, the volume is consistent throughout the song. You compensate with volume for the vibration Elvis puts in you.
KEN: What the fuck are you talking about?
ME: I'm trying to tell you you're afraid of the vibration of Elvis.
KEN: That's bullshit!
ME: No, it's not.
KEN: Yes, it is!
ME: No, it's not.
KEN: Yes, it is! Now shut the fuck up.
ME: All right. Have it your way.
KEN: Good! I will have it my way!
ME: There's no shame in being afraid of Elvis, though.
KEN: I'M NOT AFRAID OF ELVIS! If you don't shut your mouth I'm gonna pull over and kick the shit out of you.

4

The truth of the matter is, if Elvis and Priscilla ever had a yard sale on the long lawns of Graceland, they would have sold everything in three minutes, customers screaming, crushing one another to buy the King's used socket wrenches and ashtrays. It used to take me hours to sell only half the things my mother wanted to get rid of. We had a set of Sonny & Cher napkin rings that always wound up back in the attic 'til the next summer's yard sale. For five years I put on my finest Capricorn salesmanship: "And over here, ma'am, we have a lovely set of Sonny & Cher napkin rings." None of our yard-sale customers ever had dinner events fancy enough to employ the likes of Sonny & Cher napkin rings. Of course, neither did we, that's why we wanted someone else to get stuck never using them. A set of Sonny & Cher napkin rings at Elvis's yard sale would have been swiped up by some shrieking, weeping yard-sale customer. If Elvis had dropped by my own yard sale and just touched my Sonny & Cher napkin rings, they would have been transformed into the Sonny & Cher Touched By Elvis Napkin Rings. Every one of my shrieking, weeping yard-sale customers (it was very uncommon for me ever to have shrieking, weeping yard-sale customers) would have wanted one of the eight Sonny & Cher Touched By Elvis Napkin Rings. No one would have had a compete set! Yeah, Elvis would have been a big help back then. But he had his own successful three-minute yard sale to worry about. Only a few other Americans could have had yard sales as successful as Elvis's—the president, for instance, as long as he was still in office. No one wants to buy used roller-skates from an ex-president. I wonder if Jackie O was ever given a complimentary set of Sonny & Cher napkin rings. When she smiled for a photograph with them in her hands they would have become the Sonny & Cher Touched By Jackie O While Being Photographed Napkin Rings. Is it true there were also Elvis & Priscilla napkin rings? Did Sonny & Cher have a set?

"The President Lives in Washington, D.C., but the King is from Memphis!" (Graffito on the Graceland Wall)

5

If Elvis Is Not Paranoid, Someone Will Have To Do It For Him

Elvis can't hide the fact that he has a penis. He's walking down the street and everyone knows he has a penis! It's outrageous! How dare they! But there's virtually nothing he can do about it. And they imagine other penises they've seen to imagine his penis. Which isn't fair either, but he's not whipping it out to say, "Hey, stop imagining things, this is mine!" He's sick of it. Sick sick sick sick of it! How dare they think about his penis! But there's nothing he can do about it. The best thing to do is not to mention it. When someone walks up to him and begins a conversation about the rainfall expected this afternoon, he just keeps talking about rain, never saying, "I know you know I have a penis!" It's ridiculous he should even have to say such a thing! But it's the way the world is! Better to ignore it. Yes, that's it, that's best.

6

While I was walking to work today, another GODDAMNED fucking yuppie car nearly ran me down! I was FURIOUS! Then an old pickup truck stopped at a red light, Elvis on the radio rhyming tender and surrender, holding his darling in his arms underneath the bright moon.

Oooh, thank you, Elvis. I relaxed. Really, really relaxed. Sky overhead turning the jar lid of release. My sphincter opened its baby-bird mouth. Thank you, King.

7

Elvis And The Illusion Of Hemisphere

There are two windows on the wall. One for each of us. We fly through them and meet in the room. I come early, the sun catching me on its orange descent, reflecting off my back as I land on the floor, land in a rolling ball, a wreck as always. He never lands so clumsily. With him it's easy, gliding perfectly no the leather heels of his shoes. I come early so he doesn't see me crashing against the setting sun. I love him. I don't want him to see me sprawled and confused. My tender spots, my bruises, each of them a curiosity to him as we fold and unfold on the long sheets. What time is it? I'm waiting. Last time, he didn't come at all. He does that sometimes. Once, I waited half the night, making tiny pictures of him, a hundred pictures of him, smiling. They glued together nicely in the shape of an animal. Or a man, whatever you want it to be. He still hadn't come when I woke in the night and I found myself flying out the window, confused as I had ever been about my feelings. Then I was sure of my feelings the next time I saw him. Why is that? He knows what time it is. He knows I know. If he were here I'd say I understand my feelings. Any minute now he will glide through the window, the scroll of white drapes blowing aside.

8

I dreamed I was watching Johnny Carson interview Elvis on TV. Johnny told a joke and everyone laughed. Elvis told a joke and everyone laughed harder because everyone loves Elvis more.

JOHNNY: So, Elvis, tell us what you think of Madonna.
ELVIS: Oh, I think she's got some real good tunes—and she has a sweet pair of tits.
JOHNNY: She sure is a beauty.
ELVIS: Yeah, yeah, I wouldn't mind sticking my pencil in her knish.
JOHNNY: Knish?! Are you, ah, Jewish?
ELVIS: Yeah, well, you know, I thought I'd give it a try. I mean, hey, it can't hurt, right?
JOHNNY: Well, sure, sure. Ah, MAZEL TOV to you, Elvis!
ELVIS: Yeah, Mazel tov, Johnny, Mazel tov. (*Elvis says he has a surprise phone call to make. The TV audience gets real quiet while he dials. My phone rings.*)
ME: (*Never taking my eyes off the TV.*) Hello?
ELVIS: Hi, is this Conrad in Philadelphia?
ME: (*Silent. Can't believe it's true.... But I see him on TV.... Hear him and see him.... Talking to me.*)
ELVIS: Is this Conrad?
ME: Oh, uh, hello, Elvis. Yes, Elvis, it's me, it's Conrad, uh, hi.
ELVIS: (*Low and sexy.*) You've been a bad boy. Mmmm. Haven't you?
ME: Oh! I mean no, no Elvis.
ELVIS: You're lying. Mmmm. You want to suck my cock, don't you, hm, don't you, boy? (*The audience oohs and aahs.*)
ME: Me, um, I, I, uh—

ELVIS: Yeah, oooh, yeah, you'd like that, wouldn't you? Hm? My
   big, fat cock in your mouth, hm? Yeah, yeah.
ME: (*I black out.*)
ELVIS: (To Johnny.) I don't know where he went.
JOHNNY: My goodness, Elvis. I think you put him into a coma!
   (*The audience laughs.*)

9

An exhibition of the late works of Delacroix came to the
Philadelphia Museum of Art. I wore headphones, listening to my
Elvis CD, letting Elvis guide me though the 19th-century
paintings. I wanted to spend time with the painting of Ovid in
exile, but Elvis wanted lions, lions lions lions. He was singing
"Don't Be Cruel," and I STOPPED in front of the painting entitled
Young Woman Attacked By A Tiger. What is it, Elvis? What?'
   In the gift shop there are Delacroix T-shirts, Delacroix
postcards, Delacroix jigsaw puzzles, Delacroix baseball caps,
Delacroix note pads, Delacroix video tapes, Delacroix pencils
and more! The yuppies roll their eyes at my Elvis T-shirt and
whisper to one another while purchasing their Delacroix coffee
mugs. They're fools, really. They think this gift shop is any
different from Graceland with its Elvis wristwatches, Elvis
cookie jars, and Elvis shot glasses. One man wearing a three-
thousand-dollar Brioni suit purchases a Delacroix baseball cap
and a CD entitled *Music In The Time Of Delacroix*. They're absurd
Americans, just like me. We are the world's ridiculous, beautiful
clowns!

> *They are going to launch a large vessel called*
> *a clipper at noon today. Another of these*
> *American inventions to make people go faster*
> *and faster. When they have managed to get*
> *travelers comfortably seated inside a cannon*
> *so that they can be shot off like bullets in any*
> *given direction, civilization will doubtless*
> *have taken a great step forward. We are*
> *making rapid strides towards that happy time*
> *when space will have been abolished; but they*
> *will never abolish boredom.* (Delacroix, 1854)

10

Animation Family With Elvis Everyday

Every morning Timmy pleads with Mama not to draw him a penis. "You're a BOY, Timmy, just shut up!" Just because he's a cartoon, doesn't mean he can't get what he wants. Elvis is never drawn until noon, gives us a chance to have some peace and quiet. First we draw the yard real pretty, lots of flowers. Mama draws flowers the prettiest. Elvis is drawn sitting on a picnic blanket with freshly drawn meatloaf sandwiches, mmmm! Sure enough, Elvis will be singing us a song, telling jokes, and being particularly kind to Mama, when Timmy will stalk into the scene in a freshly drawn wig and evening gown to take Elvis's breath away. That Timmy ruins it every damn time! Elvis sings a love song to Timmy, stops halfway through, takes Timmy into his arms and makes love to him right there on top of the meatloaf sandwiches EVERY DAMN TIME! We busy ourselves drawings walls around their lusty, moaning bodies. "Hurry!" Mamma yells. "Hurry, draw faster! I don't want to see THIS! That boy of mine takes Elvis away from us EVERY time! I swear, and I know I've threatened this a thousand times before, but tomorrow I will draw Timmy on horseback galloping away for the day!"

WALLS
L. A. Fields

Tulsa looks out the window of the trailer and, in a quiet moment of reflection, considers the irony that they must dig deep holes to build tall buildings. Right now his construction site looks like a spacious grave with brightly colored rebar caps pointing accusations at the sky. Tulsa didn't go to college; for him deconstruction is the opposite of what he does all day, so this type of philosophical musing only goes to show how disturbed his mood is right now, just waiting to do what he has to do.

This sort of preoccupation has come upon him before. Years ago, for example, when he had built a flight of cement stairs in the middle of a building's foundation, and for a while that was all there was: just a set of steps leading to nowhere. Tulsa found himself lingering outside and moving around the thing like some photography faggot, watching it cast a toothy shadow that he knew was symbolic of something. That was an uncomfortable period in his life, right around the time he told his mother what he was. This won't be as bad as that, nothing ever will be, but Tulsa still isn't looking forward to this meeting. What can he do, though? This is the kind of stuff the foreman gets to deal with; it comes with this torn-up territory.

The problem is, is the new kid, with his big mouth. Most of the guys on Tulsa's construction crew don't care a rat's flung anus that their boss and his boss go home in the same truck and presumably sleep in the same bed. God bless them, some of the most stubborn and old-fashioned guys have just gone ahead and convinced themselves that Tulsa and Terrence carpool to save gas. Nowhere else in his life has Tulsa seen ignorance work to such good advantage.

But this new kid, Kent Jaspers, he doesn't seem to embrace the don't ask, don't tell policy. He keeps bitching about his light-footed bosses. On somebody else's site it might be standard fare to question the foreman's sexuality, but here it's too true to joke about. Besides, Tulsa has a terrible sense of humor on the topic of his sexuality. If Jaspers doesn't shut up, he might rip the blinders off this whole operation, and Tulsa isn't looking to get chained to one of his own company trucks and dragged around behind it. So he has called Jaspers in for a little gum flap. Excuse the phrase, but they need to get a few things straight.

The kid knocks and comes in, sits down across the particle board desk from Tulsa without speaking. Tulsa can barely stand being in the trailer, and he's only in here when he has paperwork to do or something he needs to set down. The floor is covered with the same carpet as the portable classrooms at his old high school, a joint he never did graduate from and doesn't like to be reminded of. The synthetic smell, the fake paneling on the walls, and the way the fucking door sticks whenever it wants to: this room feels hostile to Tulsa, like the trailer knows he doesn't belong here, doesn't belong in charge, doesn't really have the sack for it. And yet Tulsa has been cooped up in here all day, letting the office erode his self-confidence, all because of Jaspers.

Tulsa takes a second to look at the kid. The office doesn't seem to like Jaspers either, which is at least something. He's slumped like he knows he's in trouble. He probably shares Tulsa's distaste for offices, and that's why he chose to work in a shitty, unstable industry that lets him labor outside. Tulsa can almost relate. He must have twenty years on the kid, but he hasn't forgotten what it was like to be young. Tulsa used to be one of the angriest kids in the tri-county area, with a bad attitude and a real mouth on his face too. Matter of fact, if he were twenty years younger, he might have killed Jaspers over what he's been saying. He's certainly put people in the hospital for implying less than what Jaspers has been explicitly saying.

"You know what I wanna talk to you about?"

Jaspers shrugs, but doesn't answer. Tulsa can't tell whether that means Jaspers knows better than to say it out loud or whether he's as dumb as his handsome face says he ought to be. Tulsa sighs.

"You see these walls?" he says, pointing around at the room. "They're pretty thin, and I don't know if you've heard yourself lately, but your voice tends to carry, just clear as a bell." Really, Tulsa heard about the kid's trash talk from another guy on the site, someone he met during his stint in juvenile detention when he was about Jaspers' age. The guy was a reliable snitch back then, too, God love him but never trust him, Amen. Jaspers gets the point Tulsa is picking at. He looks pissed off, wondering what he's in for.

"Let me ask you something," Tulsa says. "Terrence, Mr. Jackson to you, he owns this company. If he were on site all the time like I am, would you go around calling him a nigger?"

"Hey, I'm not a racist," Jaspers says, jumping to his own defense. Tulsa holds up a hand to stop him.

"I don't care if you are," he says. "You're allowed to be a racist. You're allowed to hate fags. You're just not allowed to talk shit on my build site, you hear me?"

Jaspers shuts up with a quiet snap of his mouth, like a guppy. How much Tulsa really likes the kid is sad, all things considered. He no more wants to hate Jaspers than he wants to hate his own reflection in the bathroom mirror.

"Am I fired?" Jaspers asks.

Tulsa bites down hard on a smirk. "No. But you are free to go. Next time," he says just when Jaspers has his hand on the door, "I will fire you."

Jaspers leaves in a huff, but Tulsa feels sure he'll get over it. Friday is nearly over, and Jaspers has all weekend ahead of him to blow off steam and come back to work just fine. Tulsa can hope along with the best of the fools, in other words. Never say he is not an optimist.

He still has a few minutes until Terrence comes by to pick him up, and Tulsa spends the time holed up in the office, not wanting to poke a stick into the rattlesnake nest that the parking lot full of his employees looks to be at the moment. When Terrence's truck pulls up, Tulsa is already standing. He locks up fast, hoping to keep Terrence from honking or even slowing down for long. He jumps in the passenger seat and asks Terrence to get moving before they even exchange pleasantries. Terrence can guess why.

"D'you talk to him, then?" Terrence wears the suit in this operation ever since he inherited the building business from his uncle. The both of them used to be bottom-rung workers at Jackson Construction, and that is why Tulsa still feels like a phony sometimes in his hateful little office, knowing he only has that job because he's fucking the boss, and that's the truth.

"Yeah, I talked to him," Tulsa says, putting a hand between his face and the window as they pass a couple of guys who are yammering near the open doors of their trucks. He never really got over the shame of what he is, but sometimes when he is with Terrence he can forget about that shame for a while, and so here is the choice he has made: Terrence in the driver's seat, taking him home. "I think it'll be okay," Tulsa says.

"Then why we leaving so fast?"

"I think it'll be okay by Monday."

Terrence nods and they drive home in comfortable silence, Tulsa trying to cheer himself up with how good Terrence looks buttoned up and neatly cinched, even though he's kind of getting to be an old bastard too. Tulsa has always liked that Terrence has much bigger lips than he does, and not to be a racist himself, but it makes kissing Terrence awfully nice and spacious. He'd like to kiss him now, but by mutual agreement they keep all that sort of thing inside, which means Tulsa has to wait until they get home.

The wait isn't long by relative means, but it aches in him all the same. To take the edge off, Tulsa slides a hand over the vinyl of the seat, touching Terrence's two-toned fingers and feeling them close on his hand like a soft trap. The contact is little enough, but it keeps him going. Every day Tulsa doesn't crawl beneath a cement pourer or fall from some scaffolding is a day he gets to ride home with Terrence, and that's a good day, if you can't already tell.

SAVING
Carter Sickels

"Dean, you okay?"

I realize the engine is still running and turn the key. "Yeah."

Jillian still looks a little woozy. I had to pull over for her a couple of times after we left the highway. This is her first time in Kentucky.

"Finally." She opens the door. "Fresh air."

We left Brooklyn early this morning, and now the mountains throw long shadows. I hesitate, then get out, as Jillian strides across the overgrown lawn, marveling at the trees, commenting on the loud cacophony of crickets and spring peepers, carrying herself like she's never wanted to be in any other body. Her skirt rides up, revealing long muscular legs. Her hair is thick and red. She looks beautiful, and out of place.

My grandmother's house is a little one-story clapboard hidden in the hills behind a fortress of maples and oaks. The paint is dingy gray, sloughing away like old skin. A dented GE washer sits on the front porch. Before I go in, I take my time walking around the yard. Jillian does the same, framing her hands around her face like she's looking through a camera. A dense web of kudzu has swallowed the hen house. At the edge of the woods rests a heap of aluminum cans, old tires, and discarded appliances. From here I can hear Sugar Creek, which cuts through the lower woods. When I was a kid, my grandmother and I fished for catfish and trout, but after the coal company started stripping above us, the water turned the color of Tang and most of the fish died. A pillowcase still droops from the clothesline, as if my grandmother had been hanging clothes one day and then vanished into air. I feel like I've come back to bury her, but she's not dead: she is in a nursing home, where I put her.

I push open the door, step into the musty, warm, familiar smell. It is eerily quiet. My grandmother usually had the TV and radio going at the same time. The house is dark and gloomy except for a few drizzles of sunlight. I flip the overhead switch and look at what I'm faced with. Boxes of old medical bills and Sunday circulars, tin cans with the labels scrubbed off, piles of clothes and fabric. Empty mayonnaise jars, plastic ketchup and dish soap bottles. Stacks of newspapers, yellowed church bulletins.

"You were right, she is a hoarder." Jillian picks up a framed picture of me. I'm seven or eight, wearing a ruffled dress, a yellow bow in my hair. "I can't wait to start filming."

When I first asked Jillian to come with me, she didn't want to leave the city, but then she started seeing it as a filming opportunity. "Back to your roots," she said. "Trans guy in Appalachia."

Suddenly I feel embarrassed, her seeing where I grew up. I light a cigarette, she looks at me with disappointment. Smoking on testosterone increases the risk of high blood pressure. I've been smoking since I was fourteen. When I started injections last year, I recorded the changes in a notebook—weight gain, body hair, muscle mass—and Jillian took pictures. But after a while, the changes became too subtle, or maybe we both stopped noticing. Every day I look at myself in the mirror, wonder if this is the real me.

"God, it's stuffy in here. I need a shower." Jillian lifts her wild mane off her neck, puts one hand on her hip. "You grow up without running water?"

"Funny."

When she smiles the lines around her mouth pop out. Jillian is almost forty, six years older than me. She's got a horsey face and a yoga-trained body, and she's flirtatious and loud; when she walks into a room, people look at her, draw close. Only I get to see her in the mornings, her eyes puffy, her brow grainy with creases and lines.

While she showers, I walk through the house. Last year when I moved Grandma into a nursing home, I felt too overwhelmed to deal with the house, so I just left it stuffed with all her crap and hoped no one would break in. The coal company wants to buy the land. I told them it's not for sale. Back in Brooklyn, I started dreaming about fixing the place up. It will be Jillian's and my vacation house. She'll work on films, I'll plant a garden, our New Yorker friends will visit for long weekends. We'll have barbecues, sun ourselves at the swimming hole, read under the shade trees.

My grandmother's room looks exactly the way I remember: chenille bedspread, wallpaper printed with tiny roses, a dresser cluttered with ceramic animals and miniature teapots, and framed pictures of family, including her husband. My grandfather died before I was born. He was a deep miner and a drinker, and one day he was discovered by the creek, his skull cracked. He'd gotten drunk, fell on a pile of rocks. My grandmother never remarried or even showed interest in another man, at least as far as I know. I moved in with her after my mother died. I was eight years old. My grandmother wasn't affectionate, but she raised me and always thought I'd come back one day to take care of her.

In the walk-in closet, her faded dresses drape from the wire hangers like the skins of animals, the coats and blouses moth-eaten and old as the bones of this house. Bulging boxes of scrapbooks, photo albums, and loose pictures are stacked next to my grandmother's thick-soled brogans and a pair of navy blue church shoes. I take out a handful of snapshots, shuffle until I find one of my parents. My dad in fatigues, slim and handsome in a weaselly way. My mother in a blue cutout dress, her thick hair falling below her shoulders. She's leaning against him, her face open and smiling. I don't remember them ever looking this happy.

"Find something?"

Jillian is standing naked in the doorway. Her ropey wet hair is a tangled nest, her skin pale and freckled and smooth. A Japanese-style tattoo of a pink budded tree stretches across her ribs. Her heavy breasts hang downward, the large pale nipples like a pair of closed eyes.

For the first time in weeks, she reaches for me.

"Not here," I say, stepping out of my grandmother's closet.

Back in the front room, Jillian slips into a T-shirt and underwear. I've missed my chance. She is thinking about her film again, studying the room. Jillian's work is experimental, and I usually don't understand it. She has shot me hundreds of times, but there is still so much she doesn't know.

She asks about the history of the house, about my grandmother's collections of junk. I don't know where to start. Grandma was always a pack rat, but it wasn't until after I moved away that she started to save so much. I push open the window by the sofa, blow a line of dead flies off the sill. They scatter like ashes.

I tell her it's my turn to shower. "We can talk about all that stuff later," I say.

In the steamy bathroom, I strip and wipe a clean circle on the mirror. My eyes are milky brown, like my father's. My face is more square now, also like his. My hair is short and spiky, and stubble peppers my chin. It is strange to think that I am here and that my grandmother is not. It is strange to think that my lover is on the other side of the wall. I hear her moving things around. I flex my muscles, clench my jaw, admiring the angles. This is what I used to dream about, years before I had language for any of this. My chest is flat and scarred, the nipples numb. After the surgery, nasty blue and yellow bruises made it look as if I'd taken a beating. I remember how it felt the first time I could run my hands down my chest without feeling the rise and knots of soft flesh, how that nothingness, that hardness, thrilled me.

Exhausted, we collapse on my bed. Grandma never took down the posters from my youth—Madonna, Depeche Mode, and INXS—now yellowed, curling at the edges. I turn off the light, and when I reach for Jillian, she doesn't move. It's been like this for a while.

"Dean," she says sleepily.

"Yeah?"

"Tomorrow you promise to talk about your parents? For the film?"

I haven't told Jillian much about my family, about my childhood. This has always been a sore point. Jillian wants to know everything. Transparency, she says. Trust, she says. I was an only child, didn't have many friends. Grandma and I did not need to talk about what was in our hearts, we weren't that kind.

"Okay."

Soon, she is sleeping. She breathes open-mouthed like a child. I lie here for a long time, wide awake, trying to make myself little. Jillian takes up most of the twin bed. I finally get up and fish a couple of blankets out of the cedar chest and make up the couch. But I still can't sleep. Can't stop thinking about what I'll say to my grandmother. Can't stop thinking of my parents, their fuzzy faces materializing like Polaroids behind my eyes. It's all the stuff in here, I think, it's suffocating me.

I slip on shorts and sneakers and head out to the creek, breathing in the country air. The silver moon leads the way. This was who I used to be, a country kid who loved the woods. Not boy nor girl, just a kid. People think that the decision to transition is something you've always known, or that one day you experience a single earth-shattering epiphany. Maybe for some it's like that, but for me, for so long, I've both known and not known; I've had experiences that led me here, took me away, and brought me back, a tide I can't predict. Something rustles in the brush, probably a coon. The warm air smells clean and woody. This is my home, I say. But the words, spoken aloud, sound empty.

In the bright daylight everything about Perry looks worse. Burned out storefronts, rows of old coal camp houses pressed close to the road. I start to drive through quickly, but Jillian asks me to slow down. Jillian grew up in the rich suburbs of Long Island, a train ride away from the city. We met at a mutual friend's birthday party in Williamsburg. She pulled me onto the dance floor, pushed her hips against mine. She told me I was handsome, her voice low in my ear.

"What did you do for fun around here?" She's wearing big sunglasses, and her hair is piled on top of her head like a stack of flower petals.

"I don't know," I say. "What did you do?"

"Hung out in the East Village, and went to clubs."

"No clubs here. People had parties in the woods."

"You're such a country boy." She says, "It's sexy."

I glance over to see if she's kidding. The glasses make it hard to see her expression. "I just mean, you know, it's so different from how I grew up." She adds, "More real."

What I see are poor people and falling apart homes and hardscrabble lives and junker cars on blocks. Families that go back for generations, and keep going, sprawling with cousins, half-siblings, step-kids. But not my family, whittled down to just me and my grandmother. A tight, closed-off circle, we will die out. I drive by a duplex where a girl I used to have a crush on lived, and then to where my parents' house once stood, now rubble.

"Do you miss your parents?" she asks.

"I try not to think about them very much."

We pass the diner where my grandmother used to work. Jillian wants to eat breakfast there, but it would be too complicated. "I might see people I know."

I continue on Route 12, taking us out of Perry and toward Murphy, where my grandmother now lives. It's a bigger town, feels safer—I don't know anyone here. On the way Jillian asks me questions about my parents, trying to open me up. The digging makes her happy. She's won awards for her films, shown them in art galleries.

I exhale a stream of smoke, remembering how my mother's hair fell out after the chemo. "My dad was only nice to my mom after she got sick," I say.

"He felt guilty." Jillian clears her throat and hesitates like she's just thought of this question but I know she's been wondering. "Did he hit you, too?"

Earlier, when I admitted that my father sometimes hit my mom, Jillian's face cracked with interest, and I quickly backpedaled, downplaying it. She wanted to know why I'd hid something that big from her. "I wasn't hiding anything, I just don't like to talk about it," I said.

Now I say, "He never paid much attention to me. After she died, he spent even more time on the road." My father was a long-haul truck driver. Whenever he'd first get back from a trip, things were good, but they never stayed that way for long.

"My parents would sit in the kitchen and eat doughnuts, listen to the radio. He'd tell stories about what he saw on the road, sometimes he played checkers with me," I tell Jillian, remembering how when he laughed, which was rare, his eyes crinkled, his thin moustache jumped.

"He didn't know what to do with me, so he gave me to my grandma," I explain.

"You were twenty-one when he died?"

"Twenty." Willowy and athletic, with shoulder length hair and slender hips. "I was away at college when my grandmother called with the news," I say. "He had a heart attack on the road. A few days before, I had just had sex with a girl for the first time." At the funeral I couldn't stop thinking about her, I remember, her hot breath on my face, the way she'd bucked against my hands. "I don't think I could have ever come out to him ... as anything," I add.

"You came out to your grandma though. As a lesbian."

"A long time ago. She was cooking soup beans. She stopped what she was doing and said, 'To each his own.' Then she kept right on stirring. We never talked about it again."

I pull into the nursing home parking lot.

"What do you think she'll say when she sees you now?"

"I don't know." Last year the sheriff called to tell me that my grandmother had taken to wandering. She'd stolen the neighbor's mail, driven his pickup across the county line. I had sensed from our phone conversations that she'd grown forgetful and nervous, but I didn't know how bad it was. I'd just started hormones and there was nothing noticeably different about me; some saw me as male, others as female. I booked a round trip flight, didn't stay long. After several doctor appointments and meetings with nursing home staff, I signed the papers. She didn't fight me. Half the time, she didn't know who I was.

Before we get out of the car, Jillian takes off her glasses and looks at me with clear blue eyes. "I'm glad you brought me here."

"For your film," I say.

"No, not just that." She reaches for my hand. "It means something, you sharing so much. I know it's not easy." Her long fingers curve over mine like ribs of a small animal. "Telling me all this, it's good for you, too. Don't you think?"

"Yeah, maybe." I add, "I'm glad you're here."

Her smile is big and loose, and gives me the extra encouragement I need to go inside. Before we walk through the doors, Jillian asks if I'm sure I'm okay with her filming, and I tell her it's fine. She carries the camera under her arm like a pocketbook, and I suddenly wish I'd brought something to give to my grandmother, flowers or a cake. I try not to look at the old people parked in wheelchairs, slobbering, sleeping, staring, and I walk up empty-handed to the woman at the desk and tell her that I'm Gertrude Pearson's grandson. She doesn't bat an eye. Jillian and I pass as a straight couple, no problem, a thin, delicate boy and his sexy girlfriend. Sometimes I still feel nervous inside my skin, wondering how people see me, what they think. Jillian says I worry too much: "Just be yourself."

Outside Room 12, I take a deep breath. I've played this scene in my head over and over, but I don't know how I'm going to explain to my grandmother who I am. It's not like I've radically changed. My clothes, hair, all of that is the same. For years I've been presenting as male. But my voice is deeper, and the hair on my arms and legs is dark and thick. I debated whether to shave my sideburns, but left them, the faint soul patch, too.

There are two beds, two beat up TVs. The roommate is not here. My grandmother sits in a pale green armchair staring at her palms as if she's reading her fortune.

"Hi," I say.

She looks up, thinner than I've ever seen her, an emaciated elf with long ears and a nose two sizes too big for her face. Gigantic glasses slide down the bridge. She wears a pink terrycloth robe and fuzzy slippers, clown shoes.

I go to her, kiss her forehead. "How are you?" She looks at Jillian, then back at me.

"Is that the new nurse?"

Jillian's lost her big smile and she seems nervous now, like she's afraid to get too close. I wonder if all this is too much at once. The junk in Grandma's house, the dilapidated town, the stink of the nursing home. All this decay. But then she recovers and steps toward my grandmother with her hand outstretched, and I think about the way she used to smother my hands and face in kisses when we first started dating. Jillian's face is tender and kind. My grandmother doesn't take her hand though, and Jillian drops it to her side.

"I'm Jillian," she says loudly. "Dean has told me so much about you."

The blank expression on my grandmother's face doesn't change.

"Grandma," I say, moving closer to her.

As I do that, Jillian quietly lifts her camera. "Pretend I'm not here," she instructs.

I put my face in front of my grandmother's. "Do you know who I am?"

Her eyes narrow. She purses her thin lips, then opens her mouth. "Last night a man come in here through the window and tried to rape me," she says.

Everything inside me locks together and then explodes into pieces in a matter of seconds. "Grandma, that's not true."

She smacks her lips. She's wearing new-looking false teeth that are straight and white. "Yesterday they strangled that girl."

"Grandma."

She shakes her head, impatient. "You don't know what goes on around here."

"What are you talking about?" She's quiet, then mumbles under her breath, "My Jell-O."

"Wait, what you said about that man."

"I'm hungry."

I take a deep breath. "Grandma, do you know who I am?"

She lifts her gnarled hand, brushes my face. The skin of her hand is shiny like bone, the wrinkles like the ridges on a shell. I wait, my heart pounding.

"I'm your granddaughter," I say because I don't know how else to do this. "I'm Anne."

She spots Jillian's camera. "What's that thing she's got?" She looks alarmed. "What is she trying to do?"

Jillian lowers the camera, nervous again, like a kid caught stealing candy. My grandmother glares at her, then orders Jillian to bring her a bowl of Jell-O. She says to me, "These people, they don't know what real work is."

I sit behind the wheel, shaky and sick. "I shouldn't have put her in there."

"The place isn't that bad."

"I could have come out to stay with her. I'm all she has."

"You can't live here."

I swallow hard and close my eyes, feel Jillian's hand on the back of my neck.

"What if there's some guy really hurting her?"

Jillian softens her tone. "Dean, she's confused, delusional. Maybe she's getting mixed up with things that happened in the past."

I open my eyes and start to ask what she means, but stop as her hand falls away. I turn the key, the engine rattles, starts.

"You look so sad," Jillian says.

"I'm fine."

"Don't think I'm fucked up." She stops. "I'd really like to film you."

"Doing what?"

"Nothing, just be yourself." I'm quiet and can feel her waiting, worried about what I'm thinking of her. Then I tell her to go ahead. I drive back to my grandmother's, the wheel pulsing in my hands, the camera on me, a weird monster eye. Everything rushes past. I don't see any of it.

The next several days go by quickly. I put in a few hours of work, but without internet service, I can't do much. Our cell phones don't work either. New York is far away. Jillian spends the days behind her camera, filming me, filming the house. I spend the days organizing and cleaning, still thinking about how I can fix it up. Wondering if I should move my grandmother back here where she belongs. She wouldn't recognize the place now. I'm only throwing out what's clearly junk, but still, that's a lot. The rooms are beginning to open up, to feel brighter.

The closest neighbor, Paul, lives on the other side of the hill. He comes by each day to complain about something, and he offers to haul my grandmother's junk to the landfill for free. He's some relation to the old guy that used to live there, and he has no idea about me: he assumes that Jillian is the granddaughter, that I'm her husband.

"New York," he says with disgust. "Why in the hell would you want to live there?" Paul is in his late fifties and can't talk for too long without breaking into a heavy smoker's cough.

We stand outside by his pickup. When Jillian walks by, waving, he winks at her. Then he says to me, "Watch out for that one." He hasn't said much to Jillian, but he's always polite. She says he leers.

"I don't like him," she says. "I'm not straight. That's not who I am."

"We've got to be safe," I tell her. "We can't be raging queers out here."

Jillian has dated trans guys and non-trans guys and women, and she told me early on, "All of my relationships are queer, doesn't matter if I'm with a guy or not."

Now she says, "It's fucked up."

Still, we fall into a kind of routine and move easily around each other like the married couple Paul imagines us to be. I tell myself this is who I am-there's no hiding anymore. I pretend this is where we live, that we are happy.

Tonight Jillian volunteers to make dinner. I'm on the front porch, looking through my old sketchbooks that I found in the back of the hall closet. The pages are soft, velvety. I used to draw all the time when I was a kid. I flip the page to a leggy princess with rhinestones in her hair, then a boy pirate with quick fists and the power to turn invisible. There are also a lot of strange animals that fill the pages, mythological deer and horses and owls.

I can see Jillian through the window at the kitchen counter, her back to me. She moves quickly, with purpose. Chopping, tossing. My grandmother used to can in the summers, steaming up the kitchen. She'd warn me to stay away from the hot mason jars. She always seemed old to me, her hands bent and gnarled, her back hunched.

She still doesn't know who I am, although she seems to be getting more used to me. One of the nurses thought I was Anne's brother, and I let her believe it; another called me by my old name, and I didn't deny it. Jillian comes with me in the mornings to film. They're growing more at ease around each other, even though my grandmother still thinks that Jillian is a nurse and orders her around. Sometimes in the afternoons I go back alone, and we sit and look at each other. Grandma always has a horror story, someone hitting her or trying to shoot her. I asked the nurses about it and they looked at me with pity. "Oh, you poor thing. Nobody's hurting her."

We eat outside, swatting at mosquitoes. Lightning bugs hover, and the bushes look like they've been sprinkled with glitter.

Jillian needs more material. "What are your most vivid memories of your parents?" she asks.

When I think of my mother, I see her crying or cowering from my father. Nothing was ever right—the food she cooked for him, the house she cleaned for him. I know this is what Jillian means when she says "material." Jillian's parents give us tickets for the opera, and over dinner, they discuss the Whitney Biennial. Everyone in the family goes to therapy; they're always telling each other what they feel.

"What about good memories? Did you ever go on vacations or anything?" she presses.

I start to say no, then remember. "Once we went camping in the Smoky Mountains." Jillian wants more, how did the trip make me feel? "My mom fried bacon over the fire and sang country songs, and my dad, he seemed at peace, for once," I say. "We all slept in a tent together. I never wanted to leave."

"What was it like when he was on the road, when it was just you and your mom?"

I remember her looking out windows, staring at the phone, always waiting for him, always sad. "She missed him," I say. "How fucked up is that?"

"Do you think your grandma knew about how he treated her?"

"I think so. At church she used to ask the congregation to guide her lost son."

"Is she scary religious?"

"Everyone down here is religious. Grandma is a good Christian lady, but she's also superstitious, and I don't know, spiritual. Everything counts. Animals, trees. Everything's connected, the dead and living."

"So she's Buddhist. In a way."

"In a way." I don't want to talk anymore. I set down my bowl of pasta salad and lean toward her, and push my lips against hers, force her mouth open with my tongue. I move my hand under her shirt, but she does not soften to my touch. The noise of the crickets is a hum inside of me, my heart trying to get out.

Jillian pulls back; we untangle.

"Maybe we should go out. What do people do? Honkeytonking?"

"You want to?"

"Maybe tomorrow." She picks up a sketchbook, thumbs the pages. "You had a wild imagination."

"Grandma used to tell me stories."

At first, after my dad left me with her, my grandmother didn't know what to do with me. I stayed out of her way, the way I was used to doing with adults. Then one night after supper she called me out to the front porch. She was sipping homemade wine that she got from old man Ruffy up at the head of the holler. After a couple of jelly glasses, she started telling me about ghosts, about the creatures that walked the hills. "I know you sense them out there," she said, "just like I do."

"I want to use these sketches in the film." Jillian flutters the pages.

"I don't know."

"Come on. These will be great. They tell a story."

"What story?"

"Your story." She pauses dramatically. "Dean." The way she says my name scares me.

"What?"

The pause again, but then she shakes her head. "Oh, nothing. I'm just tired." She stands and stretches. "I'm going in, I'm beat."

I crack another beer and wonder if she's missing the city. Jillian's friends are artists and queers, and she's always taking me to openings and parties and films. I don't have many of my own friends. I moved to the city to escape the isolation of my childhood, but it followed me, a disease in my bones. Grandma encouraged me to go off to college. "Live your life," she ordered. I just kept going and going, a wind blowing me north, rarely came back to see her.

I've been spending the nights on the couch. We haven't said much about this. Jillian asked if anything was wrong and I said no, and she said, "The bed really is too small for two people," and I agreed. Now I lie here staring up at the ceiling and thinking of my mother on the couch. Whenever my dad was on the road, she would just lie there, forget to make supper. She didn't put on makeup, didn't do her hair. I would comb it out for her, and she'd absently pat my hand and call me a good girl. She'd tell me stories about how they met, how he swept her off her feet, saved her. I never learned from what. When she got sick, her hair falling out, her breasts cut off, my father became desperate, hugging and kissing her, and finally, she was happy. Happy and light, rising to heaven.

I can't sleep. I go in the kitchen and watch moths flutter wildly against the screens trying to get to the light. After another beer, I walk past the couch and go into my childhood room. I can't tell if Jillian's sleeping or not. I put my hand on her hip, waiting, my heart beating fast. Jillian sighs, shifts away. I start to get up, but then she changes direction and moves against me, her ass pushed against my hips. When I move my hand between her legs I feel her wetness and she moans. I want her to feel all of me. I hold down her wrists with my hands and press my flat chest against her, and we stare at each other in the dark, and I am waiting. I am waiting for her to tell me what is wrong. She gives me a sad little smile; I loosen my grip.

"He tried to kill me last night."

Rain pelts the only window, which does not open and looks out onto a parking lot. The light from the lamp next to the bed is a sickly yellow.

"He's after me."

"Who?"

"There are things," my grandmother says. "Things you wouldn't understand."

I hold her hand until the anger in her face subsides. I've shaved off my sideburns and soul patch. I've shown her photographs of my parents, herself, me, her parents, her dead brother, her dead husband. I've played the music she used to listen to, like Patsy Cline, Hank Williams. Nothing works, nothing pulls her back into herself.

"Remember that time you caught a snapping turtle when we were fishing? Remember?" I try again. "Grandma, I'm your son's kid. You remember your son? Do you remember Charlie?"

"You're going to be late for school," she says, suddenly perking up. Then, nothing more.

Before leaving, I ask to see the director. The receptionist picks up the phone and in about fifteen minutes, he's next to me, a chubby, balding man in khakis and a baby blue golf shirt.

"I'm Gertrude Pearson's grandkid. From New York."

"Right, um, Anne," he stumbles.

"It's Dean."

"Dean."

He is still smiling but his nose crinkles. I tell him what she's been saying, that I'm thinking of moving her out of here, maybe someone is hurting her. He rests his hand on my arm, then looks nervous and removes it.

"It's the dementia. People get confused, hallucinate."

"Why would she say those things?"

"She's getting it from the TV, probably. The nightly news, TV shows. Could also be her medication. We'll talk to her doctor about it." He pauses, thinking. "Or maybe she's remembering something from her past and mixing it up."

"No," I say. "I don't think—"

"I know you're worried, but I promise you, she gets the best possible care." He lowers his voice like he's telling me something nobody else should know. "I promise, we're taking good care of your grandma."

When I wake up, I don't know where I am. I sit up, my heart racing. Then I see all the boxes, the mantle cluttered with pictures and figurines. I reach for my cigarettes, and the dream slowly comes back, my mother standing over me, clumps of hair falling out. Jesus. I've gone years without thinking about her or my father, but now that I'm here with Jillian, everything is stirred up. I stretch, look down at my naked body. Touch the scars on my chest. After my mother had the mastectomy, she refused to wear the falsies that my father bought for her. Her chest was flat like mine.

In the kitchen I find a note from Jillian: *Went to town, be back soon.*

After I shower, I swab my skin with alcohol, draw in the testosterone. I do this once every two weeks. There is not this single moment that you transition, Clark Kent ducking into the phone booth. It's not a magic pill, you don't go instantly from girl to boy. There is not a clear start or end. It's ongoing. The way you dress, the name you choose. If you have surgeries or not. Hormones or not. There is no easy path, no before or after. You're the same, and yet more yourself. More the person you imagine yourself to be.

When I met Jillian, only a few people knew me as Dean. But Jillian introduced me to everyone by my chosen name. When she talked about me, she used male pronouns, like there was nothing strange about it. I remember how right the "he" sounded, how everything else melted away, and this part of me, so hidden and protected, was finally seen. She's been with me every twist and turn of my transition, but now that I'm here, at last growing comfortable with who I am, I'm scared she's not.

The needle sinks into my flesh, a shot of sweetened pain. I am a project, I think, that will never be finished.

Someone is knocking at the front door. I pull up my underwear, zip my jeans, grab a shirt to hide the scars.

Through the window, I see a fraction of a person. I open the door, and Paul greets me. "Hey, how you doing?"

"Good. You?"

"Alrighty." He pulls at the bill of his hat, which says, *Sit Down and Shut Up.* Paul is a big guy, over six feet. His belly hangs over his jeans. He's got a craggy face, a head of thick dark hair.

"I just come by to see if you needed me to haul anything."

"Uh, not today. Maybe tomorrow."

He stands there lingering at the door, so I ask him if he wants any coffee.

"I could use a cup. Thank you." He follows me into the kitchen. "Where's the little lady?"

"Oh, she went into town."

"You better keep an eye on that one." I laugh uneasily, wait for the coffee to brew. Paul coughs for a long time, his face turning red and sweaty. Then he catches his breath, looks at me.

"I'm heading to town too. Got to take care of some paper work." He shakes out a cigarette. "Care if I smoke?"

I tell him I don't mind and he offers me a cigarette and I take it. He mentions the paper work again, like he's waiting for me to ask. So I do.

"The ex-wife." He makes a sour face. "Goddamn trying to clean me out. This house that Thomas left me, it's about all I got left."

He tells me that they got divorced a year ago. "Women." He shakes his head. "*Women.*"

Paul blows on his coffee, drinks it black. I don't say anything, and he keeps talking.

"She was messing with one of my buddies. I wanted to kill the both of them, but then he got throwed in jail for drunk driving. She moved out, served me with papers." He looks at my hand. "Thought you said you was married. I don't see no ring."

"Oh, well, we're not really married yet. We're engaged."

I sip my coffee, trying to act like this is normal, the two of us hanging out.

"You best think twice before you get married," he says. "You best think twice."

If Jillian wasn't with me, Paul probably wouldn't be such a friendly neighbor. He would peg me as a queer, an effeminate New Yorker. Jillian is what he recognizes: she gives me hetero credibility. Paul goes on about his ex-wife and women in general, and I just sit there, feeling ashamed, listening to his rant. Jillian would be disappointed. I'm a coward.

He takes a long drag on his cigarette. "For a goddamn year she was running around on me. I was too damn pussywhipped to see it."

He shifts his long legs. He has no idea who I am. For so many years I tried to ignore my feelings. I was scared for a lot of reasons. But one of the biggest ones was that I would turn out to be like him, the one who taught me what it meant to be a man.

"I better get back to work," I say. "I'm trying to get a lot of stuff packed up."

"You think y'all are going to stay?"

"I don't know."

"You thinking of selling?"

"Thinking about it," I admit.

"Well, I wouldn't blame you none."

Then he reaches out, catching me off guard, and we shake hands. Something crosses his face, just a subtle twitch.

"Catch you later," he says.

I drag boxes out of the back room. One is as light as a carton of eggs. Inside I find folded clothes in plastic, like evidence from a crime scene. Little clothes. My clothes. Tiny T-shirts and shorts and dresses, ruffled socks and shoes the size of my hands. I hold them up in front of the mirror and wonder how I ever fit into them. My grandmother was glad I'd been born a girl. "The female's got a harder lot than the man, but we're better for the earth." She didn't say much about the men in her life. Her husband, father, son. They only caused her pain.

When I hear Jillian come in, I set the clothes aside, thinking she'll want to use them for the film. She's in the kitchen, putting away groceries.

"What's all this?"

"Stuff to grill, and liquor. I thought we could make margaritas." She's wearing short-shorts and a T-shirt that dips into a V at her breasts. "I got some good shots of the place where your parents used to live. I'll show you later, if you want."

I tell her about Paul coming by.

"He was ranting about his ex-wife."

"I'm glad I wasn't here." Jillian takes peppers and onions and mushrooms out of a bag. "I think it'll feel good getting back to New York. Don't you?"

I nod, but I'm afraid of returning, what will happen to us. Jillian was the first person to see me for who I was. Now I don't know what she sees.

"I'm going to the nursing home," I say. "Did you leave the keys in the car?"

"Wait. Do you have to go now? I was thinking we could have a few drinks. Talk."

I've told her too much, I think. She's stripping me down, turning everything inside out.

"More recording?" I ask.

"No, just talking." Her smile is small, forced. "About us."

She looks tired. I see crow's feet around her eyes, a few new lines hugging her lips. The light coming from the windows shines on her face and glints on a single silver strand of hair. Her face is open and sad, and wanting too much.

"Please, Dean," she says.

"Later," I tell her, "when I get back."

Her face clouds as I give her a peck on the mouth, taste her waxy lipstick.

Instead of going to the nursing home, I turn on a back road that leads to the cemetery. My grandmother used to take me to visit my mother's grave, but I never knew what I was supposed to do or say. I take a few wrong turns, then find the headstones planted at the bottom of a hill. There are no flowers. The day is bright, hurts my eyes. Many of the headstones are flanked by little American flags, framed pictures, plastic flowers. I wonder if I should take Jillian here for the film. My chest feels heavy, like it's sprouted phantom breasts. After I first got my surgery, there were nights I'd wake up panicked, swearing that I could feel my breasts growing back, and I'd have to touch my chest over and over.

I sit down in front of my parents' graves, but just like when I was a kid, I don't know what to do or say. The cemetery is butted up against a forest, and a crow caws. My grandmother used to say that some spirits never rest. Her husband was one of them. My father, too. Now I know what she means. He's still out there, stumbling through the forest, tripping over tree roots. But not my mother, her soul is at peace. She's not here in the ground but in a big nest somewhere, high in a tree, protecting a clutch of tiny blue eggs. Hidden from my father. Hidden from me. Before I go, I pull up the weeds, revealing my parents' names, the dates that they lived and died.

Jillian has started the grill, and she stabs the vegetables through the skewers. By the time I finish my first drink, she is on her third. Her cheeks are red, her laugh too loud. She puts her hand on my crotch, and a hotness shoots up to my chest. Then she pulls back. Studies me.

"What?"

Her eyes flick past me, toward the house. "Have you decided what you're going to do about this place?"

The junk pile is still there at the edge of the yard, the washer sits on the porch. The paint is peeling away, the roof caving in. Fixing it up is not going to bring her back, and none of our friends will visit, I know that. It will always be a separate part of my life, the part that is the deepest and oldest.

"I don't know," I say.

The blackened vegetable bits on my plate look like pieces of bone. My mouth tastes charred. I start to ask what she thinks I should do, but a loud rumbling blasts from the driveway; both of us jump.

Paul climbs out of his pickup. "How y'all doing?"

I offer him a drink, but he's on the wagon. He asks me if I want him to take a load of junk to the landfill.

"I thought you were coming by tomorrow."

"Shit, you're right, I forgot." He rubs his face, leaning in. "I didn't sign those damn papers." He talks low. "She ain't gonna get another cent from me."

Jillian grabs our plates. "I'm going to wash up, honey," she says in a fake polite voice, but her face is hateful.

Paul doubles over in a coughing fit, then sits in Jillian's chair. He takes a deep breath, wipes his eyes.

"I kind of gotta get in there, Paul. We're, you know, talking."

He grins, thinking we're on the same page at last. "Don't let her boss you."

I start to laugh, but then I don't. I wonder if Jillian can hear us from the house. "It's not like that," I say. "We've just got things to figure out."

Paul's eyes crinkle, like he's going to cry. His face is splotchy from too many years of drink, his hands tremble. He's just a lonely old man, heartsick. "Things are gonna be all right," he says. "You go in there. Everything's going to be all right."

Jillian's at the table, resting her forehead against her fist, her hair falling around her. I can't see her face.

I slowly pull out a chair, careful with my movements, as if I'm carrying loose eggs. She finally looks up, tears in her eyes.

"I don't know how much you want to know." I want to know all of it and none of it, but I stay quiet for a while.

"Someone I know?" I finally ask.

"No."

"Tell me."

She says he's a guy who has a studio in the same building that she does. He's an artist, like her. I hear her words but can't look at her.

"How long?"

"A few months," she says quietly.

I'm staring at the scratched table, my hands clasped together so hard that the knuckles whiten. Everything feels speedy and wild, my heart beating too fast, my mind racing. My face throbs with heat, like I'm standing too close to a fire. I clench my teeth and squeeze my hands tighter, trying to stop this thing that's growing inside me, this rage that fills my throat like bile, that spreads through my body burning me.

"Is he trans?" My voice sounds too loud, strange, an echo.

"Dean," she says. "You know that doesn't matter."

"It matters," I say, but I don't know if it does. I just want something that will make me understand, a clear answer, a reason.

"I knew you would think that, that's why I couldn't tell you, I knew you wouldn't understand. Would you look at me? Listen. It's not like he's some straight dude. We're still queer."

The *we* slices through me, and I don't want to look at her but I do. She is still weepy, but when she talks about him there is a light in her eyes. My face is burning. I let go of my hands. Words are thick in my throat; I force them out like I'm spitting teeth.

"You love him?"

She doesn't answer, and I want to hit her, I want to hit her the way my father hit my mother. All this rage that's been inside me all my life, waiting. I force myself to flatten my hand against the table. She rests her hand on top of mine. I clench my other hand into a fist, dig it into my leg.

"I wanted to give this another chance," she says. "I thought coming here would do that."

"You just wanted to make a goddamn film."

"That's not true, that's not the only reason. I wanted to feel closer to you, to fix things." She shakes her head. "It's not working, Dean."

Her hand on mine is warm and beating like a heart. Finally, something snaps, movement returns. I get up and go outside, leave Jillian crying at the table. The air is stagnant, covers the yard like a sheet of plastic.

At the creek a school of tadpoles dart behind a rock. The gnats are thick; sweat rolls down my neck. My father stood over my mother when she was on her deathbed, cried like a baby, but it was too late. I crouch down like I'm going to be sick, but nothing will come out. My hands press into the damp dirt. All these months have been a lie. This trip, a lie. A dull thumping rises from my chest to my skull. She doesn't love me anymore—she didn't say that, but she didn't have to. I've known for months now, just couldn't admit it. Maybe I don't love her anymore either. I loved her because she knew me, but maybe that's not enough.

I take a deep breath, walk back. Early evening light slants across the house.

"Where are you going?"

"Town," I say.

"I'm coming with."

I don't tell her yes or no. She gets in, and I shift into gear, the tires grinding dirt and gravel. I've never spent much time on the road, but my father trucked thousands of miles, all of it blurring by like the years, gone. I punch in the lighter on the dash, hold the red circle to my cigarette.

Jillian tells me she didn't mean for it to happen, she wasn't expecting it. Things sometimes just happen, she says. "I felt terrible, all this time. He did too, he really did, Dean." She explains that they have a lot in common. He grew up near the city too. He makes paintings. He goes to therapy. They talk. She feeds me details that I don't want. The sun is going down, turning the sky a dusky, depressing blue. I drive faster, and as soon as I get cell service, I make the call to the coal company.

"What was that about?" Jillian asks.

"Nothing." When I look over at her the rage returns. I feel sick with it. I look at Jillian and I see her with a cock in her mouth, I see her waking up in the mornings with her soft puffy eyes, I see her laughing in his arms.

I speed up. Something shifts in the road. I don't swerve fast enough and there is a loud, sickening thud.

"Stop," Jillian yells. "You hit something."

I pull over and look in the rearview and see a dark lump. Jillian scrambles out, and I chase after her. I pull up short. It's a puppy, a mutt. Chocolate brown with floppy ears. Positioned weirdly on its side, shuddering. Blood seeps from underneath it, and its hind legs look tangled, like the roots of a gnarled plant.

"Oh, God," Jillian kneels next to it. "Dean."

I touch the dog's velvety head and it bares its teeth, whimpers, and then is still. Its belly is limp and I can't tell if it's alive or dead. It's not much bigger than the length of my forearm.

"We have to find its owners," Jillian says.

There are no houses, only an empty field, a patch of dying woods. A burlap bag is tangled in the high weeds. "Someone dumped it," I say.

Jillian is on her knees, like she's going to give the dog mouth-to-mouth, and I run back to the car and get a blanket out of the trunk, drape it over the dog, leaving its head exposed. I'm crouched next to Jillian. I can smell my own sweat, the blood of the dog, the expensive product that Jillian uses to tame her curls. No other cars drive past. Swallows or bats sweep across the field. I reach out and touch the dog through the blanket. Its body is still.

I stand and take a deep breath, and Jillian stays crouched, her shoulders hunched like an old woman's. "Come on, it's dead," I say, reaching for her.

She knocks my hand away, then suddenly jumps up and rushes at me, punching my chest, smacking me.

"Look what you did," she yells.

I grab her wrists. She tries to break free, but I won't let go. Her breath is ragged, cheeks flushed, the way she looks when we fuck. Her face crumples and there are tears in her eyes. "I'm sorry," she says. "It's not your fault, I'm sorry." I tell her I'm sorry, too. I let go and she wraps her arms around me and we stand there in the fading daylight, our hearts pounding against each other, until a truck rumbles by blaring its horn.

When I pick the dog up, still wrapped in the blanket, blood drips through onto my hands. It's heavier than I expected, like a sack of oranges. I carry the body into the field and set it under a tree. Jillian watches from the side of the road, arms crossed over her chest, hair lit up by the setting sun. I feel like I should say something, a prayer, or a goodbye, but I don't have any more words.

There are specks of blood on my palms. I shove my hands in my pockets. This man Jillian loves, he's not afraid of himself, not afraid of what he comes from.

"Hi, Grandma."

But she is looking at Jillian, sunglasses perched on her head, T-shirt clinging to her breasts. Grandma says, "Sara." My mother. "I'm so glad you're here."

Jillian doesn't look at all surprised. It's the first time she's come in here without her camera and she walks over to my grandmother and cups her face in her hands and pretends to be my mother. "So am I," she says.

"No. Tell her who you really are. Jillian, tell her. Grandma, this isn't Sara."

My grandmother isn't listening. She touches the hand on her face, then holds it in hers. Jillian and my grandmother holding hands. "Honey, are you okay?"

"I'm fine," Jillian says. "I'm okay, I promise."

My grandmother looks at me. "Charlie."

"No, no. I'm not Charlie," I say. "And this is not Sara."

My grandmother just smiles. At my father's funeral she did not shed a tear, but she said, as we left the cemetery, "I tried to raise him right." She knew there was something in him that was wrong, just like something was wrong in her husband. But wasn't something also wrong in my mother? One time my father was punching her, and when I ran over to put myself between them, my mother pushed me away. I always told myself that she was protecting me. But she didn't even look at me. She rubbed her jaw and gathered herself, and then she followed him into the bedroom and locked the door behind her. The violence haunts me, just like it does my grandmother. My father's blood is in me, so is my mother's.

"Charlie?"

"Grandma, no. It's me. Your grandchild. Sara and Charlie's kid. I go by Dean now. I used to be Anne."

"Anne's gone," she says. "Who's Anne?"

My grandmother blinks wildly like she's woken up from a long dream. She can't stop talking. She's not saying anything about anyone hurting her—she's just repeating names and dates and little bits of memories, nothing bad. She calls me Charlie, her son, she calls me John, her husband. Him, a man she rarely spoke of, but I know that he is the one who is after her now. Like father, like son. She goes on and on, calling me the names of the dead, these men who beat their women, and I am afraid to say a word. I'm afraid to meet Jillian's eyes. I want to apologize to my grandmother, how sorry I am for leaving her. Grandma leans in closer to me, I smell her rotted breath. My grandmother who kept a room for me all these years, waiting on me to come back home.

Jillian and I sit by Sugar Creek, not touching. The mountains and trees hide the stars, but there is still enough light to see each other.

I tell her about the box of baby clothes. "You want to use them for your film?"

"I think I've got enough."

"You're finished?"

"Yeah."

She tells me she will go back to New York tomorrow. She already bought a plane ticket. She twists her hair with her finger, curling it even more. She's got so much of it, whenever we had sex it used to get stuck in her mouth, stuck in mine.

"What do you think the film's going to be like?"

"You know, it'll be like my other stuff. It's not traditional."

I know what she means—that once she pieces it together, the story of my father's death and my mother's death, my grandmother's fears about her husband killing her, and all the beautiful and sad shots of the mountains, the house, my grandmother's junk, my flat chest, the pictures of my mother who lost her breasts, the baby pictures of me, none of it will add up, there will not be an easy story. I will not recognize myself.

Now here I am, leaving what I know. I got rid of what my grandmother was saving and put her in a nursing home and now I'm selling her land. She used to hang my drawings on the refrigerator. The princess was her favorite, but I liked the one with the angry fists, the invisible one.

"Dean, I wasn't just here for the film," Jillian says.

I think how things could have turned out differently. If I hadn't hit the dog, we could have taken him home with us, I think, to our house in the mountains, and everything would be fine.

"If I had just stopped a second sooner," I say. "The dog."

Jillian doesn't reply. Tomorrow she will go, and in a week or two, I will leave too, and no one will be here, except Paul, bitter and lonely, and all these old ghosts wandering the woods. When I come back to visit, my grandmother won't know who I am.

The peepers, impossible to see, grow louder. They're all around us. I thought Jillian was the first one who ever saw me, but that's not true. For a few seconds the noise suddenly stops. Silence reverberates. Then there's a single chirp and they all join in. My grandmother taught me to look at what was hidden, to see what was right in front of my eyes.

This afternoon, before I left, I promised her nobody would ever hurt her again. She reached out her old claw hand and cupped my face.

"You're a good boy," she said. "A real good boy."

MY SPECIAL FRIEND
Christopher Lord

By the time Harley and I leave to visit my parents for Christmas I'm barely speaking to him.

A few weeks ago I was promoted to night manager at Shari's Restaurant and I've been having trouble making the switch from days to nights. These days our—formerly my—little apartment has been feeling pretty close.

Because we were going home for Christmas I decided we wouldn't get a tree even though Harley wanted one. Just when I think we're agreed he goes and buys a Noble fir, some strings of lights, and puts everything up while I'm at work. I'm still cleaning up his mess when he comes in the door.

"Why didn't you pick up this shit?" I ask.

"I ran out of time, Rudy," he says, slipping out of his coverall and letting it fall to the floor.

I'm on my knees, the fir needles in the carpet pricking my fingers. "You should've thought of that before you started."

He walks over to me, puts his business near my face.

"You wanna play?" he asks, a little shy, a little teasing.

"Play with your own self," I say. "I'm busy."

An hour later, after eating dinner in silence, we're on our way, the first time I've ever brought a man home to meet my parents.

We're off the interstate now and familiar signs tell the miles to Foster, Sweet Home, other rural Oregon towns. Side roads beckon as they trail away in the fog and darkness.

I see the house—it's a little box with a low-pitched roof, the porch a pouty lip drooling out rickety stairs. Chimney smoke trails into the fog and spreads in veins. Already I can feel the heat inside, the cramped rooms, the low ceilings.

I pull the car into the gravel driveway. "We're here."

It's the first time I've spoken to Harley in more than an hour. My voice is husky, probably sexy, too.

"It looks nice," he says.

The house looks the way it did when I was growing up, only smaller, a few cedar shakes loose and paint peeling in the light of the full moon. Not quite in the country, not quite in town, my parents' house sits on a quarter acre at the end of the paved road that crumbles into gravel the next house down. It's the first house past the trailer court where OotieMae lived until the second hip replacement, the reason for the telephone call from Mom that has led Harley and me here. Mom—or more probably OotieMae—has persuaded Pop to put up Christmas lights. They are stapled in place. Clown colors of orange, yellow, red, blue wink at us as we get out. The curtains are closed; the triangular glow of the tree shows through.

Harley stumbles on the porch. I reach out and grab him so he doesn't fall.

"Thanks," he says, brushing his knee.

As I'm holding Harley's arm the front door opens. Mom and Pop are standing in the doorway, Pop squinting into the darkness. I let go of Harley and we finish climbing the steps. My parents are on the porch now. Pop's arms come around my sides. He smells like dry firewood.

"Good to see you, son," he says.

Mom gives me a closer hug; the dough of her body is warm, a hint of bath talc.

Pop is shaking Harley's hand. "You must be Rudy's special friend," he says.

"Harley, Mr. Sampson." Harley uses his deepest, most polite voice.

"Call me John."

"And I'm Wilma," Mom says, clasping Harley's large flat hand in her own small hands. "So nice to meet you."

Pop steers us into the house. My glasses steam up.

The pellet stove is decorated with garlands. A Douglas fir—a real one from the woods—holds strings of white lights and Hallmark ornaments.

"Take off your coats, men," Pop says. "Set a spell."

The stove's hellish warmth radiates to every corner of the living room. The furniture is familiar—the long couch with the orange-and-brown crocheted afghan on the back, the twin green Barcaloungers. The new big-screen television competes with the tree trying to illuminate the room. Somebody's hit the "mute" button. Bing Crosby and Rosemary Clooney move ghost-like across the screen.

Harley and Pop sit across from one another, big crooked smiles on their faces, but they're not talking.

"Is that who I think it is?" The voice is a rasp, a growl, a wheeze.

"OotieMae?" I ask.

"Bet your ass, kiddo."

From the kitchen comes OotieMae Winsocket, my father's stepmother. She's been old since forever—she's about eighty now. She's a dynamo not quite five feet tall, once somewhat broad, now thinner, racked with lung disease and every other ailment known to man. She's wearing a white velour caftan decorated with a giant sequined Santa face. She's got a hand on one of her bony hips, which project out from the caftan like antler buds. Her elbow propels her upper body forward as she takes one step, then another, in jerky motion. Her other hand holds a wooden cane, gnarled and polished, almost black. A cigarette hangs from her lip and produces a wreath of smoke that envelops most of her face.

"Give Ootie a hug," she says, sidling up to me, her voice somewhere between Tallulah Bankhead's and Andy Devine's.

Even though I'm only five six, I tower over her, and my face gets buried in her engine-red hair, scratchy, smoky, and flying in all directions. She tries to put her arms around me, pokes me in the side with the handle of her cane.

"It's about time you came back," she says.

I pull away. "You're right, Ootie—it's been too long."

She looks at me, swivels on one foot, gives Harley the once-over. "Who's this tall drink of water?"

Harley's just over six feet. Some of our friends call us Mutt and Jeff.

"This is Harley," I say.

"Come here," she says to him.

"Harley is Rudy's special friend," Mom says. Her hands are clasped in front of her flower-print dress.

"Well that's just ducky," Ootie says.

Harley bends down, lets Ootie hug him. She pulls back, puffs on her cigarette. Her fingernails are two-inch talons polished in alternating green and red.

Mom and Pop sit in their recliners. Ootie has a special chair of her own, a cracked vinyl rocker that's piled with throw pillows that she can arrange around her achy bones.

Harley and I sit together on the couch, several feet apart.

"So," Pop says, "any bad weather on the way down?"

"The weather's the same in Portland as it is here," I say. "It's less than a two-hour drive."

"Then why don't you visit more often?" Ootie asks. Ash falls from her cigarette onto a metal tea tray sitting next to her chair.

"Let's hear about the big promotion," Pop says.

I can't tell what it is: the heat, the strangeness of being here with Harley, Ootie's eyes ranging over us both, or embarrassment at Pop's pride when he emphasizes "big." Whichever, I feel my face flush.

"Do you like it?" Mom asks.

"It's better than serving—well, not always, since I could get good tips most days, especially the breakfast crowds. I miss days. But I like the managing. I'm getting to use my education."

After waiting a few years to start college I finally finished night school a year ago, got an 'associate's degree in business from Western Community College. My parents came to Portland for the graduation, took me out to dinner.

"You're the boss," Ootie says.

"I guess."

Harley's spatula hands are on his knees, large fingernails, flat and square. I notice that he's scraped away the grease.

"Are you hungry?" Mom asks. "There's tuna casserole in the refrigerator."

"We ate before we came."

"What about you, Harley?" Pop says.

He looks at me, shuffles his hands. "No, thanks," he says.

"You work for Midas?" Mom asks.

"Yes, ma'am," he says.

Mom's hair picks up the light of the television, shimmers with the colors. "Wilma, please," she says.

"Wilma—yes. I do brakes. Discs, pads, fluid—you name it." Harley pushes himself back in the couch.

"We go to Midas here in town," Pop says.

"They're a good employer. I've been there two years."

"Steady job," Pop says.

Mom's face, Pop's, Ootie's inscrutable pucker—I'm looking for signs that they're wondering about the two of us in the bedroom, whether the difference in height is a handicap. I shiver in the heat.

"Well, Munchkin," Ootie says, after she finishes a cough, "I'm sure as hell glad you're here."

"We got a turkey—first one in several years," Pop says.

"I haven't cooked a big Christmas dinner since you moved out," Mom adds.

"You're making me hungry," Ootie says.

Harley and I go outside to get our luggage; when we come back in we start up the stairs.

Mom stops us. "Ootie's staying in your old room." I put down my bag. "Since the hip replacement. We had her in the family room until she could climb the stairs. But she didn't like sleeping there."

Harley and I go upstairs to the guest bedroom. I turn on the light. Twin beds pushed against opposing walls, tight neat bedcovers. A framed poster from Aunt Tilda's trip to Germany twenty years ago. Mom's waterfall Lane cedar chest, topped with a yellowed crocheted runner, hugs the wall opposite the beds. The room is chilly, with an empty smell, but it's clear that it has been cleaned, straightened, made ready for me and my "special friend."

I open the top drawer of the dresser and I put in my underwear, socks, extra shirts. Harley does the same. Our clothes touch; we don't.

We go downstairs. Harley looks like a man too big for his skin. I can't tell what he's taking in. I told him about OotieMae—but I didn't expect to see her so frail, even after what Mom said on the phone.

Pop's standing at the foot of the stairs; as we come down he puts his hand first on my shoulder, then on Harley's—he rubs Harley's pretty hard.

"You fellas have everything you need up there?" he asks.

"I put extra towels in the bathroom," Mom says; she's talking to me, but looking at Pop. She almost sings the words. "All I had were the ones with seashells."

"I left the bedroom door open to warm the room a little," I say.

"I'll check the vent," Pop says. "I'm about ready for bed anyway. I still have to work tomorrow—half a day, at least—and six o'clock comes pretty early. But you boys can sleep like slugs."

My dad's a plumber; he plans on working just one more year until he's sixty-two. He's put on weight; either that or the plaid pattern of the Pendleton shirt makes him look broader than when I last saw him.

"Night, Pop."

"Night, Rudy," he replies. "Harley, glad to meet you finally."

He gives Harley a good look, shakes his hand again, then climbs the stairs one at a time and disappears into the dark.

Mom is at the bottom of the stairs, takes Harley's hand, too, then stretches up on her toes, kisses me on the cheek. "Goodnight," she says. The rustling of her dress fades as she climbs.

"You get your butts over here by me," OotieMae says, a bony arm flailing out from her caftan like a twig in a storm. Her fingernails wink the reflected light of the television.

"Nice nails," I say, as Harley and I sit down in the recliners.

"You like them? Delpha at The Hairport does them for me."

"How long does it take?" Harley asks.

"How would I know? I'm never there!" She slaps a hand on her brittle knee. "I love that joke—Dolly Parton says that all the time about her hair."

"It's a good one, Ootie," I tell her.

"I glue 'em on, honey," she says to Harley, fanning the nails at him.

I go to the kitchen. The fridge is filled with cellophane-wrapped bowls, casseroles, fresh vegetables. The turkey's thawing on a towel. So much food for only five people—four, really, since I suspect OotieMae doesn't eat more than a child. A part of her stomach is missing.

Mom's always had a clean kitchen, little appliances lined up and covered with plastic or fabric. The room hasn't changed— the thick, white-framed glass cupboard doors with the old-fashioned pulls, the Formica countertop clean but discolored. Mom's duck collection—ceramic, wooden, glass, clay and other odd materials—lines the counter.

"What are you rooting around for in there?" OotieMae calls out.

I get a couple of Barq's and a Bud for Ootie.

"You're something in shoes?" she's asking Harley when I get back.

"Brake shoes," he says. "I repair brakes at Midas."

"Oh, yeah. You said that before. The muffler people." She sucks at her beer bottle, smiles, and shows both sets of dentures. She leans back in her chair, gives us a long look. "You've been away too long, Rudy."

"I get so busy."

"You're never too busy for family," she says.

"What with moving and all—" I start to explain.

"And you, Harley—" she says, "well, you're the real Megillah." She drums her Christmas nails against the head of her cane.

"Thank you," Harley says politely.

"You're going shopping tomorrow?"

"Yes," I say. "I still have to get a few things. So busy, you know..."

"Nothing like waiting until Christmas Eve to buy presents," Harley says.

"I want you to buy something special for John," Ootie says. "He and your mother have been extra good, letting me come here after the surgery and all."

"Sure," I say. "What?"

"A new fishing rod. It's on sale at the G. I. Joe. I'll give you the money." She reaches into some fold in her caftan and pulls out a wrinkled newspaper ad. She holds it between two fingernails, one red, one green. "This one." She hands me the crinkled paper.

"We can get this tomorrow, no problem," I say. I put the ad in my wallet.

She finishes her beer. "I better be getting up to bed," she says. She closes her fingers around the head of her cane.

Harley rises, starts to help her, but she whips out a bony arm and shushes him away until she's standing as tall as she can. Her hair is wild, maroon flames.

"*Now* you can give me a hand," she says to Harley, her voice breathy. "I still hitch up on the stairs."

I turn off the lights, the television, and make sure the door is locked. When I finish they're still making the climb, Ootie putting both feet on each tread before starting up the next one. Harley towers over her. He's cradling her small craggy elbow with the palm of his hand. Ootie is talking to him in a low voice. I can't hear and I stay back so I won't crowd her.

Harley walks Ootie to the door of my old room. She pats his hand, says goodnight to me, and shuts the door behind her. She starts to cough almost at once; more than a minute passes before she stops.

I go into our room while Harley leaves to brush his teeth. I leave when he returns and when I come back he's undressed and in bed already, the covers pulled up to his waist. I see his broad hairy chest. I want to be naked next to him, want not to be mad at him.

"I like your parents," he says.

"My friends always have," I say.

"And OotieMae—she's a real trip."

I turn out the light, undress in the dark and climb into the cold bed, the sheets crisp against my skin. The room is black, a hint of bitterness and Harley's cinnamon aroma.

"What's a megillah?" he asks, his deep voice poking a hole in the dark. "Some kind of monkey?"

It's Christmas Eve and I'm pissy.

I wake up, hard as a rock, and see that Harley's already gone.

I think about Harley again when I'm in the shower, him snaking out of that coverall last night, and the soap and water feel good, sexy. I think about relieving the pressure but that's too weird and anyway, I'm still mad at him.

When I come down, Harley's at the table with OotieMae, almost lost behind a shroud of cigarette smoke. Mom's frying bacon—some things about home stay golden.

"Hey, sleepyhead," Ootie says.

"Morning," Harley says.

I respond with a yawn, give Mom a kiss on the cheek, and steal some of the bacon that's on the plate under paper towels.

"We've been having a little visit, Harley and me," Ootie says.

Harley looks up from his plate; he's been stoking himself with scrambled eggs. He smiles.

"Ootie did most of the talking," Harley says, as if the scowl on my face told him what I was thinking. "About when you were little."

"A little shit is what he was," she says.

Her hands are even smaller today; she's removed the press-on nails and her fingers look like crinkle-cut French fries.

"He was a good kid most of the time when I came for a visit," Ootie says, "except when he'd come around when I was standing in the bathroom in my undies and bra and slap me on the butt saying 'bosom bottom bosom bottom' until I'd shoo him out and slam the door."

"Bosom bottom?" Harley works his mouth around the words like they were foreign.

"Maybe I picked it up in church," I say. "I never could sing 'Rock my soul in the bosom of Abraham' without thinking of OotieMae."

"And my big ass," she adds.

"And the smell of Avon Skin-so-Soft."

"I still use it," she says, "and Christmas is coming."

Mom nods at me from near the stove, her smile small and thoughtful.

Ootie's taking Harley in with great big gulps of her eyes, checking him out as he shovels in the food. He doesn't talk with his mouth full or anything like that, but he looks like a big child as I watch her watch him, a big child with huge muscled forearms and wide shoulders. I'm getting hard again, and I'm still mad at him, but I'm beginning to forget why.

Ootie drags on her cigarette. I forgot how those Kools smell, rotten minty dirt in the air.

"Say, Harley," Ootie says, "I need some things downtown, some special things to make Christmas perfect. Could you get them for me?" She stubs out the cigarette, pushes herself up from the table with her spindly arms. "You come in the other room with me," she says. "Where they can't hear." Harley rises to help her and they disappear into the living room. "Rock my soul..." she sings, then cackles.

Mom loads the dishwasher, turns it on, and sits at Ootie's place with a cup of coffee. She pushes the beanbag ashtray away, wipes her hands on her apron. Her eyes are warm brown pools, the skin around them wrinkled at the edges. The pupils are dark too.

"Ootie thinks quantity is as important as quality when it comes to presents," she says.

"I'll keep that in mind."

"Harley's a nice man." Mom sips her coffee. "Your father and I—"

"I should have shopped earlier," I say, "but this job change really has me jumpy—I've got my days and nights all tumbled up."

She waits. I see her thinking. "Are you happy?"

"I like the new responsibilities—I feel too young sometimes to supervise the older servers."

"Are you happy at home?" The voice is patient.

We've never had this talk before. I've told them the minimum things they needed to know.

"We get along fine," I say.

"Harley's been there—what is it—five months?" Her hands cradle her coffee cup.

"Almost six."

"He's got a good job."

"He wants to go to night school for an associate's degree, maybe do bookkeeping or something. He doesn't want to be a grease monkey forever."

"There's nothing wrong with manual labor," she says.

"He wants to learn stuff, too."

"You're careful, aren't you?"

"Mom—"

"I read horrible things."

"Other people, Mom. Not us." I put my hand on hers, warm from her coffee cup. "Yes. We're careful."

I see her face change, a twitch at the corner of her eye. She looks away, then back at me.

"We haven't bought Harley anything," she says. "We didn't know what to do for him until we saw him."

"You don't have to get him anything."

Ootie and Harley come back into the kitchen. "He's big *and* he's smart," is all Ootie says before she starts to laugh, then gives way to a long, painful cough.

Even in the car I'm getting horny. I want Harley to mention the tree, say he's sorry, and then we can go back to the way it was, sex nearly every day, the yeasty smells of sweat and semen.

"What did you and Ootie talk about?" I ask.

"Just some errands she wants me to run. Nothing special." Harley's voice pushes the warmed air.

We split up at the mall and agree to meet in a few hours.

I've made a mental list and I need to follow it. Something personal for Mom. For Pop, Ootie's fishing rod and something from me. My usual gifts for Ootie. For Harley—well, I haven't made up my mind, yet. I could use a little more charity in my heart, move the feeling for him up from where it seems to be stuck.

There's Harley a hundred yards ahead, going into the music shop. From the back—that's how I saw him the night we met at the Cinco de Mayo party. I'd had a boyfriend for six weeks but he dumped me and I was in a lousy mood. I was planning on drinking a lot of margaritas and going home early when I saw Harley's broad, flat back. He turned and I saw his face and instantly I got interested. But he was too handsome until I saw the chipped tooth when he smiled.

That's when I knew I wanted him. I remember staring at Harley's hands, grease under his nails, and I started imagining those flat big fingers on my back, my stomach, the other places. I liked everything about him and didn't mind at all that he didn't have any college or a career job.

I was jittery that night but the more we talked the more I noticed that he was calm, at home in his skin, had some deep center that was at peace. And that took the edge off me as well.

I could tell he was interested. Since I lived alone my place was the obvious choice. I started cleaning up the bedroom but he was right there kissing me, taking off my clothes, being both gentle and demanding at the same time until we fell on the bed naked and did the wild monkey sex thing three times before morning.

He moved in six weeks later when his roommate got busted for drugs and Harley said he'd had enough. So we just fell together like that. He brought over his boxes of things— clothes, some CDs, a few science-fiction novels.

I didn't tell my parents right away. We don't talk about me being gay, not in any explicit terms. So when Mom asked if I would bring Harley when I came home for Christmas I paused before I said I'd ask him and then see.

He wanted to go, couldn't wait. So I said we'd be there without giving it much more thought, without wondering what kind of signal it sent to them, to Harley, or, for that matter, to me, about what our arrangement might mean.

I think about the Christmas tree back at home. I'm not quite sure now what got me so angry so fast. It wasn't about money and it wasn't about style. I could care less what the tree looks like.

I go into one of the men's stores and look at ties and stuff. I see this great wool sweater, almost too heavy, but somehow I see Harley's chest underneath it, filling it out. So I buy it. It's dressy, not something he would wear any day of the week. I see us sitting in a restaurant and we're eating Caesar salads and Harley's wearing this sweater and there's a candle at the table.

For Pop I get a new Pendleton shirt. For Mom, a sweet perfume. For Ootie, the gifts are the same as always—another beanbag ashtray, a carton of Kools, some lottery tickets, and something I pick up at the music store that makes me chuckle—something I'll give her early.

Harley's already waiting at the Orange Julius when I get there. He's got a big shopping bag. We eat Chicago dogs, then go to the car. If he would just apologize then we could get back to the way it was.

We ride pretty much the whole way in silence.

At home the smell of baking hits us like a warm glove. The kitchen table is covered with wax paper. Chocolate chip, chocolate crinkles, peanut butter, and oatmeal cookies are lined and stacked in neat rows.

For once Ootie's not smoking. She sits at the table and removes cookies from a cookie sheet with a spatula she's holding in both hands.

Ootie shovels a cookie into Harley's big red hand. "Have one," she says.

"Snerkle-derkles," I say.

Harley looks up, his face full of cookie. He fills the kitchen with his body.

"Snickerdoodles," Ootie says. "He couldn't say it right when he was a kid."

"They're delicious," Harley says to Mom.

"I'm going to take a nap," I say. I kiss Mom on the cheek.

"We'll eat dinner at six."

"And then we're going to the Living Nativity," OotieMae says.

"What's that?" Harley asks, sneaking a cookie from underneath Ootie's watchful eye. She gives him a sly grin.

I turn to Harley. "People standing out in the cold pretending to be the Holy Family. They pose in costumes with animals and stuff."

"It's at the Holy Christ Redeemer Church," Ootie tells him. "This year I'm going to get Lester Simms to say 'hey' when I go by."

I go up to the guest room, take off my shoes, and lie on top of the bed. I'm almost asleep when the door opens a bit and Harley comes in.

"You need something?" I ask.

"Presents to wrap," he says, gruff-like, and picks up his packages. "Don't worry your pretty little head about it."

I wake up and it's dark. I've had one of those naps that make you feel like you've been hit by a truck. The feeling lasts just long enough to put a little more edge on my temper.

I can hear muffled sounds from downstairs, Ootie's laugh, Pop's voice deep and cottony. The cookie odor has slipped under the door and draws me downstairs.

"Hey, kiddo," Ootie says from the living room.

The Lennon Sisters are singing on the stereo. That reminds me.

"I got you something today," I tell her as I stop on the stairs. "I think you'll like it." I go back to my room and bring down a small package.

She's wearing her Christmas nails and scratches open the wrapping paper.

"Hot damn!" she exclaims. "Put it on now."

Harley's watching from Mom's recliner; Pop's sitting in his. I put on the disk, wait for it to start up.

The background vocalists, their voices washed out like eunuchs, begin to "aah" as the four opening chords of "Rockin' Around the Christmas Tree" sound and the singer begins:

> *Rockin' around the Christmas tree*
> *At the Christmas Par-ty hop....*

Ootie smiles. "It ain't Christmas 'til Brenda Lee says it's Christmas."

Harley's puzzled. "It sounds like she's burping," he says. He doesn't make eye contact with me.

"Don't you knock Brenda Lee," Ootie says. She comes over, takes my hand and steps forward, raises my arm as we start a swing step:

> *Rockin' around the Christmas tree*
> *Let the Christmas spi-ir-it ring*
> *Later we'll have some pumpkin pie*
> *And we'll do some car-o-ling.*

I give Ootie a careful twirl and pull her toward me the way I learned in junior high dance class. She's all bones under the sweat suit she's wearing today.

I'm afraid of hurting her, she's so small and her hips bad, but she's smiling big, her hair a bright shock of flame and she's laughing while we dance. When Brenda finishes the song, Ootie collapses back into her chair, her final laugh turning into a cough.

"You all right?" I ask.

"Best ever," she says when she stops. She's breathing hard now, reaches for a cigarette.

Mom comes in from the kitchen, turns down the stereo.

"That's the first record Ootie bought us the year we got our stereo," she says, mostly to Harley.

"Back in the early sixties," Pop says. "One of those fancy console models."

"Danish Modern," Mom says. "With spindly legs and cloth all around the front, real teak veneer on the lid. We played this record until we wore a hole in it."

"It was the only one we had for a while," Pop adds.

"That was the same year you had the aluminum tree," Ootie says.

"Aluminum?" Harley asks.

"A fad," Mom answers, sitting on the couch and chuckling, wiping flour from her hands. "Before Rudy was born. An aluminum tree with a color wheel that sat on the floor and made the tree change from yellow to red to green to blue."

"Psychedelic," Harley says.

"Bad taste," I say.

Harley gives me a look.

After dinner—roast pork Midwest style, cooked dark and crusty, with a milk gravy, crescent rolls, and green beans— we're all bundled up, headed for town. Ootie, small and insulated in a faux fur coat and muffler, looking like a burning can of Sterno, sits between Harley and me in the back seat of Pop's Crown Victoria. She doesn't smoke in the car. She's humming along with Brenda Lee, although the radio isn't on.

"Town looks so different," I say.

A steady line of cars enters and leaves the church parking lot. The grounds are lit up; from here I can see some of the Living Nativity actors.

"They must wear long underwear under those robes," Mom says.

We snake through the parking lot, find a space. I help Ootie out while she tries to put on her gloves. The glued-on nails are causing her some trouble.

"Oh, hell," she says, throwing one glove at me. "I'll just stuff my hands in my pockets." She hooks an arm through mine. "Let's go."

She leads me ahead of the rest, leaving Harley to fend for himself. Pop and Mom bring up the rear.

Cordons guide visitors around the block. Four or five men (and one woman) stand with crooks among several tethered sheep on a small knoll near the outside of the nave of the church. The sheep chew the grass while shepherds look toward a giant gold plywood star lit by flood lamps.

Small children in front of me gasp and goo, pointing with stubby fingers at the animals. A child tries to pet one of the sheep.

"I'm glad you came home," Ootie says to me as we walk past the sheep.

The crowd has backed up at the next scene. I look behind me; Harley is several groups back, standing near Mom and Pop. They're chatting.

"What's wrong with you, anyway?" Ootie asks me.

"I don't understand."

"You're ashamed of who you are. And you don't know what you've got, either." She gives me a look, expects me to chew on what she just said.

I don't want to understand her, but I already have a feeling that I will.

Here are Mary and Joseph. They've got a cow, another sheep, and a piglet in a small stable behind the manger, all flooded in light. Mary is draped in a blue robe, hardly looking as if she's just been through childbirth. The manger itself is raised so you can't see whether there's a baby in it. In the background "What Child is This?" plays. Joseph is a young man made older with a fiber paste-on beard.

"Isn't Mary beautiful?" Ootie asks. "She's new. They finally got rid of LaiLoris Doody; she'd played Mary for *way* too many years. 'Our Lady of the Menopause,' some of the women called her."

"Ootie," I say, chiding her gently.

"Don't think I've lost my train of thought," she says. "I've been watching you since you got here. The way you are with that boy."

"Harley's twenty-seven."

"You're all boys to me." Harley is still with Mom and Pop behind us. "He's the real thing, Rudy."

We move slowly. OotieMae feels like a bag of sticks; her arm is almost weightless in mine. The flesh I used to jiggle as a child is no longer there, just spongy bones and skin under sweat pants and her gigantic parka.

The Wise Men stand at stiff attention, their gifts in plywood painted chests on the ground, too heavy to hold. The church can't afford camels, so Christ the Redeemer has used llamas instead, draped with elaborate gaudy saddles streaming colored ribbons.

"There's Lester," Ootie says. "Say 'hey,' Lester Simms!"

"Hush," I tell her.

I walk between her and the scene, fearful that she'll take another stab at Lester. But as we walk toward the corner of the church, she looks up at me instead.

"You're my favorite stepgrandson," she says.

I look down. "I bet you say that to Jerold and Keith as well."

"I've been watching you and Harley since you got here."

"There's nothing to see," I tell her.

"That's the point. You act like he's a stranger, not your 'special friend,' or whatever you call him."

"We've been fighting," I say.

"The anger's all coming from you—I can feel it. So can your mother."

"Harley snapped at me this afternoon."

"Why shouldn't he? You've treated him awful since you got here. Ever since the Christmas tree—"

"He told you."

"I wormed a few things out of him while you were having your beauty sleep."

We turn the corner. "Really, Ootie—"

"You've been jumping around like water on a griddle and that boy has just sat and let you do it. That's how much he loves you."

I stammer something, but she nudges me with an elbow.

"You know he's the one, too," she continues, "but I'm thinking you're too stupid to believe it."

My face starts to burn in the cold air.

"There's no shame in love," Ootie says to me, more quietly this time. "No shame at all—only joy, sometimes hurt. Your parents love you, I love you, but you're ashamed of who you are." She pauses. "You can see how he loves you, the way he talks about you. You better watch yourself or he'll be gone and you'll get just what you deserve—a big heap of lonesome. And I'm getting to like him a lot." Ootie turns around, looks behind her. "Harley!" she calls. "Come here."

Harley's beside us now. Ootie grabs one arm; she's between him and me.

"There," she says. "I'm the luckiest gal at the show—except for the Virgin, I guess."

When we get home, Ootie asks Harley if he'll help her upstairs. Mom's in the kitchen making tea, Pop and I sit in the living room watching the tree's lazy blinking lights.

"Sorry you have to go back tomorrow," Pop says.

I'm thinking about what Ootie's said. I'm all knotted up, but something's about to break.

"I am too," I say. "But I've got to get some sleep before I go to work at eleven."

Pop frowns. "Seems wrong, having to work on Christmas day."

"Where would people eat?" I ask.

Pop thinks about that for a minute. "Harley's a good man," he says. I hear echoes of Mom's words earlier in the day, Ootie's more recent reprimands.

"I know."

At the same time I'm getting some message that whatever I thought about before we got here, whatever fears I hadn't fully considered before I plunged full tilt into this visit, just weren't what I thought they were. It's like I'm tired, like all of the meanness has gone out of me, the anger dribbled out somehow as we walked in the cold.

But my heart is beating fast, a pressure behind it that I have to let out. I'm afraid.

Mom brings in the teapot, four cups. Harley comes back a few minutes later carrying several poorly wrapped packages. He puts them under the tree with the others.

"Ootie says Santa can't make it through the smokestack," he says.

"I hope you're both warm enough upstairs," Mom says as she finishes her tea. "I could get you extra blankets if you need them."

"I'm fine," I say. Harley nods.

"Well, I'm off to bed," she says, rising and moving toward the stairs. "Merry Christmas."

Pop follows, rests his hand first on my shoulder, then on Harley's as he walks away behind her.

Harley sits almost in the dark, just the lights on the tree and the glow of the pellet stove glass door. His face is dark red, the planes of his cheekbones glinting like knives. I can barely see him; I assume he can barely see me. This makes me feel better for what I think is coming.

"You still tired?" he asks.

My heart starts pounding when he opens his mouth.

"Not so much," I say. "The nap helped."

"I'm still full from dinner. Your mom's a great cook."

"It's good to have home-cooked meals again."

Silence.

"The tree's nice," he says, giving a nod toward it. "Good shape."

"Yeah." I take a breath. "But not as nice as the one you got."

He looks over, a silver slice of light across his cheek. I'm seeing that deep calm I saw the night I met him, that peaceful center. It's pulling me out, stretching me until I snap.

"Too bad we didn't get to look at it before we left," he says.

That tree—now I understand. It wasn't anger—it was fear. It was a new thing, like a tradition, starting between us. And I wasn't ready for what that said about what was happening to me, to him—to us. Everything is now clear.

"We can," I tell him. "When we get back home."

We're sitting almost in the dark and there's only a metallic sound every now and then from the pellet stove. I can't stop myself now.

"I love you," I say.

For the first time.

"I've been waiting," he says.

"For what?"

"For that," he says. "I've known—I guess since you started working nights."

His voice is low, smooth dark sugar, soothing me out of my panic, but I don't know what he's going to say next.

"You move faster than I ever could—I like that about you," he says. "But you don't know much about yourself. I knew when I moved in that something was clicking for me—what made me more comfortable made you more nervous."

"So?" I ask. I need to hear something more or I'll burst.

"So I decided to wait it out. But I don't know that I could've waited much longer." He laughs, mimics Ootie. "A little shit is what you've been."

"Harley—"

"I love you, Rudy," he says. "I have for months."

We sleep in one twin bed, don't even bother to mess up the other sheets.

Besides Ootie's fishing rod and my Pendleton shirt, Pop gets a new tool box from Mom and some handkerchiefs from Harley. Mom does pretty well, too. She's pleased with her perfume, a new thick cotton robe from Pop, a jar of bath salts from Harley, and from Ootie a gift certificate for a makeover at the Hairport.

Ootie loves her cigarettes and the new ashtray, wins five dollars on one of the lottery tickets. Besides a bottle of Avon Skin-So-Soft, Mom and Pop have gotten her a fancy new cane with four rubber-tipped feet. She looks at it, leaves it by her side, her face a puzzle. Harley gives her a box of chocolates.

Harley brings in a haul—all clothes, a new parka from Mom and Pop (bought while we were out shopping), gloves from Ootie.

"I made him buy them himself," Ootie says behind a veil of smoke. "I told him that he and John had the same-sized hands." She laughs at her cleverness.

From me he gets the sweater—tries it on right over his T-shirt—flexes his lats as he turns—and wears it the rest of the day.

"Don't you look like the stud," Ootie says. Harley blushes.

I get a small haul of my own. Ties—"Dark," Ootie says, "so the food won't show"—a sports jacket from Mom and Pop. Harley gives me a tie bar with a small pink triangle on it.

"What's that?" Ootie asks.

"It means gay pride," Harley says.

Mom and Pop exchange glances.

"Too bad it's not bigger," Ootie says.

Harley's other present to me is a framed enlargement of a picture taken of us at a late summer picnic. We're shirtless—Harley's chest so far superior to mine—arms around each other's shoulders, big shiny faces for the camera. What I see now clearly in Harley's face is that he loved me that day already. And now I know, looking into my own eyes—bright, slightly squinting—that I already loved him, too.

"I'll keep this," Ootie says, taking the picture from me with her gray talon-less fingers. She looks at Harley. "You can get another, right?"

"You bet," he says. He stands up, puts one arm around Ootie, and squeezes. On his way back to his seat on the floor his hand glides across my shoulder.

When it's time to go after dinner suddenly I don't want to—Mom and Pop and Ootie all warm smiles, stuffed from the turkey, dressing, mincemeat pie, and all the rest—Harley offers to drive so I can get some sleep on the way.

Hugs and squeezes at the door. Brenda Lee's singing Christmas.

Mom folds me in her arms, leans in.

"Pray for Ootie," she whispers. "And come visit again—soon." The last word has extra urgency.

I give Ootie a careful hug, feel her frailty, lose myself in the dull light of her hair.

"You take care of yourself," she says, her voice broken. "Take care of each other."

Pop shakes Harley's hand, Mom gives him a hug. Ootie almost disappears in his embrace.

"Welcome to the family," she says to him as I open the door.

BOYS AT THE RODEO
Judy Grahn

A lot of people have spent time on some women's farm this summer of 1972 and one day six of us decide to go to the rodeo. We are all mature and mostly in our early thirties. We wear Levis and shirts and short hair. Susan has shaved her head.

The man at the gate, who looks like a cousin of the sheriff, is certain we are trying to get in for free. It must have been something in the way we are walking. He stares into Susan's face. "I know you're at least fourteen," he says. He slaps her shoulder, in that comradely way men have with each other. That's when we know he thinks we are boys.

"You're over thirteen," he says to Wendy.

"You're over thirteen," he says to me. He examines each of us closely, and sees only that we have been outdoors, are muscled, and look him directly in the eye. Since we are too short to be men, we must be boys. All the other women at the rodeo are called girls.

We decide to play it straight, so to speak. We make up boys' names for each other. Since Wendy has missed the episode with Susan at the gate, I slap her on the shoulder to demonstrate. "This is what he did." Slam. She never missed a step. It didn't feel bad to me at all. We laugh uneasily. We have achieved the status of fourteen year old boys—what a disguise for travelling through the world. I split into two pieces for the rest of the evening, and have never decided if it is worse to be thirty-one years old and called a boy or to be thirty-one years old and called a girl.

Regardless, we are starved so we decide to eat, and here we have the status of boys for real. It seems to us that all the men and all the women attached to the men and most of the children are eating steak dinner plates; and we are the only women not attached to men. We eat hot dogs, which cost one tenth as much. A man who has taken a woman to the rodeo on this particular day has to have at least $12.00 to spend. So he has charge of all of her money and some of our money, too, for we average $3.00 apiece and have taken each other to the rodeo.

Hot dogs in hand, we escort ourselves to the wooden stands, and first is the standing-up ceremony. We are pledging allegiance for the way of life—the competition, the supposed masculinity, and pretty girls. I stand up, cursing, pretending I'm in some other country. One which has not been rediscovered. The loudspeaker plays "Anchors Aweigh." That's what I like about rodeos, always something unexpected. At the last one I attended in another state, the men on horses threw candy and nuts to the kids, chipping their teeth and breaking their noses. Who is it, I wonder, that has put these guys in charge. Even quiet mothers raged over that episode.

Now it is time for the rodeo queen contest, and a display of four very young women on horses. They are judged for queen 30% on their horsemanship and 70% on the number of queen tickets which people bought on their behalf to "elect" them. Talk about stuffed ballot boxes. I notice the winner as usual is the one on the registered thoroughbred whose daddy owns tracts and tracts of something—lumber, minerals, animals. His family name is all over the county.

The last loser sits well on a scrubby little pony and lives with her aunt and uncle. I pick her for the dyke even though it is speculation without clues. I can't help it, it's a pleasant habit. I wish I could give her a ribbon. Not for being a dyke, but for sitting on her horse well. For believing there ever was a contest, for not being the daughter of anyone who owns thousands of acres of anything.

Now the loudspeaker announces the girls' barrel races, which is the only grown women's event. It goes first because it is not really a part of the rodeo, but more like a mildly athletic variation of a parade by women to introduce the real thing. Like us boys in the stand, the girls are simply bearing witness to someone else's act.

The voice is booming that barrel racing is a new, modern event, that these young women are the wives and daughters of cowboys, and barrel racing is a way for them to participate in their own right. How generous of these northern cowboys to have resurrected barrel racing for women and to have forgotten the hard roping and riding which women always used to do in rodeos when I was younger. Even though I was a town child, I heard thrilling rumors of the all-women's rodeo in Texas, including that the finest brahma bull rider in all of Texas was a forty-year-old woman who weighed a hundred pounds.

Indeed, my first lover's first lover was a big heavy woman who was normally slow as a cold python, but she was just hell when she got up on a horse. She could rope and tie a calf faster than any cowboy within 500 miles of Sweetwater, Texas. That's what the West Texas dykes said, and they never lied about anything as important to them as calf roping, or the differences between women and men. And what about that news story I had heard recently on the radio, about a bull rider who was eight months pregnant? The newsman just had apoplectic fits over her, but not me, I was proud of her. She makes me think of all of us who have had our insides so overly protected from jarring we cannot possibly get through childbirth without an anesthetic.

While I have been grumbling these thoughts to myself, three barrels have been set up in a big triangle on the field, and the women one by one have raced their horses around each one and back to start. The trick is to turn your horse as sharply as possible without overthrowing the barrel.

After this moderate display, the main bulk of the rodeo begins, with calf roping, bronco riding, bull riding. It's a very male show during which the men demonstrate their various abilities at immobilizing, cornering, maneuvering and conquering cattle of every age.

A rodeo is an interminable number of roped and tied calves, ridden and unridden broncos. The repetition is broken by a few antics from the agile, necessary clown. His long legs nearly envelope the little jackass he is riding for the satire of it.

After a number of hours they produce an event I have never seen before—goat tying. This is for the girls eleven and twelve. They use one goat for fourteen participants. The goat is supposed to be held in place on a rope by a large man on horseback. Each girl rushes out in a long run half way across the field, grabs the animal, knocks it down, ties its legs together. Sometimes the man lets his horse drift so the goat pulls six or eight feet away from her, something no one would allow to happen in a male event. Many of the girls take over a full minute just to do their tying, and the fact that only one goat has been used makes everybody say, "poor goat, poor goat," and start laughing. This has become the real comedy event of the evening, and the purpose clearly is to show how badly girls do in the rodeo.

Only one has broken through this purpose to the other side. One small girl is not disheartened by the years of bad training, the ridiculous crossfield run, the laughing superior man on his horse, or the shape-shifting goat. She downs it in a beautiful flying tackle. This makes me whisper, as usual, "that's the dyke," but for the rest of it we watch the girls look ludicrous, awkward, outclassed and totally dominated by the large handsome man on horse. In the stands we six boys drink beer in disgust, groan and hug our breasts, hold our heads and twist our faces at each other in embarrassment.

As the calf roping starts up again, we decide to use our disguises to walk around the grounds. Making our way around to the cowboy side of the arena, we pass the intricate mazes of rail where the stock is stored, to the chutes where they are loading the bull riders onto the bulls.

I wish to report that although we pass by dozens of men, and although we have pressed against wild horses and have climbed on rails overlooking thousands of pounds of angry animalflesh, though we touch ropes and halters, we are never once warned away, never told that this is not the proper place for us, that we had better get back for our own good, are not safe, etc., none of the dozens of warnings and threats we would have gotten if we had been recognized as thirty-one-year-old girls instead of fourteen-year-old boys. It is a most interesting way to wander around the world for the day.

We examine everything closely. The brahma bulls are in the chutes, ready to be released into the ring. They are bulky, kindly looking creatures with rolling eyes; they resemble overgrown pigs. One of us whispers, "Aren't those the same kind of cattle that walk around all over the streets in India and never hurt anybody?"

Here in the chutes made exactly their size, they are converted into wild antagonistic beasts by means of a nasty belt around their loins, squeezed tight to mash their tender testicles just before they are released into the ring. This torture is supplemented by a jolt of electricity from an electric cattle prod to make sure they come out bucking. So much for the rodeo as a great drama between man and nature.

A pale, nervous cowboy sits on the bull's back with one hand in a glove hooked under a strap around the bull's mid-section. He gains points by using his spurs during the ride. He has to remain on top until the timing buzzer buzzes a few seconds after he and the bull plunge out of the gate. I had always considered it the most exciting event.

Around the fence sit many eager young men watching, helping, and getting in the way. We are easily accepted among them. How depressing this can be.

Out in the arena a dismounted cowboy reaches over and slaps his horse fiercely on the mouth because it has turned its head the wrong way.

I squat down peering through the rails where I see the neat, tight-fitting pants of two young men standing provocatively chest to chest.

"Don't you think Henry's a queer," one says with contempt.

"Hell, I know he's a queer," the other says. They hold an informal spitting contest for the punctuation. Meantime their eyes have brightened and their fronts are moving toward each other in their clean, smooth shirts. I realize they are flirting with each other, using Henry to bring up the dangerous subject of themselves. I am remembering all the gay cowboys I ever knew. This is one of the things I like about cowboys. They don't wear those beautiful pearl button shirts and tight levis for nothing.

As the events inside the arena subside, we walk down to a roped off pavilion where there is a dance. The band consists of one portly, bouncing enthusiastic man of middle age who is singing with great spirit into the microphone. The rest of the band are three grim, lean young men over fourteen. The drummer drums angrily, while jerking his head behind himself as though searching the air for someone who is already two hours late and had seriously promised to take him away from here. The two guitar players are sleepwalking from the feet up with their eyes so glassy you could read by them.

A redhaired man appears, surrounded by redhaired children who ask, "Are you drunk, Daddy?"

"No, I am not drunk," Daddy says.

"Can we have some money?"

"No," Daddy says, "I am not drunk enough to give you any money."

During a break in the music the redhaired man asks the bandleader where he got his band.

"Where did I get this band?" the bandleader puffs up, "I raised this band myself. These are all my sons—I raised this band myself." The redhaired man is so very impressed he is nearly bowing and kissing the hand of the bandleader, as they repeat this conversation two or three times. "This is my band," the bandleader says, and the two guitar players exchange grim and glassy looks.

Next the bandleader has announced "Okie From Muskogee," a song intended to portray the white country morality of cowboys. The crowd does not respond but he sings enthusiastically anyway. Two of his more alert sons drag themselves to the microphone to wail that they don't smoke marijuana in Muskogee—as those hippies down in San Francisco do, and they certainly don't. From the look of it they shoot hard drugs and pop pills.

In the middle of the song a very drunk thirteen year old boy has staggered up to Wendy, pounding her on the shoulder and exclaiming, "Can you dig it, brother?" Later she tells me she has never been called brother before, and she likes it. Her first real identification as one of the brothers, in the brotherhood of man.

We boys begin to walk back to our truck, past a cowboy vomiting on his own pretty boots, past another lying completely under a car. Near our truck, a young man has calf-roped a young woman. She shrieks for him to stop, hopping weakly along behind him. This is the first bid for public attention I have seen from any woman here since the barrel race. I understand that this little scene is a re-enactment of the true meaning of the rodeo, and of the conquest of the west. And oh how much I do not want to be her; I do not want to be the conquest of the west. I am remembering how the clown always seems to be tall and riding on an ass, that must be a way of poking fun at the small and usually dark people who tried to raise sheep or goats or were sod farmers and rode burros instead of tall handsome blond horses, and who were driven under by the beef raisers. And so today we went to a display of cattle handling instead of a sheep shearing or a goat milking contest—or to go into even older ghost territory, a corn dance, or acorn gathering ....

As we reach the truck, the tall man passes with the rodeo queen, who must surely be his niece, or something. All this non-contest, if it is for anyone, must certainly be for him. As a boy, I look at him. He is his own spitting image, of what is manly and white and masterly, so tall in his high heels, so well horsed. His manner portrays his theory of life as the survival of the fittest against wild beasts, and all the mythical rest of us who are too female or dark, not straight, or much too native to the earth to now be trusted as more than witnesses, flags, cheerleaders and unwilling stock.

As he passes, we step out of the way and I am glad we are in our disguise. I hate to step out of his way as a full grown woman, one who hasn't enough class status to warrant his thinly polite chivalry. He has knocked me off the sidewalks of too many towns, too often.

Yet somewhere in me I know I have always wanted to be manly, what I mean is having that expression of courage, control, coordination, ability I associate with men. To provide.

But here I am in this truck, not a man at all, a fourteen-year-old boy only. Tomorrow is my thirty-second birthday. We six snuggle together in the bed of this rickety truck which is our world for the time being. We are headed back to the bold and shaky adventures of our all-women's farm, our all-women's households and companies, our expanding minds, ambitions and bodies, we who are neither male nor female at this moment in the pageant world, who are not the rancher's wife, mother earth, Virgin Mary or the rodeo queen—we who are really the one who took herself seriously, who once took an all-out dive at the goat believing that the odds were square and that she was truly in the contest.

And now that we know it is not a contest, just a play—we have run off with the goat ourselves to try another way of life.

Because I certainly do not want to be a thirty-two-year-old girl, or calf either, and I certainly also do always remember Gertrude Stein's beautiful dykely voice saying, what is the use of being a boy if you grow up to be a man.

ABOUT THE CONTRIBUTORS

Andrej Longo was given his first name by his father in honor of Prince Andrey Bolkonsky from Tolstoy's *War and Peace*. After graduating from Bologna's School of Art, Music, and Performance, he worked as a lifeguard, a waiter, and a pizza maker. His first book, *Più o meno alle tre* (*Around Three O'Clock*) was published in 2002, and his later works include the novels, *Adelante, Chi Ha Ucciso Sarah?*, and *Lu Campo di Girasoli*, and a collection of short stories, *Dieci*, inspired by the ten commandments, which garnered several literary prizes. He divides his time between Rome and Ischia.

C. Bard Cole is the author of a collection of short stories, *Briefly Told Lives* (St. Martin's Press, 2000), and a novel, *This is Where My Life Went Wrong* (Blatt Books, 2010). An East Coast native, he currently lives in Memphis, TN.

CAConrad is the author of seven books including *ECODEVIANCE: (Soma)tics for the Future Wilderness* (2014), *A Beautiful Marsupial Afternoon* (2012), and *The Book of Frank* (2010), all published by Wave Books. A 2014 Lannan Fellow, a 2013 MacDowell Fellow, and a 2011 Pew Fellow, he also conducts workshops on (Soma)tic poetry and Ecopoetics. Visit him online at http://CAConrad.blogspot.com.

Carter Sickels is the author of the novel *The Evening Hour*, a Finalist for the 2013 Oregon Book Award, the Lambda Literary Debut Fiction Award, and the Publishing Triangle Debut Fiction Award. He is the recipient of the 2013 Lambda Literary Emerging Writer Award, and has been awarded fellowships or scholarships to the Bread Loaf Writers' Conference, the Sewanee Writers' Conference, and the MacDowell Colony, among others. His fiction and nonfiction appears in the anthologies *The Letter Q: Queer Writers' Notes to Their Younger*

Selves, The Collection: Short Fiction from the Transgender Vanguard, and *Walk Till the Dogs Get Mean: Essays on the Forbidden from a New Appalachia*. He is the editor of the anthology *Untangling the Knot: Queer Voices on Marriage, Relationships, and Identity* (Ooligan Press) and the fiction editor of *Gertrude Press*, a national queer literary journal. Carter is Professor of Fiction in the Low-Residency MFA Programs at West Virginia Wesleyan University and Eastern Oregon University. He lives in Portland, Oregon.

Christopher Lord is the author of The Dickens Junction Mysteries, set in and around his home town of Astoria, Oregon. His latest book, *The Edwin Drood Murders*, was published in September 2013 by Harrison Thurman Books. He lives in Portland with his husband, who is not a writer.

Dean Durber received his PhD from Curtin University in Perth, Western Australia, in 2005. He also holds an MA in theatre studies and a BA in Chinese and Japanese studies. He has lectured extensively in the areas of queer theory, media studies, cultural studies, and gender studies. The academic world is a far cry from the government housing estate where he (mis)spent his youth. His publications include a novel, *Johnny, Come Home* (Marginal Eyes Press, 2002) and short stories in such anthologies as *The Best Gay Erotica 2003, Straight? Volume 2*, and *Boy Meets Boy*. He has also published numerous research articles in academic journals.

John Gilgun writes: "In 1999 I retired from teaching because of my deafness. I retired with Social Security and a generous pension from the state (my final school was a state college). I decided immediately to become an artist. At 78 years of age, I do my art, using two programs on my computer, Pixilmator and Photostudio. I did ceramics for many years and made ceramic masks. I now do digital collages using my Apple. I am happy, fulfilled, healthy and, as Edith Piaf said, "I regret nothing." I send the collages out on Facebook. I have friends who click "like" to my art every day. I am a totally satisfied man." Gilgun is the author of *Everything That Has Been Shall Be Again: The Reincarnation Fables of John Gilgun* (Bieler Press, 1981), *Music I Never Dreamed Of* (Amethyst, 1989), *The Dooley Poems* (Robin Price, 1991), and *Your Buddy Misses You* (Three Phase, 1995).

Judy Grahn is internationally known as a poet, woman-centered cultural theorist, early gay activist, co-founder of lesbian-feminism, and early contributor to literature of women's spirituality. She grew up in a working-class home in New Mexico. After she was discharged from the Air Force for being a lesbian, Grahn became involved in lesbian activism and began writing poetry and publishing lesbian literature. Her poetry collections, considered foundational to the development of cultural feminism, include *Edward the Dyke and Other Poems*, *The Queen of Wands* (American Book Award), *The Queen of Swords*, and *The Common Woman Poems*. In addition to her poetry, Grahn has written extensively on what it means to be a lesbian and a lesbian writer in such books as *Another Mother Tongue: Gay Words, Gay Worlds* and *Blood, Bread and Roses: How Menstruation Created the World*. Her memoir, *A Simple Revolution*, was published in 2012. In 1995, she was awarded The Publishing Triangle's Lifetime Achievement Award. She is currently an executive core faculty member in the Women's Spirituality program at Sofia University.

Keith Banner, a writer and a social-worker for people with disabilities, lives in Cincinnati, Ohio. He teaches creative writing part-time at Miami University and has published three works of fiction, *The Life I Lead* (a novel) and two short-story collections, *The Smallest People Alive* and *Next to Nothing*. He has published numerous short stories and essays in magazines and journals, including *American Folk Art Messenger*, *Other Voices*, *Washington Square*, *Kenyon Review*, and *Third Coast*. He received an O. Henry prize for his short story, "The Smallest People Alive," and an Ohio Arts Council individual artist fellowship for fiction. He is also cofounder of Visionaries & Voices and Thunder-Sky, Inc., two non-profit arts organizations.

L.A. Fields is the author of The Disorder Series and *My Dear Watson*, a queer Sherlock Holmes pastiche. Her short fiction has appeared in anthologies of horror, erotica, and academia. Find her online at la-fields.livejournal.com. Her collection *Countrycide: Stories* was published by Lethe Press in 2014.

Marcel Devon is a thirty-eight-year-old bisexual writer and artist recently released after serving eighteen years in Texas prisons. During his confinement, he developed his artistic and writing skills as well as a grasp of four other languages. His current work includes the comic strip "Ambiguous Ambrosia" and contributions to *Fanorama*, a LGBTQ punk rock 'zine (www.freewebs.com/fanorama). "There Are No Pretty Girls at the Tabernacle" is his first published story.

Rane Arroyo, who died in 2010, was a Puerto Rican poet, playwright, and scholar. Born in Chicago to immigrant parents, he started work in a factory at the age of thirteen, later holding temp jobs and working as a banker, an arts administrator, and a dancing ape at a Mormon disco. His work dealt extensively with issues of immigration, Latino culture, and homosexuality, and he was the author of eleven collections of poetry, including *Home Movies of Narcissus*, *The Buried Sea: New and Selected Poems*, *The Roswell Poems*, and the Carl Sandburg Prize-winner, *The Singing Shark*, as well as of a book of short stories, *How to Name a Hurricane*, a collection of his experimental fiction about gay and Latino identities. At the time of his death, he was a professor of English and Creative Writing at the University of Toledo in Ohio, where he had taught for many years.

Renny Christopher is a poet as well as a teacher and scholar, and she currently serves as Vice Chancellor for Academic Affairs at Washington State University, Vancouver. Her first book, *The Viet Nam War/The American War: Images and Representations in Euro-American and Vietnamese Exile Narratives* (1995), was named Outstanding Book on Human Rights by the Gustavas Myers Center for the Study of Bigotry and Human Rights. *My Name is Medea* won the New Spirit Press chapbook award in 1996 and *Longing Fervently for Revolution* won the Slipstream Press chapbook competition in 1998. Her memoir, *A Carpenter's Daughter: A Working-Class Woman in Higher Education* (2009), addresses her experiences as the first in her family to attend college. Before she earned her PhD, she worked as a press operator, typesetter, carpenter and horse wrangler.

Rick Laurent Feely finds inspiration for his writing in his past as a chronic runaway and street kid. His short stories have been published in *Everything I Have is Blue* (2005) and *The Harrington Gay Men's Literary Quarterly* (2006). Rick graduated cum laude with a B.A. in English from the University of Pennsylvania as a Jonathan Lax Scholar and Newcombe Scholar and received Honors in Creative Writing for the first manuscript draft of his multimedia memoir, *Evidence*. Rick continues to work on his memoir in Philadelphia, where he lives with his life partner, Andrew Campbell.

Rigoberto González is the author of fifteen books of poetry and prose. He is the recipient of Guggenheim and NEA fellowships, winner of the American Book Award, The Poetry Center Book Award, The Shelley Memorial Award of The Poetry Society of

America, and a grant from the New York Foundation for the Arts. He is contributing editor for *Poets & Writers Magazine*, on the executive board of directors of the National Book Critics Circle, and is professor of English at Rutgers-Newark, the State University of New Jersey. Visit his website: www.rigobertogonzalez.com.

Robby Nadler is a doctoral student in the creative writing program at the University of Georgia. His poetry, fiction, and nonfiction have been or will be published in such journals as *Gulf Coast, Lana Turner, Bloom, The Southeast Review, Unstuck*, and others. He is the recipient of a Fulbright fellowship and the 2011 Discovered Voices prize for poetry. He currently resides in Athens, Georgia, and works as an artisan baker.

Royston Tester is an associate editor for *Cha: An Asian Literary Journal* (Hong Kong). His work has appeared in numerous journals and anthologies in Canada, the U.S., and Asia. Two short-story collections (*Summat Else* [2004] and *Fatty Goes to China* [2012]) were published by Porcupine's Quill and Tightrope Books respectively. A third book, *You Turn Your Back*, will appear in 2014. Currently, he lives in Spain and is working on a novel, *Buggerlugs*, and a non-fiction book, *Pictures of Kinky Things: How to Exit Canada*.

Tara Hardy is a working-class queer femme poet who writes and teaches in Seattle, Washington. She is the founder and current creative director of Bent, a writing institute for LGBTIQ people based in Seattle. A daughter of the United Auto Workers, she holds an MFA from Vermont College in fiction writing and an MSW in community organizing from the University of Michigan. She is a member of the Bullhorn Collective and has performed at the Rolling Thunder Democracy Tour, Vancouver's Rock for Choice, Sister Spit, the Washington Poet's Association's Burning Word Festival, Portland's Youth Pride, and San Francisco's Harvey Milk Institute. Tara's work appears in the anthologies *Without a Net: The Female Experience of Growing Up Working Class* and *Sex and Single Girls: Women Write on Sexuality* as well as in the literary magazines *Blithe House Quarterly* and *Switched-on-Gutenberg* and in her self-published chapbooks *Vs* and *Rant-some*.

Timothy J. Anderson is a writer, horseman, and truck driver with seventeen years of over-the-road trucking experience throughout North America. He holds an MFA in creative writing from Seattle Pacific University. He is co-author of the study, "Chicken Haulers and the High Liners: CB Talk Among Interstate Truckers" (*Communicating Ethnic and Cultural Identity*, 2004) and past president of the Gay Truckers' Association. He has served as a consultant on the NIH/Emory University Community and Truckers' Health Project and as the Spokane Regional Health District's Trucker's Health Project Coordinator. His writing has appeared in *Guide, Frontiers, Stonewall News NW*, and the anthologies, *Second Essence* (1999), *Bend, Don't Shatter: Poets on the Beginning of Desire* (2004), and *Archipelago: Stories, Poems, and Essays* (2011). He resides in Pend Oreille County, Washington. "Hooters, Tooters, and the Big Dog" is based upon actual events.

Wendell Ricketts was born on Wake Island, an atoll in the middle of the Pacific Ocean, and raised in small towns on O'ahu, Hawai'i. Over the last thirty years his writing has appeared in such publications as *Contact Quarterly, The Advocate, Out, Dance Ink, Spin, Gay and Lesbian Literary Heritage, Blithe House Quarterly, James White Review, Mississippi Review, modern words, Harrington Gay Men's Fiction Quarterly*, and the anthologies *Rough Stuff: Tales of Gay Men, Sex, and Power* and *Bum Rush the Page: A Def Poetry Jam*. He holds a perfectly useless master's degree in creative writing and today makes his living as a full-fledged member of the "precariat." He can be reached at wendell.ricketts@gmail.com.

CLASS/MATES: FURTHER OUTINGS IN THE LITERATURES AND CULTURES OF THE GA(Y)TED COMMUNITY—AN AFTERWORD
Wendell Ricketts

I.

> "We're here! We're Queer! We're not going shopping!"
> (*Chant at an early Queer Nation demonstration at a California mall.*)

I have a confession to make. As much as I reject the notion of group identities, as much as I despise the Stepford Fag mass hallucinations of gay "community" rhetoric, and as much as I long to be the fierce and independent warrior of spirit that the label "queer" conjures, the genesis of this book was a much more fragile concept. We.

As in: Where are we? How do we imagine our lives and reconstruct our histories? Given the chance, what kinds of stories would we tell?

That last question intrigues me particularly. I am more and more convinced that imaginative literature—creative writing— possesses the ability to embrace ruction and rupture, union and invention, slippage and paradox in ways that are simply, inevitably absent from pride marches, consciousness-raising groups, "lifestyle" magazines, tavern guilds, gay churches, waves of same-sex couples lining up to get married at city hall, press releases, election campaigns, award-winning documentaries, civil-rights-litigation teams, queer-theory classes, gay-dad potlucks, square-dance clubs, and cadres of activists, no matter how pure of heart.

Short stories, novels, poems, and other kinds of creative writing capture the extemporary, plastic, kaleidoscopic, everything-at-once nature of being alive. They stand in marked contrast to those other mannerisms of culture and community whose goal is the reduction of reality to a proposition on which a majority can agree. It's not for nothing that creative writing is never produced by committee.

And that's why this anthology. Men and women who come from or live in or were formed by the working class—who cannot or will not compromise that piece of their complicated selves—and who also love/fuck/pine for/build lives around/experience themselves in common cause with lovers, tricks, spouses, partners of the same sex, well, we don't see ourselves much in American queer literature. Though perhaps that only makes another question inevitable: Why bother to look there in the first place?

For someone coming out in 1976, as I did, what was remarkable about being gay was that you simultaneously knew so much about it and almost nothing about it. Before I came out, I had never read a book with a gay character in it; I had never seen a gay character on a TV show or in a movie. Even in the entire first year after I did come out, the number of gay or lesbian people I knew personally remained a single digit. Of course, I intimately understood every loathsome, despicable thing about queers that everyone else did, because in America you imbibe that much with your colostrum.

So what was a boy to do? Fortunately, I also came out at a time when it was still possible to give a friend fifty dollars, send him on his annual pilgrimage to San Francisco, and have him return with a copy of every new gay book that had been published during the previous year. Today, fifty dollars wouldn't cover the sales tax on a year's worth of queer stories.

The point is, my coming out, because it was essentially a small-town one, took place against the backdrop of the lives of the gay people I found in books. Later, a friend moved away to Laguna Beach, and we read *The Tales of the City* together long-distance, inspired by our reading to write each other long, gossipy letters in which we referred to Armistead Maupin's characters by their first names and pretended they were our buddies, boyfriends, neighbors.

Well, but wasn't that precisely the point?

Cliché as it sounds, I read in those days to discover myself and my "people," and the characters in novels and short stories *were* more real to me than the few flesh-and-blood queers I knew. Books offered alternative possibilities; they promised a world in which secrets were optional, in which longing was quite often requited, in which figuring out where "gay" was and going there was The Quest, was the answer to—well, to *everything*.

I don't know if that goes on anymore—whether seventeen-year-old American gay boys and girls still look for their first glimpse of life "outside" or their first, vicarious experience of "community" between the pages of books. The Lambda Literary Foundation's "A LGBTQI Book Saved My Life!" campaign suggests that maybe they do.[1]

I can report that something similar happened in Italy in 2003, where I happened to be when the publication of the translation of the first volume of *The Tales of the City* (ironically enough) was greeted with both genuine delight and a certain samizdat zeal: If you were too embarrassed to walk into a bookstore to buy your own copy, a friend would slip you his. Everyone was talking about it—and fantasizing trips to the other edge of the world. I can't recall the last time a gay novel in America got that kind of reception.

The Italians, of course, were reading against invisibility and as counter-propaganda, just as I had done in 1976. (Anita Bryant mounted her "Save Our Children" campaign two months after I came out.) In a country where gay community—even in the restricted sense of gay-friendly physical spaces—barely exists, *I Racconti di San Francisco* described Oz.

But perhaps we have no need for that anymore in America. You can scarcely watch an hour of primetime television these days without seeing a gay or lesbian character who's doing all right, and the producers of reality television are positively obsessed with gay men (though lesbians remain an unfathomable mystery), so we're not exactly invisible, right?[2]

---

[1] See https://www.facebook.com/groups/abooksavedmylife. "A LGBTQI Book Saved My Life!" is a crowd-sourced video project associated with the LLF's annual book awards, the Lammies. See also "LGBT Readers Share How A 'Book Saved My Life,'" Advocate.com (2014, 6 June). Web: tinyurl.com/nqknuyn.

[2] Lance Loud was arguably television's first "real" gay man: He came out on national television in 1973 during the broadcast of *An American Family*. When sections of the series were shown again in 2002, on the occasion of a documentary about Lance's death, what stood out to me was how deeply the Louds' story is rooted in class. Lance himself

Or are we?

The "boom" in lesbian and gay writing, which began as a trickle in the mid-seventies and was already a flood by the mid-eighties, was related in major ways to the enormous social and political changes that were taking place then—the Anita Bryant campaign; the defeat of the Briggs initiative in 1978 (which attempted to outlaw gay and lesbian school teachers in California); the election (and later assassination) of San Francisco Supervisor Harvey Milk, the first openly-gay elected official in the United States; waves of queer-produced documentaries and of movies with more-or-less sympathetic gay characters; and even primetime television shows. By the early '70s, in fact, talk-show hosts like David Susskind and Dick Cavett had interviewed so many homosexuals on the air that they had become the butt of newspaper cartoons and stand-up routines.

There was unquestionably a new national momentum in those years to organize, to lobby, to protest, but there was just as strong an impetus to publish, to produce movies and plays, to bring gay and lesbian literature and studies into the university. The two impulses, of course, were not separate. Literature is the propaganda of a culture, and a lot of people thought we needed better propaganda.

And that—if you can stand my mushing together more than a decade of complicated sociopolitical and sub- and mass-cultural phenomena—is how gay and lesbian literature up and married identity politics.

---

characterized his childhood as "drowning in the luxury of late-'60s suburbia," and Shana Alexander, reviewing *An American Family* in *Newsweek* in 1973, described the Louds as "nice-looking people [who] act like affluent zombies. The shopping carts overflow, but their minds are empty" (28). Lance's decision to "run away from home" at age twenty, meanwhile, in order to exist in faux poverty in New York City's Chelsea Hotel, struck me as way glam and *très boulevardier*, but not especially daring, just as Thoreau is not daring when he goes to live "deliberately" in the woods—fully cushioned by his family's money and the comfort of the knowledge he may return at any time to the mansion in Concord. Still, one understands Lance's desire to escape the WASP-y, relentless, and slightly creepy impassivity of his natal home, though the adult gay life he constructed for himself in Manhattan proved to be no less superficial, consumer-driven, lonely, and spiritually empty. Gay, in other words, couldn't save him.

Now, for someone reading as I read in those early years of my initiation, it hardly mattered. Like so many readers then and even now, I firmly believed in role models and evaluated fiction on the basis of whether it provided "positive" images of gay and lesbian people. All I wanted in my reading was some reflection of myself and of my group. But if you had asked me who I thought that was, I'd have said "gay people" and cut my eyes at you for asking such a silly question. "We are here!" Horton hears the Whos chanting. For a long time, I wasn't much concerned with figuring out what I meant by "we."

II.

Hey, faggot. The Castro is that way!

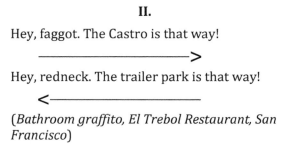

Hey, redneck. The trailer park is that way!

(*Bathroom graffito, El Trebol Restaurant, San Francisco*)

But how long could that go on? In due time I put down the naive belief that all my contradictions could be crammed into a single identity, and, when I went looking in fiction for my li(fe)(ves) to be reflected back to me, I did so with an increasing sense of disorientation.

Blue, Too and, before it, *Everything I Have Is Blue*, came about because I came to understand something I originally had not: Literature instructs us. We must be vigilant, then, as we take our pleasure in reading, because one of the main ways that literature instructs is by what it refuses to name, by what it omits, elides, or just plain fumbles. Literature is never neutral and it is never still.

In one of the first post-Stonewall gay novels to come into my hands, Andrew Holleran's *Dancer from the Dance*—a book that still haunts me—Holleran creates a mid-'70s world of Manhattan circuit queens who are rich, stylish, rapacious, desperate for sexual attention (which, paradoxically, they often reject), terrified of aging, and defiantly superficial. The main character, Sutherland, actually comes from a poor Southern family, but he affects such Ur-Blanche duBois entitlement and regal scorn that he seems more like the scion of a deposed czar.

These, Holleran suggested, were the people participating meaningfully in gay life.

The one identifiable working-class character in the book is Frankie Oliveiri, an Italian-American transit worker from Bayonne, New Jersey, who has left his wife and child to be with Malone, one of Holleran's gilded young men. Here is Holleran's description of him:

> Frankie had never gone to a bar, had never wanted to, had heard of Fire Island but considered it "a bunch of queens" and lived a life that, save for the fact that he slept with Malone, was hardly homosexual.... (82)
>
> Frankie read the papers, asking Malone to pronounce for him the words he had never come across before, and tell him what they meant.... Frankie hated tuna fish because he had eaten it so much when he was poor. Frankie was no longer poor, but he still wanted to make more money.... "Maybe I should be an electrician," he said, "we could move to Jersey and have a house. Just you and me and all those honkies." He wanted to have a skill, he believed in the unions.... [Frankie] wanted to improve his lot; he wanted to learn a skill, fix TVs, and move to New Jersey with Malone to a house in the pine barrens. He was a true American. (87-88)

In addition to being "hardly homosexual," Frankie is also pathologically jealous and becomes physically violent when he learns that Malone has cheated on him. Part of his macho charm is his lack of formal education (Malone tutors him in newspaper English); and his ethnic masculinity, while highly attractive, is ultimately incompatible with "real" gay life. Moreover, Frankie's "truly American" desire to escape Manhattan's gay scene for the suburbs is depicted as incomprehensible and when, toward the end of the book, he finds a more accommodating partner and does exactly that, Sutherland and Malone have this to say:

> "He's bought a house in Freehold, New Jersey," said Malone, as they sat down for a moment and Sutherland slipped off his satin pumps.... "He's making twenty thousand a year now and he'll have a pension, too. Never say America isn't a worker's paradise...."
>
> "Oh, well, we lived for other things," [Sutherland] smiled.... "At least," he murmured in [Malone's] ear, "we learned to dance. You have to grant us that. We are good

dancers," he said. "And what," said Sutherland, "is more important in this life than that?" (230-231)

Well, probably a lot of things, but the point of *Dancer from the Dance* is that there's something fishy about a homosexual who wants the things that Frankie wants—Frankie, in fact, is in danger of forfeiting his gay identity.

It would be an exaggeration to hold *Dancer from the Dance* responsible for the single-handed creation of a genre, but it is accurate to say that Holleran put his finger on the crack-that-would-become-a-chasm in gay male self-representation and -imagination during the 1980s. "Truly" gay men lived in cities (or fled to them) where they lived not lives but lifestyles. All other aspects of their identities fell into place beneath the capstone of gayness—a process, as any number of commentators have noted, that has only intensified in the years since.

Meanwhile, on another coast and in a darker part of the forest, John Rechy's 1967 *Numbers* also established (gay) identity as its thematic fulcrum. The protagonist of the novel, the male hustler, Johnny Rio, is another example of a more-or-less gay literary (anti)hero whose working-class upbringing is constituted as a problem that must be outrun: "[Laredo, Texas] has unpleasant memories for him (a dreary fatherless Mexican Catholic childhood; poor, poor years and after-school jobs in a laundry call-office, a department-store stockroom, and on a newspaper as a copy boy)" (22).

The main legacy of Johnny's class-inflected masculinity (to the extent that he is himself able to recognize it) is to render him more marketable to the "queens" who desire him, and his sexual activity—that of "collecting" men who are content to service him sexually without reciprocation (Johnny doesn't kiss and doesn't pursue)—collates with his need to experience himself as beautiful and not with his placement on a heterosexual-bisexual-homosexual continuum.

Frankie Oliveiri is different from Johnny Rio, of course, but they are kin. If Frankie's class-inflected desires lead him to posit a way of being gay that Holleran's Manhattanites find inscrutable, Johnny's way of living his class, gender, and erotic experiences means that he very nearly seems to have no sexual orientation at all.

Long before Rechy, Holleran, and the defining Stonewall moment that stood between them, of course, the materials existed for a rich consideration of the ways in which working-class men have loved and been loved by other men—in literature as well as out of it. Indeed, there is so much to take into account that what follows is no more than a series of notes on the stops I made as I have read, utterly without discipline, in search of "our" (that word again) lives.

I begin where so much of American literature begins—with Walt Whitman. Though Whitman's own class position may be debated (he was well educated and earned most of his adult living, in the years leading up to the 1850 publication of his famous *Leaves of Grass*, as a newspaperman and editor), it is also true that the American class system of the day bore only passing resemblance to ours. That said, Whitman's affection for working men and his poetic location within them of the most admirable traits of the new American republic, together with his long-term, passionate attachments to working-class men like Peter Doyle, Harry Stafford, and Horace Taubel, make Whitman an ancestor and an icon.

In fact, Whitman was able to envision relationships between men as a model and a metaphor for both an American political program and an American literary project because he experienced, in his affectionate, erotic, and spiritually rich interactions with other men, a convergence of social equals that was made possible by the unique nature of "adhesiveness" (Whitman's word for love between men, as opposed to "amativeness," with which he described love between men and women). Adhesiveness ensured not only that intimacy would not exclude male partners from equality, comradeship, and masculinity, but would strengthen and affirm those qualities.

Whitman's interest in masculine men and boys expressed itself as aesthetics and as pleasure (all those hours spent watching young men work, all those snippets of conversation with shop boys and printers' devils whose names Whitman recorded in his Daybooks), but it certainly also implied sexual desire. In one view, Whitman's delight in and attraction to the soldiers, drivers, bricklayers and other men of the "muscular" classes among whom he delighted to "mingle" could be seen as a kind of fetishization of working-class men, but the important consideration is that Whitman viewed them as his peers, if not at times his spiritual superiors. What he loved about them was emphatically the *opposite* of what he told Emerson he found all too apparent among "the young men of These States":

> [A] parcel of helpless dandies, who can neither fight, work, shoot, ride, run, command—some of them devout, some quite insane, some castrated—all second-hand, or

third, fourth, or fifth-hand—waited upon by waiters, putting not this land first, but always other lands first, talking of art, doing the most ridiculous things for fear of being called ridiculous, smirking and skipping along, continually taking off their hats—no one behaving, dressing, writing, talking, loving, out of any natural and manly tastes of his own, but each one looking cautiously to see how the rest behave, dress, write, talk, love.... Of course they and the likes of them can never justify the strong poems of America.[3]

In his interest in working-class men, Whitman was not unlike other of his contemporaries and kindred spirits—Charles Warren Stoddard (1843-1909), John Addington Symonds (1840-1893), Edward Carpenter (1844-1929), and E. M. Forster (1879-1970; I may be stretching the concept of contemporary slightly by including Forster, but Forster knew Carpenter, and Carpenter knew Whitman), all of whom formed sexual and romantic relationships with working-class men but who could apparently conceive of such relations only with male partners whose class status was "beneath" theirs ("I want to love a strong young man of the lower classes and be loved by him and even hurt by him," wrote Forster in 1935);[4] the American Stoddard fled to the South Pacific where he rhapsodized about "savages" and "cannibals," trading class discontinuities for racial ones.

Whitman's desire for men of the same class as the one with which he associated himself and in whom he saw a paragon of moral and democratic values may have been unfathomable to them. Significantly, John Simon reports that the life of Carpenter, one of the best-selling authors of the late Victorian period, was transformed by his contact with Whitman "because [Whitman] provided a role model and a paradigm of homosexual masculinity which escaped the stereotypes that had hitherto been available to a man of Carpenter's class" (117).

In 1851, meanwhile, only a year after the first edition of *Leaves of Grass*, what is very likely the first marriage between working-class men in American literature appeared. Here, in Herman Melville's *Moby-Dick*, the sailor, Ishmael, prepares to

---

[3] *Complete Poems* 768-69.
[4] Quoted in Oliver Stollybrass's "Introduction" to Forster's posthumously published short-story collection, *The Life to Come and Other Stories*. New York: Avon, 1976 (1972), vii-xxvii: xviii.

share his Spouter-Inn bed for a second night with his "savage" shipmate, the harpooner, Queequeg:

> He seemed to take to me quite as naturally and unbiddenly as I to him; and when our smoke was over, he pressed his forehead against mine, clasped me round the waist, and said that henceforth we were married; meaning, in his country's phrase, that we were bosom friends; he would gladly die for me, if need should be.... How it is I know not; but there is no place like a bed for confidential disclosures between friends. Man and wife, they say, there open the very bottom of their souls to each other and some old couples often lie and chat over old times till nearly morning. Thus, then, in our heart's honeymoon, lay I and Queequeg—a cosy, loving pair. (45-46)

Indubitably, Queequeg is in ways cartoonish, and *Moby-Dick* can be seen in a Rousseauvian tradition of exoticism and escape, but Melville nonetheless accomplished something decidedly "Whitmanesque" in conceiving of a close, primary relationship between men whose basis was not class differences that needed to be overcome but rather the shared affinities of working men that gave their bond its foundation and its strength.[5]

Having mentioned Symonds, the wealthy British writer, literary scholar, and early sexologist, we might also stop in our survey of historical working-class queer literary representation to consider Symonds' *Memoirs* (Grosskurth, 1984), the seventeenth and final chapter of which is dedicated to Angelo Fusato, a nearly destitute Venetian gondolier whom Symonds met while on vacation in 1881. Though both men were married to women, Symonds' "love at first sight" for the twenty-four-year-old blossomed into a relationship that lasted until Symonds' death some twelve years later, and Symonds' description of their life together is one of the loveliest accounts available—from his or any other time—of love between men (and also one of the most heartbreaking, for Symonds never stopped thinking that his passion for Angelo was rooted in "abnormal desire"). In the *Memoirs*, Symonds records the titles or sequence numbers of nearly four dozen sonnets he wrote to

---

[5] Poet and scholar John Gilgun has pointed out to me that *Moby-Dick*, because it is a book about *work* as much as it is about anything else, might also be considered the first American working-class novel.

Angelo but "mutilated ... in order to adapt them to the female sex" before they could be accepted for publication (272).

Before we leave the nineteenth century, Oscar Wilde's epic 1891 essay, "The Soul of Man Under Socialism," deserves more than a passing glance. Wilde's lengthy consideration of the state of humanity is far from a working-class manifesto, but it is nonetheless a remarkable document for Wilde's time, nation, and class. Though Wilde means nothing politically specific by "socialism," he brilliantly connects the aesthetic, spiritual, and worldly needs of human beings, eloquently analyzing the way that constant material struggle also blights the spirit:

> One's regret is that society should be constructed on such a basis that man has been forced into a groove in which he cannot freely develop what is wonderful, and fascinating, and delightful in him—in which, in fact, he misses the true pleasure and joy of living. (919). I cannot help saying that a great deal of nonsense is being written and talked nowadays about the dignity of manual labour. There is nothing necessarily dignified about manual labour at all, and most of it is absolutely degrading. It is mentally and morally injurious to man to do anything in which he does not find pleasure, and many forms of labour are quite pleasureless activities, and should be regarded as such.... Man is made for something better than disturbing dirt. (923)

In terms of his material life, Wilde is known to us today as much for the dalliances with working-class boys that were his peccadillo as for his love affair with one wealthy boy that was his ruin, and a consideration of the class-inflected nature of his sexual and romantic expression, particularly in light of the subversive philosophies expressed in *The Soul of Man* and Wilde's subsequent punishment by the class he criticized, leads one in rather fascinating directions.

At the dawn of the twentieth century, E. M. Forster provides another important vantage point from which to consider intersections of class and (homo)sexuality, a significant theme in Forster's work. Sexual contact between middle-class and working-class men emerges in some of the stories in Forster's collection, *The Life to Come* (notably "Arthur Snatchfold" and "The Obelisk"), but Forster explores the idea most thoroughly in his novel, *Maurice*.⁶ Though *Maurice* is fiction, Forster in part based the central relationship (between the middle-class Maurice and the gamekeeper, Alec) on the real-life partnership of his friends, Edward Carpenter and the working-class George Merrill, who lived together for some twenty years (until Merrill's death).

Maurice is, among other things, the story of how male-male love disrupts the scripts of social class and station and makes human connection possible between men who could otherwise only be master and employee. Alec, for his part, instructs Maurice about the realities of working-class life ("Maurice, you wouldn't believe how servants get spoken to. It's too shocking for words." [229]), and, if Alec initially rejects the idea that his dalliance with Maurice could be anything more, it is because he recognizes himself as someone with fewer options than his lover:

> "Yours is the talk of someone who's never had to earn his living," [Alec] said. "You sort of trap me with I love you or whatever it is and then offer to spoil my career. Do you realize I've got a definite job awaiting? [Alec is about to leave for work in Argentina.]
>
> Maurice saw through the brassiness to the misery behind it, but this time what was the use of insight.... Suffering was certain for him, though it might soon end for Alec; when he got out to his new life he would forget his escapade with a gentleman and in time would marry. Shrewd working-class youngster who knew where his interests lay, he had already crammed his graceful body into his hideous blue suit. (232-233)

Love nevertheless triumphs, but Maurice and Alec must first disappear, neatly amputating their relationships with family and friends in order to "live outside class, without relations or money" (239). Significantly, Forster doesn't specify where they go (other than "into the greenwood") but he fretted over and modified the ending of *Maurice* in order to make sure it remained a love story; he could conceive of no way to keep Maurice and Alec together in the social milieu in which they had met.

As early as 1903, Robert Martin tells us in his essay, "Edward Carpenter and the Double Structure of *Maurice*," Forster had begun to identify a homosexual literary tradition and was

---

⁶ Some of the stories in *The Life to Come* were written as early as 1903, and the manuscript for *Maurice* was completed in 1914, but neither book was published until several years after Forster's death in 1970.

making lists of famous homophile authors, "in part a gesture toward the alleviation of the radical loneliness that may confront the homosexual following the acknowledgment of his or her own nature" (1983: 36). It isn't difficult to see *Maurice* as both Forster's attempt to place himself within that tradition and to imagine a response to the problem of loneliness.

And so, like Forster, a working-class gay man or woman today recognizes his or her queer desires and goes in search of a/the gay "community" (frequently, a physical place, a neighborhood, a social milieu, but also the site of literary and cultural production). Quickly apprehending the tension between life as they have known it and the requirements of their "new" erotic, social, and amorous possibilities, they appear to face a choice: What part of their former lives will they leave behind/disguise/transliterate? If their kind cannot remain at home, then they must go. If their kind is not to be found in the new place—well, their kind will need to change. The magazines they leaf through, the movies and television they watch won't necessarily tell them much different. Neither will the books they read or the people they meet.

This is the conflict that runs like a river through Darrell Yates Rist's under-appreciated 1992 masterpiece, *Heartlands*, a journalistic account of Rist's three-year, one-hundred-thousand-mile "odyssey" across the United States, "a journey through sexual desire and identity" (1).

In the course of his research, Rist spends time in the gay discos of San Francisco and with the congregation of a minister in Reno, Nevada. He visits a military doctor in Colorado Springs who treats AIDS patients: "Sometimes he claimed to be gay and sometimes not. He claimed he had never had sex with a man, though his social life was almost without exception among gay men" (69). He follows the rodeo circuit and, in the Rockies, stays with the manager of a guest house whose sex life is limited to seducing the heterosexual "jocks" who come with their wives to stay at his resort. He interviews a young gay man in prison for murder in California and a New Mexico mystic who channels spirits for him. In Tupelo, Mississippi, he sits in on a forum about homosexuality in which one panel member tells the audience:

> Before gay liberation came along and made a life-style out of it, I didn't know many of my friends, on the farm or in the army durin' the war, that didn't have a hankerin' for other men. There's a lot of rednecks who

all along grew up doin' homosexual sex. Everybody likes to diddle! (272)

He hears the life stories of a Louisiana bayou alligator trapper and an Oklahoma cowboy who insists:

I'm not gonna turn myself into some damn label. There's a lot of things more important to me than that. Look around! Look at this land! This all's what's kept my family alive for a century. It's my blood. It's who I am. Do you know what I mean? (317)

All of these men, as Rist puts it, are "sometimes, at least, homosexual, not always 'gay.'" At times, indeed, they (like Frankie Oliveiri) seem barely even homosexual, which is Rist's exact point. His 485-page book charts, in a way no survey could, some of the ways that love and sex (the expression of them, the desire for them, the rejection of them) are woven into the lives of American men—many of them, notably, working-class men. His informants clearly have identities, and those identities include what no reader could fail to call a sexual component. What is instructive in Rist are the means by which the constellation of behaviors, attitudes, belief, and desires called "sex" is *admitted* into an identity; it is not, so to speak, the grain of sand in the oyster. It is not the organizing principle.

When *Everything I Have Is Blue: Short Fiction by Working-Class Men About More-or-Less Gay Life* was published in 2005, the part of the title that lay east of the colon—the "more-or-less gay" part—was no accident, and Rist's book was one of the reasons why. That title was an attempt to represent linguistically a failure of thought. It was an accusation. Then, as now, I don't presume to know how other queer people with working-class loyalties, families, lives, hometowns, sensibilities have, over the course of their lives, managed their relationship to that vexed and freighted notion, "gay." But I'll bet there's not one of them who hasn't at one time or another in his or her adult life been in conflict over the label, hasn't worn it sometimes not because it fit or was flattering but because it seemed to be the only shirt in the closet.

III.

"It is a truth universally acknowledged that a man in
possession of a gay lifestyle must be in want of a
fortune." (*With apologies to Jane Austen*)

That's the way it happens in John Caffey's *The Coming Out Party*,
originally published in 1982.

Sid and Calvin, bored and besotted with luxury and
possessions in their West Hollywood mansion, decide that the
solution to their malaise lies in finding a boy in need of gay
metamorphosis and modeling him into "The Ultimate Homo."
The more dubious the prospect, the more enviable the "rescue"
effort. Thus, when they come upon nineteen-year-old Hal,
broken down by the side of the road in Santa Monica, a pale,
overweight "Hee-Haw reject" (20) from Xenia, Ohio, they've
found their (im)perfect man.

The transformation begins (of course) with the physical: the
gym, the personal trainer, Keratin masks, the starvation diet,
contact lenses, the hair stylist, the fashion consultant. Hal is next
made to read Gore Vidal and is instructed in the appreciation of
classical music; he is taught how to engage "properly" in casual
sex and drug-taking, and he is quizzed on his ability to identify
the source of such quotations as "Jungle red, Sylvia!" and "I have
always depended upon the kindness of strangers."

Up to this point, *The Coming Out Party* is a rather broad farce
on gay male "community" mores at the time of its writing. What
makes the plot timely more than thirty years later, however, is
that the imperialist, colonizing energy of the bourgeois class and,
in particular, of its avatar, the gay-male coming-out process, has
not changed. Indeed, the comedy would fail if the serious truth
behind it were not still fully legible.

The cultural imperatives evident in Sid and Calvin's "project"
were, in fact, the running joke behind the four-part "Fagmalion"
episode of the NBC sitcom, *Will & Grace*, which aired in 2003.
Barry, the dowdy cousin of Karen Walker, has come out at the age
of 35, but his "debut" as a gay man (at a black-tie Human Rights
Campaign fundraising dinner) is unthinkable until he undergoes
a complete makeover. Jack and Will, guardians of the well of gay
knowledge, serve as Barry's guides and renovators. (Significantly,
it is Karen who arranges for—and funds—Barry's twenty-
thousand-dollar crash course in gay, but faithful viewers will
recall that the rich (by marriage) and eternally snobby Karen

comes from a working-class background; in another episode, her shame regarding her past, and the revelation that her mother works as a bartender, are explored).

What *Coming Out Party* and "Fagmalion" share is the understanding, manifest behind their "light-hearted" superficies, that the possession of a gay "lifestyle" is insufficient unto itself, but is required by its very nature to proselytize. Thus, though no one can take seriously the claim that gay men recruit sexually, the "community's" instinct is demonstrably to hegemonize *culturally*.

Gay male identity, moreover, is revealed as an almost exclusively *material* site: Barry, like Hal, is marked as "ungay" by the brands of clothes he buys (he shops at Miller's Outpost), by being "twenty pounds overweight," by his unfashionable beard and bad haircut. Will's role in the tutelage of Barry is to "work on his mind"—that is, to teach him "things like gay culture, gay politics, driving up the cost of real estate in affordable areas." The success of Barry's acculturation finally begins to be visible when he buys his first pair of Gucci shoes and when he shows Will and Jack a photo of "fabulous abs" from *Men's Fitness* magazine, stating his wish to resemble the model:

> WILL: [TO BARRY] Are those—Is that Gucci on
>   your feet?
> BARRY: Oh, yeah. Aren't they great? They kill my
>   toes and cost a fortune, but what the hell? I'll
>   take out another credit card.
> WILL: [VOICE BREAKING] I think I'm gonna cry.
> JACK: Will, do you know what this means?
>   Unrealistic body expectations.
> WILL: Choosing fashion over comfort.
> JACK: Living beyond your means.
> WILL: Boy George, I think he's got it!

Without the gay male diktat, of course, another show in which gay identity was made synonymous with bourgeois consumption, *Queer Eye for the Straight Guy*, would have been unintelligible. The humor of *Queer Eye* hinged frequently upon the ridiculing of working-class men for their grooming, clothing, living spaces, and eating habits,[7] while suggesting that the

---

[7] Food frequently emerges as a potent marker of class. The four-part 2001 PBS documentary, *People Like Us: Social Class in America*,

creation of "metrosexuality" (that is, homosexuality without the sex) depended upon the literal stripping of the classed body and its subsequent reconstruction. In every episode, then, the object of the makeover was shown all-but-naked at the moment of his transformation, just as he prepared to resignify his remodeled self with new cosmetics and new clothing.

In these precise terms, Hal is trained in *The Coming Out Party* that successful participation in male homosexual culture requires that he remove all traces—from his body, from his speech, and from his psyche—of his previous heterosexual (read: lower-class) life. That he has a home and a natal culture and may yet desire to remain fluent in their idioms is considered not only irrelevant but actively antagonistic to his homosexual rehabilitation.

Thus, the gay existence is one without a past—a life that begins *de novo* at coming out, the instant of queer conception.[8] "I am from nowhere," Andy Warhol used to remark when asked about his origins (cited in Bain, 2008).

There can be no dispute that great potential exists for the release of creative and emotional energy in processes that result in the abandonment of shame, secrecy, and self-negation, but the insistence that the newly inscribed "gay" or "queer" body must pass through the portals of the gay village *by means of* renunciation of previous moral, ethical, and cultural training and *through* abandonment of prior allegiances to geography and

---

devoted a segment ("The Trouble with Tofu") to a controversy over the building of a new grocery store in Burlington, Vermont. Low-income and middle-class residents clashed viciously over whether the new store would stock "regular" food or only more expensive "health" and "gourmet" items. *Queer Eye* episodes frequently depicted refrigerator and cupboard raids in which unacceptable food was discarded with evident disgust. In *The Coming Out Party*, Sid and Calvin are able to convince Hal to participate in their scheme because they first seduce him with a meal made entirely of frozen Stouffer's TV dinners and Sarah Lee desserts. Later, Calvin tells Hal that it's Perrier for him from then on, no longer "Cragmont soda."

[8] "Families belonged to that inscrutable past west of the Hudson," Holleran writes in *Dancer from the Dance*, "and when a queen walked out a window, and you heard the family had come east to claim the body, it was like hearing that some shroud had come out of the darkness to pick up the dead and return whence the Three Fates sequestered, in the hills of Ohio or Virginia" (235-236).

to clan is essentially to rob the individual of civilization. The indigenous baby, that is, is tossed out with the gay bathwater.

What emerges to "queer" Sid and Calvin's increasingly cruel regimen for Hal, however, is that most savage of all forces, desire. To the men's horror, their incipient creation falls head over heels in love with the decidedly déclassé Pool Man ("Not a penny to his name." [63]), and Calvin is particularly incensed by their liaison ("The Pool Man was a hunk, but Cal'd be damned if he'd have any daughter of his sleeping with the Hired Help." [65]).

It is at this point that Caffey inserts the only challenge to Sid and Calvin's project (other than Hal's own weak resistance to it), which comes, significantly, in the voice of Calvin's mother. Arriving for a visit, she accuses Calvin of "[using Hal] to be what you never were," adding, "Better the boy wants true love than what passes for it at the Club Baths"(100). By criticizing Calvin and Sid's treatment of Hal and, by extension, the entirely self-referential gay world the men occupy, Calvin's mother, like a relict of Calvin's "pre-gay" life, attempts to reassert into that world the moral, civilizing principles that were Calvin's birthright. It is to no avail, however, and Calvin's first act upon his mother's departure is to express his rage by deploying his capitalist power to fire the Pool Man.

In the end, Hal's love for the Pool Man triumphs, and they are married in a public ceremony attended by both their gay and natal families. Even Calvin comes to accept the relationship and, in a significant moment near the very end of the book, he finally asks the Pool Man his name (Beau). Just as in E. M. Forster's *Maurice*, which *The Coming Out Party* specifically references, Beau recognizes that his relationship with another man cannot survive in hostile surroundings (the heterosexual middle class in *Maurice*, the homosexual one in *The Coming Out Party*), and he immediately "whisks" Hal away (in his '71 Dodge van). They return, importantly, to the house where Beau was born—a place steeped in Beau's family and class histories—in Hawaiian Gardens, a largely Latino, working-class community in East Los Angeles.

The Coming Out Party is assuredly no manifesto of sustained proletarian resistance—Beau turns out to be the beneficiary of a large trust fund left to him in secret by an "eccentric aunt"—but it pointedly examines, in a way that perhaps only humor can (as Oscar Wilde and Joe Orton taught us), the class-inflected (and class-envious) demands of gay-cultural membership.

The question that *The Coming Out Party* raises humorously, that is, is the same one that *Dancer from the Dance* raises in deadly earnest: Does successfully entering the gay community require the assumption of a market identity? In other words, does not "gay" resemble, more than it resembles anything else, a brand name?

IV.

> It is an odd thing, but every one who disappears is said to be seen at San Francisco. It must be a delightful city, and possess all the attractions of the next world. (*Oscar Wilde,* The Picture of Dorian Gray)

Certainly, no one could blame a guy if he got that impression. But if *Dancer from the Dance*'s answer to the question is probably yes, and *The Coming Out Party*'s is probably no, Kirk Read stakes out a much more ambivalent position in his 2001 memoir, *How I Learned to Snap*. After living for several years in New York and San Francisco, Read received a contract to write a book about his experiences as an openly gay teenager in high school and, in order to focus on his project, moved temporarily to rural Lake County, California, home to "good country people, leftover hippies, and hardcore druggies" whose "prison tattoos and dirty fingernails make me wonder what in the world I'm doing around here" (vii).

Upon his arrival in a town where "Walmart and K-Mart are the cultural epicenters" (vii), Read goes to the "ambitiously named" café at Walmart for a hamburger. There, Read spots a boy he judges to be about fifteen, who is having lunch with his mother:

> His well-conditioned hair hung over the left shoulder of his Calvin Klein tee shirt.... His fingers were covered with silver rings and he ate quickly.... His mother was a round woman dressed in an embroidered Guatemalan shirt I'd seen priced for a dollar at the Hospice Thrift Shop. He was chubby from sharing his mother's snacks. I wondered how long it would take him to reach her size....
>
> I sat at the table behind his mother, catching pieces of their quiet conversation. Names like *Pa* and *Aunt Junebug* floated over to me.... [The boy] looked up from

his food to throw glances at me. As he lifted his burger, his pinkies jutted out from the sides of the bun. He was a dainty eater and wiped the sides of his mouth with a small stack of napkins after each bite....

I went through high school dreaming of being rescued by an as-yet-undiscovered older brother who would adopt me and ask me why I looked so sad....

His eyes were full of a need for adoption. I wasn't cruising him, I was gently, carefully letting him know that his tribe was out there, beyond the cinderblocks and hubcaps that filled his front yard.... In that moment, I wished I could have handed him something ... more than a soft-eyed stare that said "hang in there" or "save your money." (viii-ix)

All of this takes place in the space of Read's two-and-a-half-page prologue, which, despite its brevity, nicely compresses the semiotics of class and homosexuality. Read cannot learn, during their silent encounter, the boy's actual sexual preference or class background, of course, so he describes neither literal gayness nor literal working-class status, but their *signs*. In interpreting such signs, moreover, Read assigns a valence to each that is either positive (the escape provided by coming out as gay) or negative (the culture from which the boy needs rescue). Thus, proximity to prisoners, dirty fingernails, obesity, shopping at thrift stores, the presence of Walmart and K-Mart, relatives called "Pa" or "Aunt Junebug," and hubcaps in the yard are "coded" for their working-class (and, thus, *contra*-gay) character, while well-conditioned hair, dismay at prison tattoos and unscrubbed fingernails, Calvin Klein T-shirts, disdain for the absence of non-Walmart- and non-K-Mart-based culture, eating "daintily," and the "need for adoption" by an older (presumably gay) brother are coded for their antagonism to or differentiation from working-class milieux and, thus, in favor of gayness.

Significantly, Read desires to communicate to the boy that his "tribe" is "out there," the expression of a vision for the boy's life that is entirely hegemonic. Read seems to imagine homosexuality as a physical place (the boy must save his money in order to travel there), a "land," if you will, where the boy's true breed resides. His home culture, meanwhile—the boy's birthplace and blood family—is presumed to be an error and a detriment: the boy, "sharing his mother's snacks" (that is, her literal and metaphoric nourishment), threatens to become like her. This is pointedly *not* his tribe, and it is the discovery of that fact that legitimates escape.

To be fair, there is every reason to consider Read's concern for the boy to be completely genuine, but the question of "tribe" (that is, of community, of belonging, of membership) lies so deeply at the core of the problematics of gay male cultural (re)presentation—both as a literary theme and in our real-life experiences—that the term cannot be passed over lightly.

To further complicate matters, the body of Read's book, in which he describes his coming out as a high-school student in the small town of Lexington, Virginia, demonstrates an even more profoundly conflicted relationship with the place and people Read left behind:

> I never wanted to abandon Lexington altogether.... I loved the people I'd grown up with and even when they scared me, I held out hope that they'd come around on gay issues....
>
> It can be a challenge to go home and explain to them what I'm doing with my life, because their realities are so entirely different from mine. My exposure to sexual adventure, college, and radical politics has created painful cultural differences between us. But they're my people, and I can't give up on them. (111-112)

What is notable about this passage is Read's inclusion of the term sexual adventure in his tripartite explanation for the cultural differences that have arisen between him and the people in his hometown. Although a university education and exposure to political paradigms diametrically opposed to those of one's natal environment may lead to conflicting, even incompatible understandings of reality, they do not rewrite one's origins, dissolve personal history, or automatically replace pre-existing culture with an alternate version.

Read's addition of "sexual adventure" to his list is thus especially intriguing, containing, as it does, the premise that embedded within (homo)sexual practice lies culture or, to put it more specifically, a culture in which Walmart cafés, thrift stores, and unmanicured lawns, acceptable in one's naïveté, are revealed to have been improper all along.

In the introduction to his 1991 anthology, *Hometowns: Gay Men Write about Where They Belong*, John Preston also placed erotics at the center of identity and adopted the language of anthropology to discuss what he viewed as the gay man's dilemma: Where do I belong?

> For years, gay men thought they had only two choices: They could either sublimate their erotic identities and remain in their hometown, or they could move to a large center of population and lose themselves in anonymity. There was no way for a gay man to have a hometown and still be honest with himself.
>
> In the last three decades the choices for gay men have increased. Those exiled souls who moved to New York, San Francisco, Paris, or wherever it was that there were others like them, coalesced into a community of their own.... Having been thrown out of the tribe, they created their own new one. Once their communal existence became known, they presented the man who was coming out with a new option: he could join them. He could assume a new identity by becoming a member of a new clan. (xi)

In fact, many of the chapters in *Hometowns* reflect what Preston's writers describe as an inexorable trajectory: acceptance of their homosexuality, estrangement from their native environment, and then—particularly for writers from poor and working-class environments—what Les Wright calls in *Hometowns* an "expatriation." In Wright's case, he left behind his working-class hometown in central New York State only to return there, years later, to accept a teaching position. The "homecoming" proved a disillusionment:

> I was confronted ... with the shattering discrepancy between my long-nurtured fantasies and the realities of life outside the twin cocoons of the Castro and Berkeley....
>
> I have lived so long as an expatriate that I had completely forgotten my state of expatriation.... I had not anticipated [experiencing] myself as an expatriate in my own hometown—in my family, in the social class of my origin and aspirations—nor that I no longer understood the languages spoken around me in New York State. (150-151)

The reflections of other writers in *Hometowns* express similar sentiments. Jesse G. Monteagudo, who grew up in the Cuban quarter of Miami, Florida, wrote, "I cannot visit Calle Ocho these days without realizing that I do not belong there anymore.... As an openly gay man, I can never be reconciled with Little Havana" (19-20), while Michael Nava, describing his childhood in Sacramento, California, recalled:

> One day, walking to school, clutching my books to my chest, girl-style, I heard myself say, 'I'm a queer." It was absolutely clear to me that Gardenland could not accommodate this revelation. Gardenland provided the barest of existences for its people. What made it palatable was the knowledge that everyone was about the same, united in ethnicity and poverty and passivity.... But I knew I was not the same as everybody else. (28)

Arguably, of course, Nava *was* the same as everybody else in extremely important ways, but his comment is intriguing for the clarity with which he expresses the central theme in gay (and gay working-class) Diaspora stories: an experience of difference that demands obedience. Familiar as that sentiment may be, it deserves a much deeper exploration than it typically receives.

No one who travels from a working-class or a non-white ethnic culture (or both, such as in the case of Nava and Monteagudo) to one of the branch offices of HomoMecca can fail to understand the ways in which class, ethnicity, or gender may make her or him *not* like everybody else. And yet the so-called "gay community" seems to have a much better public-relations arm than do tens of thousands of rural or working-class towns across America, and has managed to instill the perception that racial, ethnic, class, and gender differences are more readily admitted to gay-friendly settings than sexual differences are to the average hometown. The 1984 hit "Smalltown Boy" by the Bronski Beat, which became a queer anthem when it was released and has remained so for decades, condensed the sentiment into a few lines:

> Mother will never understand why you had to leave,
> But the answers you seek will never be found at home.
> The love that you need will never be found at home.
> Run away, turn away, run away.[9]

---

[9] Lyrics by Jimmy Somerville, Steven Bronski, and Lawrence Cole. All three members of the original Bronski Beat were openly gay men. In the music video, Somerville plays the "smalltown boy" who is harassed and beaten for admiring an attractive male classmate. He decides to leave home and, accompanied by two friends, boards a London-bound train.

As newspaper stories—if not our own personal experiences—make abundantly clear, in fact, the need to "turn away" can be a matter of literal survival: sexual and gender "nonconformity" (perceived or real) "back home" may mean loss of livelihood, police harassment, social ostracism, vandalism, physical danger, and even death, especially in areas where the hold of Christian fundamentalists is strong. Terence Stamp's character, Bernadette Bassenger, probably said it best in *The Adventures of Priscilla, Queen of the Desert* (1994):

> We all sit around mindlessly slagging off that vile stink-hole of a city. But in its own strange way, it takes care of us. I don't know if that ugly wall of suburbia's been put there to stop them getting in, or us getting out.

Thus, although racism, sexism, and classism in the urban "gay community" (not to mention rigid standards of physical attractiveness, cultural inbreeding, and an inflated perception of political influence) may leave psychic scars, it seems fair to say that they less often produce physical ones or halt a life project completely in its tracks.

In his "In Defense of Identity Politics," historian Martin Duberman gave a more academic spin to Bernadette's "us":

> [W]e hold on to a group identity ... because ... it's the closest we have ever gotten to having a political home—and voice. Yes, identity politics reduces and simplifies. Yes, it is a kind of prison. But it is also, paradoxically, a haven. (2001, n.p.)

The haven that can be formed on the basis of an experience of sexual difference is one of the most significant revelations of *Small Town Gay Bar*, a 2006 documentary that explored life in and around gay gathering places in rural, Bible-belt Mississippi. As oases in a desert of overwhelming rejection and violence, the bars in the documentary brought together femme lesbians and stone dykes, sissies and passing gay men, drag queens and transsexuals, black people and white in a social context they themselves defined as "family" and "community." The bars and the social relations that formed around them were, in the literal sense, what Duberman called "sites of resistance." Perhaps more significantly, they represented a much greater "multiculturalism" and "cross-sectionality" than the average Queer Nation rally, Human Rights Campaign fundraiser, gay novel, or people-of-color-free episode of *Will & Grace*.

A look at queer demographics, meanwhile, complicates matters further. If we accept the Williams Institute's estimate that nine million gay and lesbian adults live in the United States, it follows that no more than a fraction of them can live in recognizable "gay ghettos." Where are the rest of them, and what holds them where they are? As John Weir quipped in his 1997 essay, "Going In": "There are no statistics to prove it, but if mainstream means 'majority,' I bet the mainstream of homosexuality in American today is in the Marines" (32).

More seriously, lower incomes and dead-end jobs must surely limit mobility for queer people just as they do for everyone and, as "gay-friendly" urban areas become increasingly gentrified, moving to one of them means confronting what may be an unmanageable leap in the cost of living. In addition, there is evidence to suggest that where queer people chose to live is heavily influenced not solely by what keeps them from leaving but by the factors that encourage them to stay. Race and whether or not they are raising children, for example, seem to be two of the more important.[10]

For many—arguably, *most*—people who call themselves lesbian or gay, sexual orientation may not be the sole or even the primary "subjectivity" around which they build or participate in communities, then, an entirely unsurprising fact that brings us back to the issues raised both by Read and by

---

[10] The Urban Institute's 2004 "Fact Sheet: Where Do Gay and Lesbian Couples Live," which is based on Census 2000 data, notes that the highest concentration of same-sex couples (undifferentiated by gender or race) is found, in descending order, in the states of Vermont, California, and Washington and in the Metropolitan Statistical Areas (MSAs) of San Francisco and Oakland, CA and Seattle-Bellevue-Everett, WA. Lesbian couples, by contrast, are most likely to live in the MSAs of Santa Rosa and Santa Cruz-Watsonville, CA, while gay male couples live mostly in San Francisco and Ft. Lauderdale, FL. The MSA with the highest concentration of child-rearing same-sex couples is San Antonio, TX (followed by Bergen-Passaic, NJ and Memphis, TN), though the Williams Institute reports that the percentage of same-sex couples with children is highest in Salt Lake City, UT (26%) and Virginia Beach, VA (24%) (Davidson, 2013). African-American same-sex couples, meanwhile, are most likely to live in the MSAs of Sumter, SC (followed by Pine Bluff, AR and Albany, GA) or, in terms of entire states, in Mississippi, Louisiana, or South Carolina. Hispanic same-sex couples are most likely to be found in Laredo, McAllen, or Brownsville, TX (or, by state, in New Mexico or Texas).

Preston's *Hometown* refugees: When we speak, write, or read of our group, our clan, our tribe, our community, how much do we really know about the differences between those people who perceive their sexual "anomaly" as both necessary and sufficient to serve as a basis for affiliation with others and those who choose (or who are compelled by economics or other factors) to organize their lives otherwise?

Commenting on an essay by Michael Denneny, "Gay Politics: Sixteen Propositions," John Champagne takes up this same argument:

> Denneny's remark that "Being gay is a more elemental aspect of who I am than my profession, my class, or my race" could only be uttered from a position of relative privilege. It is chiefly white, upper-middle-class professional males who can afford—literally and figuratively—to locate in their sexuality the most "elemental" aspects of their identity. (1993: 160)[11]

In fact, the whole project of gay community formation and promulgation, which is suggested in Read ("I was gently ... letting him know that his tribe was out there") and imperative in Preston ("There was no way for a gay man to have a hometown and still be honest with himself") grossly oversimplifies the very questions it purports to resolve: the nature of identity, the processes by which sexuality is infused into (or excluded from) the experiences of everyday existence, and the degree of disclosure that qualifies as "honesty."

Perhaps most curiously, it dismisses the most significant question of all: What distinguishes the relatively small group of peregrine homosexuals from the relatively large group of the more sessile variety? Though gay media and other cultural products, in the main, tend to treat the latter as sinners who refuse to board the Ark, when these subjects of disdain or pity are allowed to speak for themselves, they often balance "turning away" against questions of what they would be forced to give up ("land, blood, and family," as Rist's Oklahoma cowboy put it) if they left what they consider, for want of a better term, home.

---

[11] Denneny's essay first appeared in *Christopher Street* magazine in 1981, but has since been reprinted in *We Are Everywhere: A Historical Sourcebook of Gay and Lesbian Politics*, Mark Blasius and Shane Phelan, Eds. New York: Routledge, 1997, pp. 485-497.

At the same time, to the extent that working-class experiences and loyalties are so often conceived (and transmitted through writing and other media) as the hostile territory in which homosexuality is encamped, as the wilderness through which each individual must wander in search of admission to Beulah, it seems fair to ask how much such a premise reflects objective reality and how much it represents a colonizing discourse that has become nearly impossible to resist.

In a 2011 article about Evan Darling, purportedly the first openly gay NASCAR driver, journalist John Billow discussed the challenges Darling was facing as he sought the financial backing that would allow him to continue as a professional racer. Darling himself chalked up the reticence of potential sponsors to the workings of "a good old boy network," but Billow instantly recast (unverified) discomfort with Darling's sexual orientation as a feature of social class: "Homophobia in most sports = rednecks + beer/brain cells to number of missing teeth" (n.p.).

Comedian Margaret Cho traded on the same classist stereotypes in her 2005 standup show, *Assassin*, joking:

> [Conservatives] sidle up to these Bible thumping, cousin humping, monster truck enthusiasts and they get them all riled up and send them in to a mullet fantasia about how gays are going to move in to their neighborhoods. As if we would ever live in a trailer park....
>
> The community of Rhea County, Tennessee, tried to get rid of all the homosexuals. How do you get rid of the homosexuals? Do you tent the county and play Reba McIntyre at earsplitting levels?
>
> Well, first you're going to have to close the Abercrombie and Fitch. You can forget about Restoration Hardware. All you're going to have left is Michael's. I hope you enjoy crafts.

What is fascinating in these commentaries is not solely their blatant classism and elitism (presumably, people with dental problems would attend to them if they could afford to), but rather the two deeply insidious hypotheses about queers and about class that reside within them. First is the comfort Billow and Cho demonstrate in locating homophobic bigotry—or, at least, some more "organic" form of it—in poor, rural, and working-class settings, exploiting a shorthand they apparently presume will be clear to their audiences.

In her excellent commentary on the 1998 documentary about the murder of Brandon Teena in Nebraska in 1993, *The Brandon Teena Story*, Lisa Duggan (1995/2006) discussed this same "comfortable" connection between poverty- and working-class existence, on the one hand, and intolerance of gender and sexual "difference" on the other:

> To my eyes, the documentary ... relentlessly exoticized the "white trash" setting in which it was filmed.... The audience ... aligned itself seemingly seamlessly with that point of view [and was] comfortable projecting racism, misogyny, homophobia, and violent masculinity on to this "other" setting *where it seemingly "belonged...."* [U]rban LGBT and queer audiences, especially in New York and San Francisco, often responded similarly—with comfortable condescension and metropolitan superiority. Never mind the racism, homophobia, and violence marking the gentrifying urban settings just outside. (214; my italics)

The second is the image of gay and lesbian lives that writers like Billow and Cho construct through their totalizing discourses, diluting, discounting, occluding, and delegitimizing untold queer experiences in the process. One of those experiences, surely, is of dealing with brutality and animosity in their home environments—but being unable to escape from them for reasons of economics and mobility. When bad things happen in rural settings (Brandon Teena, Matthew Shepard), the "communitarian" gay response is typically to be appalled but just as typically to engage in a subtle form of victim-blaming: Those who insist on living among the enemy are, in a sense, asking for it.

Paradoxically, a simultaneous impulse in commentaries like Read's, Cho's, and Billow's is to subtract gay people from such presumed low-class precincts as auto racing, monster truck rallies, country music, Walmart cafés, thrift stores, and trailer parks (as if none of us ever grew up in a trailer park[12])—

---

[12] Allan Bérubé's moving essay, "Sunset Trailer Park," written with his mother, Florence, deserves mention here. It is reprinted in *My Desire for History: Essays in Gay, Community, and Labor History* (Chapel Hill: University of North Carolina Press, 2011, 182-201).

indeed from their very hometowns, if those towns are rural and not upscale—and, in so doing, to correctively rehabilitate homosexuality as a social class. Coming out (and leaving "home") is mythologized as a process of inevitable advancement in consumer behavior and acquisitive power. Through it, queer people become more intelligent, gain access to better healthcare, develop superior taste in beverages, and are given the financial means to shop at Restoration Hardware and Abercrombie and Fitch and to afford more stylish haircuts

No less remarkable is the degree to which this better-living-through-homosexuality discourse ignores the question of shame—not shame as a result of discredited sexual desire but because of what one might almost call the natural consequence of abandoning one's family and community-of-origin to a fate they may be unable to outrun. Without question, escape may sometimes be the only choice, but it can only be accomplished *without ambivalence* by those who need not worry about how harsh life will be to those who remain behind.

It is odd, in fact, that what I would consider such a commonplace poverty- and working-class experience is so little reflected in queer literature and is entirely ignored in "it gets better" coming-out narratives. Lillian Faderman's 2003 memoir, *Naked in the Promised Land*, is imbued with this ambivalence, and Faderman's sense of guilt over her unfulfilled childhood promise to save her mother from the Bronx garment-district sweatshop where she worked is a shadow over the book and her life. The more Faderman excels, the farther she seems to travel, without meaning or wanting to, from her mother's unredeemed existence, and the truth Faderman contends with is the almost inevitable guilt of the educated queer offspring of working-class parents—the realization that what the child considers good fortune, freedom, self-realization, growth, even happiness, may be seen by the parent as disrespect, even outright betrayal. Dorothy Allison, in the introduction to the 2002 reissue of her book of stories, *Trash*, touches on similar issues when she reveals that one of her motivations for writing was "an attempt to stop being ashamed of running away from the lives my cousins were living" (xii). But such examples are comparatively rare.

In the end, my point is neither to criticize Read's deeply observed and rather touching memoir or the eloquent and often melancholy reminiscences of the writers in *Hometowns* nor is it to discount the cruelty of heterosupremacy and gender bigotry. Rather, I want to call attention to the polarities of class and (homo)sexuality that have become so deeply ingrained that we are virtually helpless to avoid speaking in their language.

V.

That's why I don't raise my voice, old Walt Whitman,
against the little boy who writes
the name of a girl on his pillow,
nor against the boy who dresses as a bride
in the darkness of the wardrobe,
nor against the solitary men in casinos
who drink prostitution's water with revulsion,
nor against the men with that green look in their eyes
who love other men and burn their lips in silence.

But yes against you, urban faggots,
tumescent flesh and unclean thoughts.
Mothers of mud. Harpies. Sleepless enemies
of the love that bestows crowns of joy.
(*From "Ode to Walt Whitman" by Federico García Lorca,
Tr. Carlos Bauer*)

And yet the goal of *Blue, Too* and of *Everything I Have Is Blue*, born as they both were in a primordial soup of skepticism regarding twenty-first-century practices of identity, is not to elevate working-class experience to a place in the catechism of oppressions recited by good liberals and by smug moderates, eager to do the least they can to disguise their Darwinian politics. It isn't to ask for a place at the (literary) table or a slice of the (publishing) pie, for what would be the point? The queer bookshelf already groans, literally and virtually, beneath the weight of books by, for, and about people raising their voices to be heard: gay, lesbian, and bisexual Jews, Chicanos, African-Americans, Italian-Americans, Irish-Americans, Native Americans, Israelis, Cubans; lesbians with disabilities; lesbians and gay men who are deaf; queer youth; gay, lesbian, bisexual, and transgendered people with developmental disabilities; lesbians who are fat; gay men who are elderly.

Much of this writing speaks in some measure, just as I do here, about both invisibility and hegemony, about both silences and the difficulty of making oneself heard above deafening clamor. The least thoughtful of it goes no further than to indict media or pop culture for failing to represent "empirical realism," but almost all of it attempts to stake a claim on the landscape of queer consciousness.

Yet even as some activists and writers practice dissent because their shade does not appear on the rainbow flag, a no less dedicated group has proposed for decades to burn the flag outright. Indeed, the Gay Shame organization, founded in New York in 1998, has done literally that at their "Gay Shame Awards" and at public protests. In the Gay Shame "Statement of Purpose," organizers write:

> We will not be satisfied with a commercialized gay identity that denies the intrinsic links between queer struggle and challenging power. We seek nothing less than a new queer activism that foregrounds race, class, gender and sexuality, to counter the self-serving "values" of gay consumerism and the increasingly hypocritical left. We are dedicated to fighting the rabid assimilationist monster.[13]

Similarly, in Issue #2 of Gay Shame's successful 'zine, *Swallow Your Pride: A Do-It-Yourself Guide to Hands-On Activism*, the editors declared, circa 1999:

> We are ashamed of Chelsea homogeneity, 'community' as a corporate target market, Giuliani in the 'pride' parade, foaming-at-the-mouth praise for anti-feminist 'pro-gay' beer advertising, and reactionary 'we're just like you' gays and lesbians who ally themselves with straight, racist conservatives.[14]

Such criticisms of the "gay community," of cooptation, assimilation, and consumer-driven politics, are both long-lived and remarkably consistent over time. When they appear, they are occasionally—but by no means reliably—cast in traditional terms of capitalist injury and class stratification, but they are more often evoked without analysis as a rote feature of ritualistic complaint.

---

[13] Web: http://gayshamesf.org/about.html.
[14] Quoted by Jennifer Moon in "Gay Shame and the Politics of Identity," her chapter in David M. Halperin and Valerie Traub's *Gay Shame* (University of Chicago Press, 2010), 357-368: 360.

And yet accusations of selling out, of bourgeois complacency, of hostility to diversity and ignorance of social injustice nationally and globally, and especially of indifference to the wounds produced by capitalism were encoded into the DNA of the early modern gay-lib movement in the U.S. well before Stonewall. Readers may be aware, for example, that Harry Hay, the cofounder of the Mattachine Society, was a member of the Communist Party and specifically located the subjugation of homosexuals within the context of the oppressions generated by capitalism.

In the McCarthyism of the 1950s, however, anti-capitalist critique in any form was dangerous talk and, as Max Kirsch points out in *Queer Theory and Social Change* (2000), Hay and other "subversive" members of the Mattachine Society were purged in 1953, "culminating in [a] Mattachine convention that elected an openly anti-communist coordinating council and set the tone for more than a decade" (107).[15] By the time the Daughters of Bilitis was formed two years later, in the midst of what Lillian Faderman called "witch-hunts and police harassment" (1991: 190), the organization's leaders apparently felt they had little choice but to "[promote] an assimilationist strategy [that minimized] conflict and expressions of difference" (Kirsch, 2000: 108).

In the immediate aftermath of Stonewall, meanwhile, two competing gay-lib organizations were formed almost simultaneously in New York, the more radical and expressly Socialist Gay Liberation Front (1969-c. 1972),[16] which placed the oppression of homosexuals in the context of other social inequalities and called for simultaneous struggle against racism, sexism, capitalism, the nuclear family, and traditional gender roles; and the Gay Activists Alliance (1969-c. 1981), which was energized by dissident members of the GLF and focused on gay issues exclusively, including protests at the New York Marriage

---

[15] As lesbian activist, writer, and Feminist Studies professor Bettina Aptheker recalled in her 2008 essay, "Keeping the Communist Party Straight, 1940s-1980s," the CP itself asked lesbian and gay members of the party to resign voluntarily or be purged by as early as the late 1940s—ostensibly out of concern that they could become informants for the FBI if blackmailed. Aptheker also gives an excellent overview of the histories of lesbian activists in the Communist Party
[16] See Escoffier (2008) for a useful history of the GLF.

Bureau for its refusal to issue licenses to same-sex couples and "zaps" against anti-gay politicians and businesses.

In 1970, GLF member Carl Wittman issued his "A Gay Manifesto," a call for sweeping revolution in American culture. Wittman depicted gay people (men, chiefly) as "refugees from Amerika" and was highly critical of what he called the "gay ghetto," a place to which homosexuals came "not because it is so great here, but because it was so bad there" (3). Wittman's major criticism of the ghetto (meaning, at the time, neighborhoods in San Francisco and New York) concerned the fact that institutions in those cities were not directed by the people who frequented them—a kind of "gay nationalism" that perhaps unconsciously echoed Malcolm X's call for a black nationalism in which "the black man [w]ould control the politics and the politicians in his own community."[17] Wrote Wittman:

> It is a ghetto rather than a free territory because it is still theirs. Straight cops patrol us, straight legislators govern us, straight employers keep us in line, straight money exploits us.... (3) Ghettos breed exploitation. Landlords find they can charge exorbitant rents and get away with it because of the limited area which [it] is safe to live in openly. Mafia control of bars and baths in NYC is only one example of outside money controlling our institutions for their profit. In San Francisco the Tavern Guild favors maintaining the ghetto, for it is through ghetto culture that they make a buck. We crowd their bars not because of their merit but because of the absence of any other social institution. (6)

A number of observations may be made here. First, for as radical as he may have intended his "Manifesto" to be, Wittman was not exactly issuing a call for the end of private property or suggesting, for example, that bars and baths be transformed into co-ops; rather, the implication was simply that removing those institutions from straight hands and placing them into gay ones (gay landlords instead of straight ones, for example) would lead to self-determination. Ultimately, that transfer of ownership is just what happened in the Castro, the West Village, and almost everywhere else—with all the deleterious

---

[17] See, e.g., "The Ballot or the Bullet," delivered April 3, 1964. Web: www.edchange.org/multicultural/speeches/malcolm_x_ballot.html.

consequences of galloping capitalism that have made "gay ghettos" unaffordable for the very gay and lesbian people Wittman presumably wanted to empower; in a cruel irony, it has simultaneously tended to annihilate self-determination for black, brown, and working-class communities.

In addition, what is clear in Wittman is a criticism of the lack of "community" institutions and institutional power rather than of the institutions themselves, which only serves to make the obvious point: a critique of gay community institutions—and, with them, of "community" businesses, media, and organizations capable of setting national political agendas— wasn't possible until such institutions existed in the first place, a phenomenon that would not come to pass until responses to the AIDS crisis provided necessary fuel.

To my knowledge, no definitive analysis has been published of the ways in which AIDS-advocacy and AIDS-activist organizations both created and harnessed gay institutional power in the period between the mid-1980s and mid-1990s, though the connection now seems rather conspicuous. In 1991, in his *Millennium Approaches*, the first part of *Angels in America*, playwright Tony Kushner demonstrated his realpolitik understanding of what lack of such power meant for people with AIDS, placing his analysis in the mouth of his character, Roy Cohn.

In a scene near the end of Act I, Cohn has just rejected a diagnosis of AIDS, the disease "that homosexuals have," and angrily confronts his physician:

> Your problem, Henry is that you are hung up on words, on labels.... Now, to someone who does not understand this, homosexual is what I am because I have sex with men. But really this is wrong. Homosexuals are not men who sleep with other men. Homosexuals are men who in fifteen years of trying cannot get a pissant anti-discrimination bill through City Council. Homosexuals are men who know nobody and who nobody knows. Who have no clout. Does this sound like me, Henry? (45)

Ultimately, in fact, Cohn uses his personal and political connections to gain access to AZT, an anti-retroviral therapy that was not at the time available to the general public.

No more than a few years after Kushner wrote *Millennium Approaches*, however, homosexuals had begun to have clout—in the form of massive, well-funded AIDS and political organizations; unprecedented and increasingly supportive coverage from mainstream media as well as a proliferation of gay-owned magazines and newspapers that attracted significant name-brand advertising; a small but ultimately influential group of uncloseted gay and lesbian politicians at national and local levels; and activist organizations like ACT-UP and its offshoot, Queer Nation, which were effective, efficient, and enviably media-savvy in significant measure because their core constituency was formed of middle-class, well-educated white men with professional jobs, the presumptive "grassroots" nature of their mobilizations and the scruffy, radical chic drag of their public image notwithstanding.

At that point, the sluiceways of class-based criticism could open full bore, as indeed they did (at least to the extent that class was conflated with consumer behavior). In 1999, Yaroslav Mogutin, the first Russian granted political asylum in the U.S. because he faced death threats and imprisonment in his homeland for his gay activism, told a reporter for the Montreal-based gay magazine, *The Guide*:

> It took me almost five years of living in America to come to the sad conclusion that the whole Western idea of a gay movement is totally bankrupt at this point. My idea of being queer is totally different from singing in the gay chorus or marching down Fifth Avenue in a crowd of thousands of topless cartoon-like clones with totally manufactured, waxed bodies. If I grew up in today's Chelsea, I would probably end up being a hardcore gay-basher in order to protest and attack this scary world of the unified look, unified morality, and lifestyle. We need more Andrew Cunanans, more queer terrorists, more "faggot-individualists" like Ginsberg, queer literary outlaws like Burroughs, more bad-ass fags to prove that the pioneering gay spirit of rebellion isn't yet entirely smothered by the Great American Consumerism (Andriette, 1999: n.p.).

Around the same time, in a bodacious essay for Mark Simpson's 1997 anthology, *Anti-Gay*, novelist John Weir took a similar tack:

> If you read any of the new or newly mainstream advertising-laden gay magazines, *Out* or *The Advocate* or *Genre*, or if you saw the thousands of identically clad homosexuals who flooded New York City during the June 1994 Stonewall 25 celebration, you know where

the gay community is headed. It's not moving towards legal rights.... The collective impulse of the chic lesbians and the brave young gay Republicans who captivate the media today and titillate each other is shopping. (27)

[T]here is no more recognizable type than the self-identified, politically active, sexually predatory gay American man, the kind of guy who wants, not equality for everyone, but entitlement for himself. And big pecs. This was abundantly clear to me at the New York Stonewall 25 celebration.... It was a week-long festival of pod people twirling their multi-colored freedom rings. There were so many hairless young men in nipple-hugging white T-shirts wandering the streets that I began to wish that it was 1969 again and paddy wagons would come and take them all away. (30)

Nor are such criticisms limited, as these examples might suggest, to gay male complaints about "male" environments, social groups, institutions, and public accommodations. British scholar Yvette Taylor has produced an impressive body of work regarding the way working-class lesbians view and interact with "gay areas" (which Taylor calls "scene space"), noting that she was forced to abandon "traditional" gay and lesbian venues in her search for respondents for her research because working-class lesbians could not reliably be found there. Rather, they recognized so-called "gay-friendly" space as "ultimately market space [that] required consuming bodies within it" (Taylor, 2008: 541)—in other words, as a form of obligatory consumption. In their criticisms of such spaces as "[pretentious], 'middle-class' and male," Taylor continued,

[m]any working-class lesbians commented on the inaccessibility of scene spaces.... Often access to such spaces required movement into cities, which incurred travel expenses as well as the emotional costs involved in moving between vastly different locations.... Most women described how scene spaces were located in "trendy" areas ... with the result that particular classed displays, images and "performances" were required to enable entry.... [H]aving the "right" clothes, the right style and taste can indicate that you "deserve" to be there but "looking like a lesbian" in these settings often requires unaffordable presentations (2005: n.p.).

To the extent that "gay-friendly" spaces achieve a certain level of respectability, Taylor argues, they tend also to be gentrified and, as she pointed out in her 2008 "'That's Not Really My Scene': Working-Class Lesbians In (and Out of) Place," consequently become "variously and vividly classed ... [as is] apparent in the location of such venues [and in their] marketing" as upscale or trendy (543). Mainstreaming may provide "non-threatening, spending lesbians and gay men" with visibility and acceptability, Taylor continues, but:

> Alongside branding, "niche" marketing and the "commercial hijacking of gayness," it is important to remember that "not everyone is invited to the party" (525). Even though many of these places [have] achieved a celebrity status as the "places to be" (gay), as "redevelopment showpieces" ... interviewees spoke of very real financial barriers against entry and the tensions in accessing a space where only certain embodied presentations and ways of being were recognized and affirmed. As gay urban areas chase the younger, wealthier gay male pound, lesbians are deemed to be "other" and "unwanted." (528)

Taylor's language is academic, but the working-class concerns of her respondents ring in clear and familiar tones. Just as gay men bemoan the gentrification of the Castro or reject the "middle-class" and "assimilationist" agendas of gay rights organizations, the working-class lesbians in Taylor's work not infrequently reject—as "superficial" and fake—the neighborhoods, associations, and events whose existence purportedly provides them with opportunities to be "free." In other words, "LGBT scene space ... reproduce[s] class as a central point of exclusion, even as inclusion is celebrated, visible, and announced" (2013: 6).

Rachel Swan traces the same phenomenon in "Pride of Place" (2014). Noting that domestic duties, "compounded by the gender wage gap, are undermining the notion of a lesbian district," Swan discusses the dwindling population of artistic, anarchist dykes in San Francisco, once the force behind a thriving community of bookstores, bars, gyms, coffee shops, performance spaces, political organizations, punk bands, and workers' collectives for working-class women. Writes Swan:

> Gay men's neighborhoods that sprouted from the margins of society are transforming into wealthy,

gentrified retail corridors; meanwhile, lesbian districts are getting diluted by the onslaught of new money.... During the 1980s and '90s, gay women flocked to San Francisco for its cheap rents and open-minded spirit..... [M]any of them came to San Francisco to ply an industrial trade, which, 30 years ago, was a viable career option for any city resident.... At that time, the cost of living was still low enough that a single woman could sustain herself, working as a house painter or crane operator or electrician.

One of the most incendiary examples of what served as both "radical" critique and rhetoric during the 1990s, however, was Ian Barnard's deliberately provocative "Fuck Community, or Why I Support Gay-Bashing," published in 1996 but delivered in its earliest draft at Indiana University's Lesbian, Gay & Bisexual Pride Week in 1993.

In the final published version of his manifesto, Barnard credited the queercore movement—one of whose founding documents is G. B. Jones and Bruce LaBruce's 1989 "Don't Be Gay, or How I Learned to Stop Worrying and Fuck Punk in the Ass"—for its "reclamation of the radical roots of modern lesbian and gay activism in North America and elsewhere by guerrilla queer insurgents" (75).

"Don't Be Gay" appeared in the punk music 'zine, *MaximumRockNRoll* and, as such, was primarily concerned with carrying forward the mission that Jones and LaBruce had begun with their own successful homocore 'zine, *J.D.'s*, which published eight issues between 1985 and 1991—with, that is, as Jones and LaBruce wrote, "putting the 'gay' back in 'punk' and the 'punk' back in 'gay.'" Punk music, of course, at least in its origins, was often both working-class music and working-class protest. As perhaps the first anti-gay/pro-queer document of the modern gay movement, and because of a unique analysis that considered the ways in which both the "gay establishment" and the "punk alternative" had been "co-opted" by identical market forces, "Don't Be Gay" is an important text:

> The gay 'movement' as it exists now is a big farce.... [I]ronically, it fails most miserably where it should be most progressive: in its sexual politics.... Gay youths are abandoning the gay establishment because it's been 'co-opted' .... [In the presence of] a facile freedom that offers gay bars, discos, and fashion within a 'gay ghetto,' a

radical option sanctioned by and contained within normalcy becomes the only concession to liberation.... Although not yet 'ghettoized' to the extent of gay culture ... punks must constantly be wary of society's attempts to reduce their protest merely to fashion.... One way to avoid such co-option is to present a movement that refuses to conform to ... standards of sexual decency and moral conduct ... while avoiding the mistakes of the gay movement: ghettoization, liberal reform, class capitulation. (n.p.)

In "Fuck Community," Barnard's writing is rageful and bracing, but with respect to "Don't Be Gay" has both hardened and become less accessible through cross-pollination with feminist, queer, and leftist theory. He lifts Adrienne Rich's concept of "compulsory heterosexuality," for example, and much of the rest of the essay is a somewhat generic hybrid of criticisms of sexism, identity politics, and the military, leavened with simil-Marxist and question-begging terminology such as "reproduction of dominant structures" or PoMo lit-crit jargon like "multiple subjectivities."

"Fuck Community" is most coherent in Barnard's analysis of attempts by "the gay community" to "co-opt queer sexualities into a liberal pluralist paradigm by silencing the diversity of queer voices" (78); in his insistence that queer was a "scrupulously politicized" stance (83) antagonistic to normalization as a "lifestyle" or "a simple sexual orientation"; and in his call to reject any linkage between sexual, romantic, or affectional alliances, on the one hand, and a shared political philosophy or agenda on the other (what he called "the debilitating facade of unity" [84]).[18]

---

[18] The references to gay bashing in Mogutin, Barnard, and Weir (Weir writes, "The next time I see a bunch of dudes from Jersey beating on a faggot from Greenwich Village, I'm going to cheer them on" [34]) are intriguing. Clearly, they are meant to express both frustration with gay male self-representation and the writer's desire to situate himself at the point of the compass farthest from whatever being a "gay-community man" is presumed to signify. Still, no matter how radical the writer, it's difficult to imagine a lesbian activist invoking, even metaphorically or for the sake of hyperbole, physical violence against other women. Barnard attempts to defuse his title by adding, rather incoherently, "by saying I support gay-bashing, I decenter heterosexuality, taking for granted my rage at explicit homophobia and institutionalized heterosexuality" (84).

Nonetheless, although Mogutin, Weir, and Barnard are all at play in the fields of capitalism and corporate-created and -sponsored artifacts of community membership and identity, they are hardly offering a class analysis, except to the extent that pejorative use of terms like "capitalism" or "middle-class" is intended to strike at the heart of class hierarchies (to his credit, Weir is somewhat clearer about class than Barnard; while Barnard is adamantine when it comes to racism and engages in a rousing round of épater la bourgeoisie through multiple references to the toxic byproducts of "liberalism," his class analysis is barely developed).

In that sense, all three commentators are related to more recent radical and radical manqué writings such as Mattilda Bernstein Sycamore's *The End of San Francisco* (2013) and Ryan Conrad's *Against Equality: Queer Revolution, Not Mere Inclusion* (2014), many of which fiercely criticize "identity politics" while failing to recognize that "radical socialist" or "anti-mainstream queer" are also identities and without acknowledging the extent to which their analyses sometimes constitute nothing so much as an elaborate fantasy of being able to live outside ideology.

All of that said, radical-queer/anti-gay (in Mark Simpson's use of the phrase in the title of his 1997 anthology) writers often fail to see their own class biases and positions even as they dutifully list class in the litany of "subjectivities" regarding which "international solidarity" is required. Nowhere is this more clear than in criticisms of efforts to end the ban on gays in the military (and, some years later, to repeal DADT) and of the marriage-equality movement.

Even as early as 1970, Wittman couched his views regarding the "correct" gay position on the military in rather ambivalent terms: "[D]iscrimination in the draft and armed services is a pillar of the general attitude toward gays.... Hell, no, we won't go, of course not, but we can't let the army fuck us over this way, either" (5), he wrote.

Barnard's statement, on the other hand, brooks no dissent and can reasonable serve as an exemplar of radical-queer opposition to "gays in the military" (which is interpreted solely as support for imperialism):

> I am enraged that many lesbian and gay activists are begging for admission into a U.S. Military that executes genocidal cultural, economic, and political imperialism all over the world. (78-79)

It is not OK that Queer Nation San Diego in 1991 refused to oppose Operation Desert Storm; it is not OK now for queers to march for marriage, domestic partnership benefits, or admission to the military. (84)

Leaving aside the question of why Queer Nation could reasonably be expected to take an official position on Operation Desert Storm (which is not to argue for the opposite view, but simply to note the need for elucidation of the nexus that seemed so apparent to Barnard), "Fuck Community" ignores the classed reality of the U.S. military which, beginning in 1973, has been an entirely volunteer force and which, since the Gulf War, has increasingly been composed of young people with few other options for education and employment.

John Weir makes this point nicely in "Going In":

Radical gays, hiding behind a veneer of pacifism, are especially guilty of classism and elitism in this instance.... [I]f somebody in the armed forces complains about how the military treats him, a lot of gay men tune out. "Abolish the military altogether," radical fags say, overlooking the fact that enlisting in the armed forces is often the most viable economic alternative for working-class young men. If you're seventeen years old and you don't like musical comedy, and you don't want to move to New York or Chicago or Los Angeles, and you don't have enough money for college; and if you know that you like sweaty, male environments; and if you want to get the hell out of your small town, why not the Marines? Not every gay man in America is a chorus boy or a sensitive poet or a Harvard MBA. (33-34)

Just as Barnard somehow manages to imagine access to the military solely as an elitist alliance with power and privilege (the unskilled nineteen-year-old GED holder who joins the Army thus becomes a wielder of privilege rather than the pawn of it), so, too, have critics of marriage-equality attempted, with little evidence to back them up but with an enviable degree of endurance, to construct marriage as a "middle-class" (and, therefore, oppressive) "privilege" that is withheld from (or alien to) "the masses."

This was the tack taken by writers from the Against Equality Collective in their critique of the *United States v. Windsor* case. As a result of that case, in June 2013 the U.S. Supreme Court declared specific provisions of 1996 Defense of Marriage Act (DOMA) unconstitutional. The Against Equality writers state, quite accurately, that the plaintiff in the case, Edith Windsor, was a wealthy woman; after her wife died in 2009 (they had been married in Canada), leaving her entire estate to Windsor, Windsor sued because the federal government rejected her claim for the estate-tax exemption available to surviving spouses and forced her to pay more than $360,000 in taxes. From these facts, the Against Equality editors conclude that the real point of the *Windsor* case was "for wealthy gays and lesbians ... to keep their fortunes," adding, "Most people are unlikely to die with that much in savings, or to ever see that kind of amount accrue in their lifetimes, let alone to have to pay that much tax."

Certainly true, but equally certainly an illogical argument. Supreme Court decisions extend constitutional protections—as a legal matter, even if not always a practical one—to all citizens, and the benefits of being recognized as a "surviving spouse" (never mind as a living spouse) are considerable, regardless of socioeconomic status. In terms of the specifics of *Windsor*, it is true that the Supreme Court's decision meant that Edith Windsor could avoid hundreds of thousands of dollars in estate taxes; it also meant, however, that any same-sex spouse of a deceased worker can now receive Social Security survivor's benefits, which currently average a whopping $1,083.13 per month.[19] That's hardly anyone's idea of a fortune, but the logical extension of the Against Equality argument was this: Because striking down DOMA *also* potentially benefited wealthy people, the law should have been left intact to "protect" the downtrodden.

Among the most thoughtless of knee-jerk diatribes against marriage-equality-as-privilege was Mia McKenzie's post, "6 Things That Happened While Y'all Were Preoccupied With Gay Marriage," published on her blog in early 2013. Wrote McKenzie,

> As someone who doesn't personally or politically feel connected to so-called "marriage equality," [I] frankly can't fathom so much time and energy and money being poured into getting one more privilege for one group of people—especially since the people within that group who will benefit the most are mostly very privileged

[19] See the Social Security Administration's "Monthly Statistical Snapshot," www.ssa.gov/policy/docs/quickfacts/stat_snapshot.

already—at the expense of countless other really important and much more urgent issues facing the queer community and our society as a whole.

Before going further, this seems a good place to make clear that my aim is not to challenge either opposition to marriage equality or objections to military service by gay people. McKenzie's call in "6 Things" for greater "inclusiveness and intersectionality" is no more than the restatement of a critical analysis that has played a fundamental role in the dialectic of the modern gay-rights movements for some sixty years. In fact, any number of thoughtful criticisms exist of American militarism and of marriage—as well as, more generally, of the tendency of major LGBT rights organizations to ignore questions of social complexity in favor of easily communicated, media-ready messages delivered in the reductive semantics of fundraising.

In an insightful essay in *The Nation* in 1994, for example, Tony Kushner provided this coherent summing-up of what happens in a movement that begins and ends with the so-called "single issues" of marriage and the military that McKenzie (along with many others) criticizes:

> [I]t's entirely conceivable that we will one day live miserably in a thoroughly ravaged world in which lesbians and gay men can marry and serve openly in the Army and that's it. Capitalism, after all, can absorb a lot. Poverty, war, alienation, environmental destruction, colonialism, unequal development, boom/bust cycles, private property, individualism, commodity fetishism, the fetishization of the body, the fetishization of violence, guns, drugs, child abuse, underfunded and bad education (itself a form of child abuse)—these things are key to the successful functioning of the free market. Homophobia is not; the system could certainly accommodate demands for equal rights for homosexuals without danger to itself. (9)

Twenty years later, in the *Chronicle of Higher Education*, Suzanna Danuta Walters made closely related points in a critique of what she called the "tolerance trap":

> Shouldn't we argue that same-sex marriage might make us all think differently about the relationship between domestic life and gender norms and push heterosexuals to examine their stubborn commitment to a gendered division of labor?

[W]hen difference is erased in the quest to make us more tolerable to those heterosexuals who get to do the tolerating, when the messiness and fluidity of sexual desire and identity are put into the straitjacket of biological inevitability, when queer challenges to gender rules and regulations are morphed into nuptial sameness, and when queer freedoms are reduced to the right to wed, we all lose out.

Finally, I know of no more compelling analysis of the limitations of the marriage-equality fight than Michael Warner's *The Trouble with Normal*, a crystal clear exposition of the ways in which a focus on marriage is linked to the project of normalization (or, if one prefers, heterosexualization) and, thus, to what Warner calls a "selective legitimacy" that further marginalizes those uninterested in a state-sanctioned marital relationship and absolves marriage-equality activists "from having to recognize any connection between the gay marriage debates and the growing crackdown on all queerer forms of sexual culture" (115). Describing what he calls a "marriage license vs. sexual license" mentality, Warner explains that the latter is "everything the state does not license, and therefore everything the state allows itself to punish or regulate. The gay and lesbian movement was built on a challenge to this regulatory system" (97).

Notably, however, none of these three objectors to the so-called marriage movement—not even Warner, the fiercest among them—couches a critique of same-sex marriage in terms of opposition to privilege bestowed by social class or wealth.

Here, then, is where I want to place my objection to the neoradical-queer insistence on understanding issues such as marriage-equality and military service as "mainstream" and "middle class"—that is, as constituted largely or exclusively for the purpose of consolidating the power of the "gay ruling class" and, thus, as antagonistic to diversity and cross-sectional solidarity—and to the way in which such analyses render working-class queers invisible and insignificant even while purporting to speak for their own good.

Barnard, for example, cannot possibly have been unaware of who was actually joining the military during the 1993-1996 period when he was revising "Fuck Community"; he simply chose to ignore them. For her part, McKenzie cannot genuinely believe that the chief beneficiaries of marriage equality are or would be "one group of people who are mostly very privileged already," nor can she rationally maintain that queer poor people, working-class people, and people of color are uninterested in marriage or are absent from the population that would benefit from entering into legal marriages if they chose to.[20] To go further, she cannot seriously be advancing the argument that discriminatory treatment should remain in place for the sake of a theoretical attack on the mainstream.

Even the New Communist Party's May 1, 2013 "Resolution on the Queer Struggle" took a more nuanced view of the marriage issue than McKenzie, lambasting

> the leadership at the helm of the struggle for queer civil rights [for] betray[ing] the queer masses. With depoliticized and toothless gay "pride" parades sponsored by anti-people corporations, the poisonous racist scapegoating that followed the passing of Proposition 8 in California, and the wholesale abandonment of transgender issues, gay and lesbian NGOs like the Human Rights Campaign have shown

---

[20] Because U.S. Census statistics are currently based solely on opposite-sex couples, teasing out the class backgrounds or economic status of married same-sex couples is next to impossible. Nonetheless, the Williams Institute at the University of California-Los Angeles has been conducting careful demographic research on LGBTQ people and their families for years, and their statistics help paint a clearer picture. Specifically, an analysis by Gary J. Gates for the Institute revealed that "married or partnered LGBT individuals living in two-adult households with children are twice as likely as comparable non-LGBT individuals to report household incomes near the poverty threshold" (2013a: 5) and, in related research, that employed men in the labor force in same-sex couples had median annual personal incomes that were lower than those of men in different-sex couples (2013b). In another study for the Williams Institute, Kastanis and Wilson (2014) noted that "Regardless of race or ethnicity, individuals in same-sex couples have higher unemployment rates" (1). Finally, Badgett, Durso, and Schneebaum (2013) found that poverty rates were higher among same-sex couples than among different-sex couples across all measures of ethnicity and gender. These are indirect indicators, but they offer some counter to the notion that marriage equality does or would chiefly serve an elite and privileged class. To the contrary, there is every reason to believe that marriage would be of special benefit to same-sex couples in lower income brackets by providing access to health insurance, earned-income credits for families with children, and veterans, disability, and social security survivor payments, among other benefits.

their hand; they are not fighting for queer people at large, but are instead motivated by bourgeois class aspirations and ideology ("Resolution," 2013, n.p.).

That analysis did not, however, stop the NCP from calling for "same-sex marriages [to] be legalized on a national level and [for] state bans of same-sex marriage [to] be overturned," among its other demands. The Australian office of the Freedom Socialist Party similarly endorsed marriage equality, noting that

> [S]ame-sex marriage and women's free reproductive choice threaten the nuclear family—capitalism's cornerstone.... Based exclusively on a male-female union and his power over her and the children, this [traditional] family ... is homophobic and sexist to its core.... This is why socialist feminists fight for same-sex marriage. It's about winning equal rights for queers, while knocking down this crucial pillar of capitalism. (Brennan, 2010)

In other words, a queer politics that is aware of and responsive to issues of class and race or which is critical of the actions of *organizations* need not by definition oppose marriage equality in order to qualify as "radical."[21]

---

[21] True radicals, meanwhile, should be incensed that a deeply intellectual tradition of analysis and action has been coopted by spokespeople whose main contribution to the causes they (you should pardon the expression) espouse has been the social-media rant. A 15 October 2013 OpEd on the *New York Times* blog by Mattilda Bernstein Sycamore, classic in its use of hyperbole, straw-man argument, and non sequiturs, is an example of what "radical" thought has come to mean: "The gay movement would like us to think that gay marriage will give everyone housing and health care; that openly gay soldiers pressing buttons in Nevada to obliterate Somali villages means homophobia is on the wane; that strengthening the criminal legal system through hate crime legislation will bring murdered queers back to life" (n.p.). The train of thought that connects hate-crime laws with fantasies of resurrecting murder victims is the same one that insists on believing that withholding attention from same-sex marriage will instantly devolve into solutions for issues such as date rape, homeless queer youth, and mass incarceration, all of which, McKenzie implies in "6 Things," are the direct consequence of an "obsession" with marriage equality.

And yet that is the zero/sum, class-ignorant position repeated like a verbal tic by a particularly vocal faction of today's so-called "radical" marriage dissenters, and the terms of the debate remain substantially those stated by Barnard nearly two decades ago:

> [P]ublic debate over queers in the military, queer marriage, and the recognition of domestic partnerships is framed in such a way as to allow for only two positions: either one is progressive and supports these supposed advances, or one is conservative and homophobic and opposes them. The terms of this binary logic erase undisciplined queer voices who do not fit any of these two cozy positions, and, who, in fact, reject with contempt the binary frame itself.

Perhaps. But it is possible to construct an alternative binary: Either one opposes marriage equality and rejects the concept that gays, lesbians, and transpeople should be able to serve in the military without discrimination, or one is coopted, unradical, anti-progressive, blind to the "important and much more urgent issues facing the queer community and our society as a whole," "privileged" (a code word, in most current uses, for white and middle-class), and probably racist.

It is in this unexamined act that concern over the silencing of "undisciplined queer voices" in the false dichotomies and univocal identities so abhorrent to Barnard and McKenzie becomes hostile to class solidarity and to working-class queers themselves, submerging their legitimate concerns and denying their very presence while promoting movements that are uncongenial to working-class peoples' participation.

To a large extent, in fact, neoradical opponents of marriage-equality have abandoned all analysis of the consequences of state-sponsorship of interpersonal relationships, of the oppressive structures that potentially materialize in traditional marriage and of their relationship to capitalism, and of the damage that a constricted focus on marriage does to genuine cultural "deviancy" and sexual "queerness"—what Michael Warner calls a critique of "normalization itself":

> If queers, incessantly told to alter their "behavior," can be understood as protesting not just the normal behavior of the social [realm] but the *idea* of normal behavior, they will bring skepticism to the methodologies founded on that idea. (1993: xxvii; emphasis in original)

Overwhelmingly, they've done so in order to talk instead about "privilege," a never-defined term whose emotional connotations are nonetheless clear in today's rudderless, sound-bite- and clickbait-driven discourses about income and social inequality and which is clearly meant as a sop to the poor and working classes. They've done so in order to pursue a politics of personal affront, precisely demonstrating what Jack Halberstam meant when (in the context of trigger warnings and the new Decalogues of "offensive" language) he wrote that

> a neoliberal rhetoric of individual pain obscures the violent sources of social inequity. But newer generations of queers seem only to have heard part of this story and instead of recognizing that neoliberalism [works] by psychologizing political difference, individualizing structural exclusions, and mystifying political change [they equate] social activism with descriptive statements about individual harm and psychic pain. (2014, n.p.)

The "psychologizing of political difference" (Barnard is "enraged" by political strategies that differ from his), the "individualization of structural exclusions" (McKenzie's lack of "[personal and political] connect[ion] to so-called 'marriage equality'" establishes her authority to critique the issue), and the "mystification of political change" (Sycamore's deliberately bombastic claim that "the gay movement" equates the success of hate-crime legislation with "bring[ing] murdered queers back to life") are fully on display in neoradical queer rhetoric. Notably, just as Halberstam argues, none of these writers proposes a strategy for change that might abolish the realities they find objectionable; the public performance of outrage is an end in itself.

In maintaining stances such as these, moreover, queer neoradicals are constantly forced to proselytize on the basis of—and, thus, continuously to replicate—the image of the "enemy": the bourgeois, normalized, implicitly white, implicitly "mainstream" same-sex-marriage proponent, who is then deployed for the same propagandistic motives that encourage organizations like the Human Rights Campaign Fund or Marriage Equality USA to rely so heavily upon the same images: because they play to the (perceived) base.

In one camp, ad campaigns featuring society-page wedding galas and beautiful white lesbians in beautiful white wedding gowns respond to the accusations of perversion and degeneracy that have been leveled against queers for decades. In the other, opposition to marriage equality often seems to function as a sort of euphemism; it is as much a surrogate for rejection of the "idea of normal behavior" and for anger over real or perceived experiences of personal exclusion as it is a balm for lack of meaningful analysis of social and economic marginalization. In no case are actual working-class queers perceived as helpful to the agenda.

But if neoradical queers view proponents of military nondiscrimination policies and of marriage equality as reactionaries, the mainstream gay response to disapproval of its institutions, products, media, and propaganda—whether those critiques come from a "radical" perspective or simply from disaffected working-class gay citizens who feel alienated and "othered"—has largely been to view discontent as churlish, ungrateful, naïve, or Utopian; to dismiss it as what majority-group or class-privileged members like to call "political correctness" (on the theory, one supposes, that to be *incorrect* in matters of human interaction is the more principled position); or to characterize it, the way *Village Voice* Executive Editor Richard Goldstein did in *The Advocate* in 2000, as disloyal "backbiting" (39).

"For every three gays there are four acronyms," Goldstein quipped. "At this rate there will soon be more divisions in the lesbian community than there are lesbians." Such "constant carping," he continued, "threatens to turn our movement into an activist equivalent of the Balkans."

Nowadays, of course, not even the Balkans are the Balkans. But the goal of the *Blue, Too* project has never been to produce new acronyms or to multiply literary or media "representations" of partitioned constituencies for the sole purpose of passing queers through ever-finer sieves or of naming solidarity and "intersectionality" without actually practicing them.

Rather, the goal is to investigate and to understand how the myth of the bourgeois homosexual has achieved such a stranglehold on our literary, artistic, and political imaginations in the context of a lived reality that is not just skewed by such myths, it is their exact opposite. In fact, whether he is embraced, petted, and mass-produced by the so-called mainstream or demonized and ridiculed by self-styled "radicals," the politically callow Caucasoid plutocrat and elitist single-issue gay-identity sectarian must continuously be reified and reinvented by both factions, who faithfully reanimate their creature like a Golem. In that effort, the working class remains, as it almost always is, somehow just out of eyeshot.

In short, the goal is to ask, over and over again, not as a rhetoric but as an intellectual, artistic, and even spiritual discipline, what people like Goldstein mean by "our" and who people who are not like Goldstein have in mind when they agitate for alternative varieties of "inclusiveness" and "us-ness."

If the logical extension of an uncritical embrace of gay groupthink, of matriculation into the ranks of Mogutin's "clones" or Weir's "pod people," is a loss of solidarity and a shrinking of the capacity for critical analysis, the logical extension of the relentless insistence on a kaleidoscope of "subjectivities" is solipsism and isolation. Only I am ultimately like myself; only I can express and embody the precise titer of allegiances, experiences, and positions that constitute my social uniqueness. From the perspective of queer cultural production, which is what ultimately concerns me here, the first threatens to produce banality and mass hypnosis, but the second risks annihilating not just audience but the ability of literature to serve as a site of solidarity and resistance. It is impossible to write (or to read) anything useful from the extremities of either position.

VI.

"I must constantly assert my difference."
Gloria Anzaldúa, "To(o) Queer the Writer: Loca, Escritora y Chicana"

I refer principally in the sections above to gay *men*. Huge differences exist between the ways in which gay men were consolidating a national, public (and literary) identity in the post-Stonewall era and what many queer women and lesbians were doing. One of the most striking contrasts between lesbian and gay-male cultural production in the post-World War II period, in fact, has been the insistence by many lesbian writers, scholars, and organizers on keeping the issue of class (and, more broadly, of economics) in constant intellectual and cultural play. Much of the work of writers like Judy Grahn, Dorothy Allison, Pat Parker, Audre Lorde, Amber Hollibaugh,

Minnie Bruce Pratt, and many others, for example, has been devoted to the working-class-lesbian theme, particularly as class intersects gender, race, and butch/femme dynamics.[22]

In one of the early anthologies dedicated to surveying the state of lesbian fiction (entitled, descriptively enough, *Lesbian Fiction*), editor Elly Bulkin took special care to underscore the important contributions of working-class women writers to the expansion of the lesbian short story:

> Through much of this century and the end of the last one, lesbian literature has been almost exclusively the province of white lesbians—or of white women of indeterminate or unknown sexual/affectional preference—who are either middle- or upper-class. Only fairly recently has this situation even begun to change: white working-class characters are depicted in some of the fiction in *The Ladder* and of the pulp novels of that period [1956-1972], and a growing number of lesbians of color and poor and working-class lesbians of all races have written much poetry since the late sixties and are, along with other lesbians, producing a growing body of powerful fiction." (1981: xii-xiii)

Bulkin, like many of the women who edited lesbian anthologies in the seventies and eighties, introduced her book with a kind of framing statement in which she underscored the

---

[22] In "Feminist Class Struggle," bell hooks recalled that: "Lesbian feminist thinkers were among the first activists to raise the issue of class in the feminist movement, expressing their viewpoints in an accessible language. They were a group of women who had not imagined they could depend on husbands to support them. And they were often much more aware than their straight counterparts of the difficulties all women would face in the workforce. In the early 1970s, anthologies like *Class and Feminism*, edited by Charlotte Bunch and Nancy Myron, published work written by women from diverse backgrounds who were confronting the issue in feminist circles. Each essay emphasized the fact that class was not simply a question of money. In *The Last Straw*, Rita Mae Brown (who was not a famous writer at the time) clearly stated: 'Class is much more than Marx's definition of relationship to the means of production. Class involves your behavior, your basic assumptions, how you are taught to behave, what you expect from yourself and from others, your concept of a future, how you understand problems and solve them, how you think, feel, act'" (2000: 39).

writer's and anthologist's obligation to combat the *silencing* of lesbian voices within the culture, including the ways in which failed considerations of class, race, and disability (to reiterate the categories that Bulkin names) served as exponents of that silence. Literature—what Bulkin called "fictional truth," evoking Audre Lorde's famous formulation, "biomythography"—was thus no mere entertainment, but was a dynamic and vital tool for change. Writing and publishing, in other words, were essential cultural work in the larger project of creating and transforming *political* consciousness, including consciousness about class.

Lesbian Fiction, thus, is no less remarkable for the high quality of the work it contains than for the respect it pays to working-class writers and to the importance of working-class themes in the development of the literature Bulkin saw emerging around her. Working-class-inflected stories like Dorothy Allison's "A River of Names," Audre Lorde's "The Beginning," or Judy Grahn's "Boys at the Rodeo"—each one a classic in its own right—ultimately form something like a fourth of the anthology.

The working-class dyke,[23] meanwhile, was becoming a lesbian literary imago, celebrated in such classic novels as Leslie Feinberg's *Stone Butch Blues* and Frankie Hucklenbroich's *Crystal Diary*. Both books revolve around blue-collar, "stone butch" lesbian protagonists in the 1950s (Feinberg) or 1960s (Hucklenbroich) and, though often painful, are tales of ultimate survival and perseverance that present working-class experience as both valuable and heroic.[24]

---

[23] Anthropologist and social historian Esther Newton (1993) notes the class-inflected use of the term "dyke" in the lesbian summer community of Cherry Grove, New York, during the late 1950s and early 1960s. Though the early lesbian arrivals to the Grove were wealthy and professional women, many of whom bought homes, working-class Irish and Italian women began arriving in the 1960s. Wrote Newton, "The remaining 'ladies' [as they called themselves] intended an ethnic and class slur by calling the new women 'dykes.' The working-class women identified with the word" (529).

[24] Paris Poirier's 1993 flawed but fascinating documentary, *Last Call At Maud's*, accomplished a similar task in a different medium, organizing an exploration of lesbian community history around the story of the closing of Maud's, a working-class lesbian bar that flourished in San Francisco from 1966 to 1989. As Poirier's interviews with Maud's patrons reveal, the loyalty patrons felt toward "their bar" was tied to the need to create and exist in a social space that was safe for working-

"Underground" writer Red Jordan Arobateau's dozens of largely self-published experimental novels and short-story collections, which date back to the mid-1970s, similarly center the experiences of what Arobateau calls "street dykes." Arobateau's characters live at the margins, moving in and out of homelessness, unemployment, jail, prostitution, and drug use. The lives of Arobateau's protagonist butches are marked by violence, rage, alcoholism, and a restlessness that is only temporarily lulled by rough, marathon sex, which Arobateau describes in eidetic detail. If Arobateau's characters often lack emotional depth, the work remains interesting for its unapologetic focus on a "queered" underclass, for its exploration of gender and racial dynamics, and for its explicit centering of sexual agency as a mechanism by which powerless people experience power (and, thus, engage with the reparative function of sex).

Without question, however, the first post-Stonewall working-class gay novel was Rita Mae Brown's *Rubyfruit Jungle*, first published in 1973 (well ahead of the boom in gay men's fiction, generally dated to about 1978).[25] Widely recognized as a pioneering work of lesbian fiction and lauded for its profound effect on the development of modern gay and lesbian literature, *Rubyfruit Jungle* is less often acknowledged for its solid grounding in working-class insights and values and for the authentic proletariat voice of its picaresque narrator, Molly Bolt.

Like many of the protagonists of the gay novels that came later, Molly leaves her hometown in Coffee Hollow, Pennsylvania, a "rural dot" where "a dirt road connected tarpapered houses filled with smear-faced kids." Unlike the majority of those novels, however, Molly doesn't reject or "rise above" her past; instead, Brown's novel is the carefully delineated story of Molly's complex efforts, as she grows up,

---

class lesbians and to the desire to create a haven from the encroachment of "lipstick lesbians" and "feminist hippy dykes" who took for granted freedoms and privileges the women at Maud's did not.
[25] In Janet Zandy's "In the Skin of a Worker; or, What Makes a Text Working Class?," the author carefully delineates the themes and approaches common to working-class writing. For an extended discussion of these matters, see "Classing Queer and Queering Class: Reading Class in *Blue, Too*," the introduction to the Reader's, Writer's, and Scholar's Guide to *Blue, Too*, in this volume. *Rubyfruit Jungle*, in Zandy's schema, is an almost classic working-class novel.

leaves home, and pursues an education, to construct an existence that distorts none of what she considers most genuine about herself—including her humble beginnings. In the novel's opening paragraph, in fact, Brown introduces the theme that is the story's leitmotiv: "Mothers and aunts tell us about infancy and early childhood, hoping we won't forget the past when they had total control over our lives and secretly pray that because of it, we'll include them in our future" (3).

Like the heroes and heroines of so many coming-of-age novels that begin among the poor, Molly's academic achievement serves as a springboard out of depressed and depressing circumstances, but the psychic boost provided by Molly's awareness of her essential "queerness"—not solely her sexual preferences, which clearly set her apart, but a vision of her possibilities as a woman in the 1950s and '60s—is no less germinal:

> For a future I didn't want a split-level home with a station wagon, pastel refrigerator, and a houseful of blonde children evenly spaced through the years. I didn't want to walk into the pages of *McCall's* magazine and become the model housewife.... I wanted to go my own way. That's all I think I ever wanted, to go my own way and maybe find some love here and there. Love, but not the now and forever kind with chains around your vagina and a short circuit in your brain. (88).

Years later, after she is outed as a lesbian and dismissed from the University of Florida, Molly leaves for New York City, but not before her mother delivers a version of the classic "getting above your raising speech" and throws Molly out:

> A queer, I raised a queer, that's what I know. You're lower than them dirty fruit pickers in the groves, you know that?
> Go on and get outa here. I don't want you.... Let's see how far you get, you little snot-nose. You thought you'd go to college and be better than me. You thought you'd go mix with the rich. And you still think you're dandy, don't you? Even being a stinking queer don't shake you none. I can see conceit writ all over your face. Well, I hope I live to see the day you put your tail between your legs. I'll laugh right in your face. (135-136)

But if home has rejected her, neither is New York an unqualified haven. Molly fails to find community in the lesbian bars she explores, and the menial work she does to make ends meet is far from rewarding. She ultimately wins a scholarship to NYU's film school, but her artistic vision is greeted with derision or, worse, indifference. When a woman she is dating advises her to "bend a little" so "you wouldn't have to kill yourself like this—and you'd have some clothes, a decent apartment," Molly explodes in frustration:

> Goddammit! No matter what happens to me I'll still have the knowledge inside my head and nobody can take that away from me. And someday ... I'm going to make use of that knowledge and make my movies. My movies, you hear me ... not soppy romances about hapless heterosexuals, not family dramas about sparkling white America ... my movies, real movies about real people and about the way the shit comes down. (174)

In the novel's fascinating denouement, set at the end of Molly's senior year, she experiences a crisis that is both existential and practical: while her program-mates are creating trendy, derivative final projects designed largely to secure them well-paid jobs in television or the film industry, Molly continues to seek a way to remain true to the entirety of her lived experience and to its impact upon her artistic vision. Exhausted and overwhelmed, she hitchhikes back to Coffee Hollow to seek sustenance in the places of her childhood:

> Maybe I belong in the foothills of Pennsylvania with the Mennonites and the Amish and how the hell can I make movies out there? You can't even have electric lights out there.... [I]f I had money I wouldn't be at the mercy of chance, peanut intellects, and amputated emotions so much. With money you can protect yourself.... Well, I'm not giving up. But I'd like to rest every now and then. I'd like to see the hills of Shiloh again and lay my body down in the meadow.... Maybe the smell of clover will get me through one more winter in this branch of hell. (212-213)

Back in Coffee Hollow, she does indeed find a physical and natural environment that restores her. (Stopping beside a pond, Molly observes an enormous frog that leaps into the water, "soak[ing] half my shirt"; frogs must consider humans "inferior creatures," she muses, "since we can't go in and out of the water the way they can.") But Molly also finds a human landscape that reminds her why she left. Her first lover, for example, has ended up in a stifling heterosexual marriage, though it has provided her with children, a "neat little house," and an "enormous decorator-brown refrigerator" (218). Indeed, Brown seems to be saying, humans cannot inhabit two environments; they have no choice but to choose.

Molly returns to New York ("Putrid, packed, polluted, it's the only place where I have any room, any hope" [221]) knowing what her final project will be: She will visit her ill, aged mother, who has meanwhile moved to Ft. Lauderdale, Florida, and ask her to speak freely on camera—"just talking about her life, the world today, and the price of meat."

Molly's travels from and to New York are simultaneously metaphorical and physical journeys and, in retracing the pathways of her own life, Molly seems intent on beating an indelible line into the earth that connects past, present, and future. She does so, however, with neither self-delusion nor hostility: She is fully aware of the sadness of the circumscribed lives of those she has loved back home, and she must even absorb their attempts to erase the past (her former lover denies that she and Molly were ever more than friends, and her mother insists she never rejected Molly) even as she struggles to place herself in relationship to it. At the same time, recognizing that she is the consequence of a history that she has no desire to sever from her consciousness, she adopts a strategy of radical solidarity; she will remain intact by telling the stories of "real people" in the vernacular she knows so intimately, of "the way the shit comes down."

Her film is greeted largely with apathy in her department and, though Molly graduates *summa cum laude*, she receives none of the promising job offers of her male or more mainstream classmates. As the novel closes, Molly feels the blow, but is not deflected by it:

> No, I wasn't surprised, but it still brought me down. I kept hoping against hope that I'd be the bright exception, the talented token that smashed sex and class barriers.... After all, I was the best in my class, didn't that count for something? .... I wished I could be that frog back at [the] old pond. I wished I could get up in the morning and look at the day the way I used to when I was a child.... Damn, I wished the world would let me be myself. But I knew better on all counts. I wish I could make my films. That wish I can work for. One way or another I'll make those movies. (245-246)

Throughout *Rubyfruit Jungle*, Brown carefully develops the elements shared by so much working-class literature, especially working-class literature by women: a clear and consistent focus on issues of wages, money, and the cost of goods and services; Molly's subjective experience as a worker, including the alienation she experiences when she is deprived of the right to conceive of herself as the director of her actions; class-consciousness and self-consciousness; the impact of sexism as a multiplier of the effects of class difference; the ways in which economic unease curtails the sphere of choice; and a rueful acknowledgement that some bonds are inescapable, even when escape seems the only choice.[26]

Unlike so much of the literature that would follow by and for gay men, in which the native earth bred only wounds, Brown was writing in a tradition in which a response to antipathy, rejection, and spiritual and material poverty created the need for an act of integration, however imperfect, rather than of amputation. If the wounds of gay men in modern fiction threatened, like Philoctetes' snake bite, never to heal, Brown's solution for Molly Bolt is a version of Hemingway's aphorism, "The world breaks every one and afterward many are strong at the broken places."

The endeavors of lesbian fiction writers were firmly joined to a tradition of political and scholarly inquiry that included such works as the newspaper published by the women of The Furies Collective, a Washington, DC-based lesbian-separatist group founded in 1971, and an anthology of their writing (see Bunch & Myron, 1974); nonfiction academic studies such as Elizabeth Lapovsky Kennedy and Madeline Davis's 1993 *Boots of Leather, Slippers of Gold*, an ethnography of working-class lesbians in Buffalo, New York; and any number of foundational works of lesbian literary and social history and scholarship by such writers as Lillian Faderman, Esther Newton, Estelle B. Freedman, and Joan Nestle, to name only a few. Such work—and what I've mentioned here is merely the tip of a substantial iceberg—is evidence of a sustained, concerted, dedicated effort on the part of lesbian writers, artists, publishers, journalists,

---

[26] Though she remains estranged from her mother and leaves Ft. Lauderdale knowing she may not see her again, Molly reflects, "[My mother], who believes that if the good Lord wanted us to live together he'd have made us all one color. Who believes a woman is only as good as the man she's with. And I love her" (242).

and scholars not to allow social class simply to be named tokenistically in a litany of oppressions, but to insist that the experiences and insights of working-class lesbians be brought to the foreground. It is no more than a reflection of that effort, I think, that the important 1997 anthology, *Queerly Classed: Gay Men and Lesbians Write about Class*, was edited by a woman who identifies as queer and that the majority of the contributors were women.

Such an observation in no way intends to imply that lesbian writers, scholars, and activists have been universally successful in contending with class and privilege, nor to mitigate the historical and ongoing struggles of working-class lesbians, and especially of working-class lesbians of color, against what Lynne Uttal (1990) called "inclusion without influence" in lesbian- and feminist-centered scholarship, literature, and community life, but it is meant to hold the lesbian-feminist "example" up for purposes of contrast.

In fact, if lesbian-feminist writers' and artists' interest in class, race, and economic privilege naturally extended exploration of those issues beyond lesbians themselves, attempts to explore classed realities were not always received with unbridled enthusiasm. Jennie Livingston's 1990 documentary, *Paris Is Burning*, for example—in which black and Latino queers, drag queens, and transsexuals in Harlem described a world of voguing, "Houses," and elaborate costume balls—earned Livingston as many brickbats as awards.

In her essay "Is Paris Burning?," for example, Feminist scholar and critic bell hooks was particularly stern in her disapproval, arguing that the documentary superficially appeared "oppositional because of its subject matter and identity of the filmmaker," but that its politics were simultaneously "progressive and reactionary" (1992: 149).

Hooks' analysis in "Is Paris Burning?" is more developed than anything I could duplicate here, so I'll simply summarize what strikes me as the main bone of contention in hooks' and others' criticisms of the film: Did Livingston's own race and class position as a white, middle-class lesbian keep her from recognizing the extent to which her subjects' imitations of ruling-class culture and privilege were symptomatic of economic, racial, and gender terrorism and thus lead her to misunderstand those acts as resistance and "freedom"? Hooks skewers Livingston in particular for her "neutrality," suggesting that *Paris Is Burning* should properly be viewed as the documentation of tragedy and not as entertainment.

Hooks' point is not unfair—only a viewer who was entirely insensitive to the injuries of poverty and to the devastating impact of media images of white success, beauty, and power could miss the vein of deep sadness that runs through *Paris Is Burning*. On the other hand, it also seems fair to ask whether Livingston ever actually claimed to be neutral in her filmmaking and to note that hooks' analysis essentially denies the ball-goers all autonomy: They may say that participation in the competitions gives them a sense of self-esteem and accomplishment, but they must be mistaken.

In any event, even those who considered *Paris Is Burning* problematic accepted Livingston's work as serious cultural commentary, a fate that did not befall a 2011 film with roughly the same subject matter—*Leave It on the Floor*, written and directed by two gay men, Sheldon Larry and Glenn Gaylord.

In their film, by contrast, Larry and Gaylord seemed to have no intention to engage in social commentary or to explore reality in any meaningful sense of the word. Rather, *Leave It on the Floor* is a formulaic "feel-good" movie set in an impoverished section of Los Angeles, where mostly black, mostly trans, often homeless queer kids live to "walk" the runways in ballroom competitions identical to those in *Paris Is Burning*. *Leave It on the Floor* belongs to the same genre as *Flashdance* or the *Step Up* franchise—other films in which artistic expression is magically cleaved from material realities and posited as "liberatory" for its fantasied ability to defeat privilege and restore meritocracy.

In short, *Leave It on the Floor* is a Disneyesque hallucination of poor queers of color, the escapist, exploitative, race- and class-unconscious film Livingston's critics sometimes seemed to be accusing her of having made. Even taking differences of genre into account, it seems as unlikely that a lesbian filmmaker would produce a work like *Leave It on the Floor* as it is that gay male Hollywood would come up with *Paris Is Burning*.

I do not want to oversimplify what I would call genuine genealogical differences between the artistic and literary approaches of lesbians and gay men to questions of class, race, and privilege. I would, however, say this: When it comes to the body of class-conscious work created by lesbian writers, scholars, activists, and artists, the counterpart in American gay-male cultural commentary barely exists.

VII.

> The workman started pulling tools from his belt
> and making adjustments here and there. At last
> Billy had a man, a sweaty he-man day laborer and
> not those polite and gentlemanly teenagers at
> school. This was, he was sure, what they called
> "rough trade." He knew it was for him.
> (*Stuart Rowen,* Boarding House Chicken)

Except perhaps in pornography. Boy, are we present in
pornography. (As we are in "erotica," the sanitizing and
misleading name given to the genre that now constitutes the
overwhelming majority of all new fiction published for queer
audiences each year in America.)

I hardly need to recite the names of internet porn sites or the
plots of "adult" novels to make the point that there's no gay
male sexual iconography quite so tried and true as the sex
object who is a truck driver/prison guard/construction
worker/ranch hand/Army grunt/auto mechanic/street
hustler/beat cop/jailhouse rapist/squaddy/skateboard punk.

In fact, in the kind of irony that only a writer could love, one of
the gay publishers who rejected *Everything I Have Is Blue* in 2005
came out only a few months later with *Working Stiff: True Blue-
Collar Gay Porn.* Another publisher, which began life nearly thirty
years ago as a solidly feminist/progressive press, is now the
publisher of a significant segment of the fetish-porn category, and
classed porn for gay men is prominently featured (titles include
Hard Working Men: Gay Erotic Fiction,[27] *Hot Cops: Gay Erotic
Stories, Truckers: True Gay Erotica*[28], *Special Forces: Gay Military*

---

[27] "These sweaty studs, brawny bears, and cocksure construction
workers go all out to turn on, tune up, and fulfill every work order.... In
the world of *Hard Working Men*, hats aren't the only things that are
hard." (From the book description.)
[28] "Truckers [are] a favorite queer sexual icon, joining such types as
sailors, cops, firemen, and other guys who 'service society.; For some
gay men, life on the road conjures up images of hairy, sweaty, blue-
collar Joes traveling from town to town in their big 18-wheelers,
pulling into all-night diners, gas stations, cheap motels, and highway
rest stops for food, rest, companionship—and sex." (From the book
description.)

Erotica, Nasty Boys: Rough Trade Erotica,[29] and *Hard Hats: Gay Erotic Stories*[30]).

In each of these cases, of course, the "consumer's" gaze is assumed to be inexorably drawn to the fetish quality of sex with a (class) difference. In the pornographer's imagination, moreover, working classness in men means masculinity and lots of it, such that, in gay male porn, the fetish category "laborer" is indistinguishable from the fetish category "he-man." In porn and erotica intended for lesbians, interestingly enough, marking a character as working class serves a parallel function: it's no easy task to find a non-working-class butch.

Because (pornographic) art so often imitates life (while studiously avoiding the actual depiction of it), the work of social scientists Joanna Brewis and Gavin Jack on the phenomenon of "gay chavinism" in Britain is especially intriguing. The authors describe chavinism as gay male erotic fetishizing of working-class "chavs"—imagined to be young and white, to live in public housing, to "[fail consistently] to participate in paid employment [and to be] defined by virtue of their supposedly debased consumption activities" (252), which involve

> a particular penchant for Burberry, Nike, Louis Vuitton and Adidas, as well as sportswear like football shirts, tracksuits, trainers and baseball caps. To accessorize, they wear ... gaudy diamond and gold jewellery and they are avid consumers of tanning products and mobile phones alike. (257)

Though the term "chav" is generally meant pejoratively and chav behavior is officially considered debased and tasteless,[31]

---

[29] "Thugs, brats, street toughs, studs with chips on their shoulders and men packin' heat.... Don't miss these hot gangsters, dirty cops, street punks and hunky ex-cons who just want to get it on...and on and on!" (From the book description.)

[30] "Construction workers, plumbers, gardeners or any hard working man with a tool belt play a part in many gay male fantasies. In this steamy collection we take a ride to the top of a high rise under construction for a precarious steel beam encounter, go down in the belly of a dark steamy mine, hang out with some hunky sweaty landscapers and slip into the construction manager's office for a quickie.... [I]n this world the hats are not the only thing that's hard." (From the book description.)

[31] See, e.g., Owen Jones' *Chavs: The Demonization of the Working Class*. London: Verso, 2012.

the authors point to a proliferation of British web sites, telephone sex lines, internet chatrooms, and pornographic movies dedicated to "scally dick," a market that somewhat parallels a subset of gay male porn niches in the U.S. ("gangstas," "thugs," "skinheads," "saggers," "jocks," "devil dawgs," "punks," "frat boys," etc.).[32]

These fetish categories, however, don't quite match chavinism's specific focus on the classed nature of the erotic object because, as Brewis and Jack put it, the chav is "a commonplace *socioeconomic* signifier in the British cultural lexicon" (257; emphasis added) in a way that none of the American categories precisely is.[33] In "Scally Lads," for example, Eror (2014) discusses the way "scally fetishism perpetuates a long-standing cycle of re-appropriation of working-class aesthetics within the gay scene" (n.p.).

But what the British chav-as-gay-male-sexual-fantasy does have in common with its cousins across the pond lies in the view that the "'harder' forms of masculinity that chavinism implies are strongly, even inextricably, aligned with the working class," including an "intrinsic" contempt of homosexuality, the potential for homophobic backlash, and a sexual allure that "pivot[s] ambiguously on the promise of rough sex and the threat of violence (even queer bashing and rape)" (261).[34]

---

[32] See also "'Rude Boys': The Homosexual Eroticization of Class" (Johnson, 2008).

[33] "White trash" or "redneck" might give something of the flavor, though neither seems to be especially popular as a gay male porn category and neither appears to have the same cultural/sexual cachet for gay men in the U.S. that chavs do among gay male Brits. For American gay men, the vessels of pornographically-imagined working-class masculinity remain soldiers, athletes, and construction workers.

[34] "Scally porn is largely violent and degrading" says Eror (2014); see also his observations regarding the proliferation of scally hookup and fetish-porn sites and such practices as "trampling." The fantasy of the hypermasculine man who is sexy because he is dangerous isn't limited to gay men, as Rosemary Daniell made clear in her gutsy and under-appreciated memoir, *Sleeping with Soldiers: In Search of the Macho Man* (New York: Holt, Rinehart, and Winston, 1985). Although Daniell's tale of her years as a testosterone junkie and Don Juanita is ultimately recast in the context of coming to terms with a brutal, alcoholic father, her desire for masculinity serves the same reparative function as it so often seems to in gay male fantasy.

278 | *Class/Mates: Further Outings*

As the authors make clear, however, the topic of classed desire and how it is expressed and commodified is wildly complicated. Some male chavs surely participate willingly in gay sex, and the existence of the fetish category may actually provide them with opportunities for sex with other males that they might not otherwise have. Just as surely, some working-class men who are not chavs may be attracted to chavs, and some chavs are no doubt attracted to each other. In other words, we must take care not to fall into the trap of the fantasy itself, which erases queerness through its reliance on what is essentially an invention: the notion that male chavs are hypermasculine because they are identified as working class and, as such, can be erotically imagined as "straight"—that is, they do not engage in sex with other males as a frank expression of desire, but can be persuaded to do so if paid (or baited with alcohol, drugs, or pornography, all of which are a kind of payment). The pornographic imagination demands that they not "want it," though "it" can be obtained through the mobilization of a capitalist purchasing power.

Meanwhile, to the extent that the chav belongs to a cultural construction whose visual element requires the display of distinctive consumer products and of specific dress, grooming, language, and posture, "chavness" can be (and has been) widely copied by people who may belong to any social class at all in such cruising venues as "chav club nights" at gay bars in London and elsewhere. The result is that we can never be certain that the sexual valence, so to speak, flows exclusively from the privileged-class "actor" toward the working-class "object" in the context of exploitative sex tourism, nor can we discount that class envy may manifest itself in downward mobility (or a fantasy of the same).

In fact, one intriguing feature of classed porn intended for a gay male public is the degree to which it disguises masculinity-envy which, in a certain light, can be seen as the gay male wish to legitimize erotic impulses by incorporating masculinity (literally or figuratively) into his queer body. More than one writer has noted, for example, the duality inherent in gay male erotics: the desire *for* the object and the desire to *become* the object. Indeed, masculinity, especially as a classed attribute, seems to provoke ambivalence and desire about equally.

On this point, Peter Hennen's 2005 anthropological study of "Bear culture" is instructive. Reviewing the scholarly literature on the Bear community, Hennen focuses on the question of whether, in the context of feminist analysis, Bears "make gender trouble" or, alternatively, simply reify what Hennen and others call "hegemonic masculinity"; his conclusion is that the question remains vexed. "Bears have been largely successful in divorcing effeminacy from same-sex desire and creating a culture that looks like a bunch of 'regular guys,'" Hennen writes, but the "subversive implications ... have everything to do with reorganizing sexuality and very little to do with challenging gendered assumptions. Most of these men would like nothing more than to have their masculinity accepted as normative, something that is largely accomplished within the group but remains problematic outside of it" (41). Hennen concludes, "Bears make a claim to radical similarity; a similarity to both heterosexual men and conventional masculinity" as distinct from the claim to radical difference of "queers, sex radicals, and activists."

In other words, by constituting themselves as "regular" masculine males who just happen to like sex with other males, Bears challenge the heteronormative assumption that same-sex desire among males is emasculating. At the same time, their associative principle requires the rejection and denigration of "feminized" gay men (twinks, club boys, sissies, "body fascists," metrosexuals, etc.)—those whom they are *not* like—a posture that is essentially identical to traditional heterosexual masculinity. Indeed, Hennen makes note of the frequency with which his respondents described their interest in Bear culture and activities in terms that aligned them with the presumed values, behaviors, and pastimes of "straight men."

I would add that Bear culture's focus on "traditionally masculine" pursuits, demeanor, and interests specifically reflects a late-twentieth-century fantasy of *working-class* masculinity. As David Thane points out in an intriguing review of the lost novels of the late British writer Angus Heriot (1927-1964):

> [Heriot's novels] represent a middle class version of gay life that was robust and even dominant in its day.... [M]asculinity was broad enough to embrace clean cuffs, witty conversation, and well-polished shoes. This class-bound version of queer was ... dealt a deadly blow by the gay liberation culture that emerged from Stonewall.... Thus we enter a world in which to be straight-acting is to act like a working-class man. (29)

Similarly, as Jay Clarkson (2006) discusses in his discourse analysis of gay men's personal ads on the dating site

StraightActing.com, the concept of "straight-acting" trades heavily in a fantasized masculinity coded as working-class as well as in misogyny and condemnation of "in your face queens."

Such images of "classed" masculinity and quasi-heterosexuality run throughout queer literature, in fact. Think of John Rechy's eponymous Johnny Rio, whose "one-sided sexual scene is: the single homosexual act which is his symbol of sexual power: to have his body adored" (169); Genet's butch, sexy, sociopathic sailor, Querelle; James Baldwin's Giovanni, a refugee who has left behind both his native country and a failed marriage to a woman and who is ultimately executed for strangling his effeminate, predatory gay employer to death; or James Barr's Karl who, in "The Bottom of the Cloud"[35] restrains and physically tortures his future lover in order to "free him of an artificially superior attitude" and more specifically, from an insufficient appreciation of the seriousness of bonding with another man.

Among women, in contrast, the deeply class-inflected debates over butch/femme of the last half of the twentieth century have expanded in the form of organizations such as the Brown Boi Project. In discussing one of the Project's leadership retreats, Hoofatt notes that BPP's "mission is to break down the often negative perceptions that accompany an identification with masculinity" and to encourage "a wide range of identities [including] butch, stud, aggressive, tom, macha, boi, dom" (n.p.).

The Brown Boi Project's mission, according to its website, acknowledges that

> traditional expectations of masculinity and femininity ... tend to box us in and make embodying femininity negative in our culture. Instead, we are fighting with others to build healthy and affirming ideas around gender. We are talking about our responsibilities and privilege as masculine people, and we are working hard to change the power dynamics in our relationships, families, and communities.[36]

In other words, as one might expect from an organization grounded in feminist analysis and dedicated to "gender justice,"

---

[35] Available at the Still Blue Project: stillblueproject.wordpress.com/fiction/barr.

[36] Mission and Values. Brown Boi Project, n.d. Web: brownboiproject.org/mission_and_values.

the Brown Boi Project's approach to masculinity is much more nuanced than is the Bears', is more openly concerned about the problematic aspects of "the privilege of masculinity," and is more keenly focused on nurturing expressions of "masculine-of-center" identity that are "non-oppressive" and "rooted in honor, community, and empowerment of others."

There's a very good deal more to be said about gay male pornography's obsession with race and class as markers of iconic masculinity, about gay male pornographers' profound ambivalence regarding masculinity in the first place and, indeed, about the ways in which the classed themes of so-called gay pornography and those of so-called gay literature complement one another, but I want to focus here on several expressly *non*-pornographic examples of the ways in which working-classness is both fetishized and robbed of specificity in media intended for gay male audiences.

A 2011 magazine interview with Tom Skidmore, a San Francisco-based general contractor and carpenter who was "hit hard by the 2008 recession," purported to discuss Skidmore's "surviv[al of] the downturn" and "his intense work ethic" (Killian: n.p.). Instead, the interview became a series of suggestive double-entendres (beginning with the title: "Tom the Carpenter is Good with Wood and Likes Men Who Work with Their Hands") in which each of Skidmore's references to his economic position or working-class values was studiously deflected. Skidmore noted that he "came from a working-class family where we thought only rich kids went to college [and] everyone had blue collar jobs" and added, in response to a question about the impact of the recession:

> Last winter was the first in ten years I didn't work, and the previous two winters were pretty rocky.... [W]ith the economy now, people aren't doing huge remodels.... Plus you're competing against carpenters from outside the city, guys who are willing to do the same job for less money.

Skidmore thus overtly broached issues of economic difficulties, unemployment, and the precariousness of blue-collar work, but in the context of the interview as a whole, his ability to foreground the unsexy realities of working-class life in a ferociously gentrified city like San Francisco—that is to raise those subjects as *material* factors of his existence—receded before the magazine's desire to establish and deploy his working-class cred in the service of pornographization.[37]

When the interviewer asked whether Skidmore had any regrets about the profession he had chosen, for example, Skidmore said, "The only ... frustration I have is that I spend all this time making the dreams of others come true, but live in a city where I can't afford to buy a house of my own." The interviewer's comeback was: "Maybe that's why you've got such a great body."

Later, the interviewer speculated that Skidmore might get more calls after the interview was published, provided he "agree[d] to come to work naked" ("I want to be known for the work I do, not how I look when I do it," Skidmore responded).

To be entirely fair, the interview appeared in *BUTT* magazine, an Amsterdam-based quarterly widely distributed in the U.S. and not known for keeping its hands out of its pants. Also in fairness, however, *BUTT* describes itself as "*the* place where gays can speak candidly about their ideas, work and sex lives" (emphasis in original) and as "the most admired and influential gay-interest publication of the last decade" ("About *Butt*," 2014, n.p.). Thus, though *BUTT* contains heavily sexualized imagery and content, its publishers clearly view *BUTT* as a so-called "lifestyle magazine" and not strictly as a venue for pornography or erotica. Or, perhaps more accurately, they deliberately blur those genres in a way that is presumed to titillate gay male audiences.

Whether Skidmore's story would have been featured in *BUTT* had he not been attractive, muscular, and white may seem a petulant question but it isn't an entirely irrelevant one. It is true, in any case, that Skidmore agreed to be interviewed for and to pose nude in a magazine whose style he was likely well aware of. No convincing argument can be made, then, that

---

[37] British writer Mark Simpson coined the term "sporno" to describe what he considered a new variant on "commodity fetishism" in which sport and pornography mingled to create advertising in which "naked, pumped and tweezed 'gods,' often in full body make-up, clutch[ed] strategically placed rugby balls like fat leather erections and gaze[d] longingly into the camera, or into each other's eyes...." (See "Sporno" at marksimpson.com/blog/2010/04/17/sporno.) But if advertisers and clothing designers had begun embracing sporno by the time Simpson's article appeared in *Out* in 2006, writers for gay men's media had been serving up "pornalism" for decades.

Skidmore was exploited without his consent. On the other hand, it is interesting to speculate about what purposes were served in the creation of a media transaction that functioned precisely because it spoke in an idiom so familiar in gay-male discourse: the deliberate confusion of working-class realities with working-class sexual fantasy. There can be no doubt about how readers perceived the message *BUTT* had molded for them: Of thirty online comments on the story, twenty-three mentioned Skidmore's physical appearance or availability as an object of sexual desire ("Hot bull of a man!"; "Tom, pound me with your hammer"; "I wish there [were] such hot carpenters round here"; "Hands down the sexiest guy *BUTT* has featured or will ever feature"; "I just jizzed in my pants").

No reader responded to Skidmore's comments about the difficulty of making a living as a manual laborer during a recession or the ironies of working hard in a city in which blue-collar people can barely afford to live. His specific and personal lived reality as a working-class gay man, which Skidmore conveyed in unequivocal terms, was rendered illegible by the dispersive, despecifying power of the working-class fetish.

The material reality of working-class lives was similarly caricatured in a two-page spread entitled "Blue-Collar Brawn" which appeared in that stop-calling-me-gay magazine, *Men's Health*. Complete with color photos, "Blue-Collar Brawn" described a "blue-collar workout for men." The exercises, which include the "Sandbag Lift," the "Shovel Lift," and the "Car Push," purported to duplicate the "real life" activity of guys who "spend [their] days moving big stuff around for a living" (118). The magazine's call to reproduce a (fantasized) working-class male body invited the reader to envision the musculature (and masculine attractiveness) that might result from physical labor, but simultaneously required the reader to annul all knowledge of the actual blue-collar man who "moves big stuff around for a living." That man—whose "blue-collar brawn" is a mechanism of survival and not a form of recreation; whose literal body ages prematurely, is often scarred and burned, and is plagued by early arthritis, bone degeneration, and tendonitis; and whose pain and injuries not infrequently go unattended for lack of adequate health care—was rendered invisible by the need to re-imagine "blue collar" as a fetish-commodity category.

J. G. Hayes' fine short-story collection, *This Thing Called Courage: South Boston Stories*, suffered a similar "re-invention" when it was published in 2002. Michael Lowenthal, whose "prepublication review" is included in the book's front matter, lauds Hayes' work:

> Though they're only blocks apart, there's a world of difference between Southie, Boston's blue collar Irish stronghold, and the South End, its gentrified gay ghetto. Likewise, there couldn't be a greater gap between Hayes' authentically muscular storytelling and the steroidal puffery that passes as some gay fiction. Unlike so many gay characters whose heroism depends upon fleeing their origins, Hayes' heroes prove their courage by staying put. From the tectonic violence of his hometown's class conflict, Hayes' voice thrusts to craggy heights.

Lowenthal could certainly not have known, when he wrote his comments, that his words would occasion a strange irony, because "steroidal puffery" describes to a T the image Hayes' publisher chose for the cover: the nude torso in profile of a young, muscular white man, his right deltoid decorated with an obviously fake tattoo in which the words "South Boston" (and not "Southie") surround a Celtic cross.

That such a body is chosen to represent—indeed to embody and exemplify—the blue-collar or working-class "condition" of Hayes' writing exemplifies the ways in which mainstream gay male cultural representation actively refuses to acknowledge working-class men, even when they are gay, beyond the fetishized, sexualized category.

The flawless, evenly tanned skin in the cover image— entirely free of hair and entirely free of scars—marks the body in question as the opposite of a working-class body and, indeed, inscribes its owner unequivocally as a denizen not of Southie but of the "gentrified South End." It is a body created not through the physical demands of working-class labor but through the decidedly middle-class exploitation of the leisure time and disposable income necessary to belong to and attend a gym, to eat well, to spend time in the sun.

Like *Men's Health*, Hayes' publisher sought to evoke the real working class by quoting an imaginary working-class body— one, in this case, onto which fantasies of young, sexually attractive, tough (meaning masculine) Irish kids in South Boston were meant to be projected. That the photo is cropped at the neck seems significant as well. Robbed of the individuality of a face, the body becomes more generic and, thus, more pornographically available.

It is essential, however, to underscore the fact that none of Hayes' stories has anything to do with the cover image; his work is by no stretch of the imagination "erotica," and Hayes is not particularly concerned in his seven stories with his characters' sex lives. But his publisher could not release itself from the rapture of the commodified fetish-consciousness to which contemporary gay urban middle-class sexual culture is in thrall, literally could not read the non-erotic experiences that Hayes' book sought to illuminate.

This, I would argue, is a peculiarly gay male alexia. A few years before *This Thing Called Courage* appeared, Beacon Press published Michael Patrick MacDonald's heartbreaking memoir, *All Souls: A Family Story from Southie*. Though *All Souls* is nonfiction and though MacDonald is heterosexual, he and Hayes traverse corresponding territory. There is not the remotest possibility, however, that Beacon Press would have considered a cover similar to the one that appeared on *This Thing Called Courage*; indeed, in a non-gay context such imagery would have been viewed as vulgar in light of the book's serious content. For a gay men's publisher, however, the appeal to the (perceived) interests of gay male consumers trumped concern about whether the sexualized cover art neutralized the working-class gay voice within.

That transaction, too, recapitulates the familiar power dynamic in which the products of the labor of working-class people (creative writing, in this case) comes to be "owned" by the holder of capital (many people don't realize that writers do not control the cover and design of their books, never mind have a say in their marketing and distribution).

Once writing is transformed into a physical or virtual object destined for the marketplace, to be sure, it necessarily becomes subject to the laws (or, rather, the superstitions) of advertising, and that's true of most any book. What is instructive about the example of *This Thing Called Courage* is the publisher's assumption that a sexualized, idealized male image was required both to invoke working-class men as the subjects of fiction (that is, was tied to the content of the book) and to render that content attractive to the consumer (that is, was tied to the gay male buyer's inability to "read" without the mediation of beefcake).

The omnipresence of such subcultural cryptography may serve to illuminate another phenomenon. If there is one kind of story I rejected more than any other for these anthologies and for the Still Blue web project, it's the one with the implausible soft-porn plot featuring (and I am not making this up) construction workers. The fact is amusing, but also telling.

So successfully have our minds been colonized that writers—perhaps especially gay male writers—have difficulty seeing full-fleshed working-class characters with complex lives, and they find it no simple matter to project working-class men into the imagination. When they look there, they tend to see clichés and advertisements, Stanley Kowalski and the Marlboro Man, the hyper-inflated cops and cowboys of Tom of Finland, the generic white boy with gym muscles who is transformed into a "he-man laborer" by the strategic application of a tattoo or a smear of axle grease.

Given such projections, it isn't difficult to understand why gay male pornography and erotica so frequently fail to qualify as working-class texts: The working-class body in those fantasies is either deployed and acted upon by a non-working-class character or is *in service to* that character's sexual desires; it rarely exercises agency of its own even when it might be called, in the semantics of sexual fantasy, "active." Only very occasionally does the working-class character control the point of view in the scene as "I"; rather, "he" does (or is done) but is almost invariably constructed and endowed with erotic functionality through the desirer's gaze.[38]

Precisely because the imaginations of writers of gay literary fiction are so readily pollinated by the classed clichés of erotica, however, the result is that relatively little gay "literature" can also be called working-class literature. Jeff Mann's 2014 short story "The Painters" illustrates this point clearly. In "The Painters," the gay male narrator and his long-time husband, who "in middle age ... [have] become ... less lovers, more cruise buddies," hire two men to paint the interior of their house in southwest Virginia. The painters are both "good-looking, well-built young guys"—one a bearish "daddy" type with "dark beard, bald head, stocky physique, and tattoos," and the other a "lean, pale, clean-shaven, very buff boy" whose ripped, too-tight cargo shorts barely conceal a "bubble butt."

---

[38] In that sense, the depiction of both working-class men and of men of color in gay erotica and pornography can be analyzed in broad analogy to Susan Griffin's central argument regarding images of women in heterosexual porn; see her brilliant *Pornography and Silence: Culture's Revenge Against Nature* (New York: Harper & Row, 1981).

The bulk of the story consists of the narrator's erotic fantasies about the painters, including detailed observations of their bodies and speculation about what they would look like unclothed. The painters speak in a single line. One of them (we aren't told which) asks, "Hey, guys, could you turn up the air-conditioning? It's really hot in here." The narrator considers refusing and wonders "How high would we have to crank the heat before they stripped to the waist?"

Though the story is meant to be a bittersweet reflection on the narrator's relief at being able to metaphorically "add color" to his relationship through the transformation of the physical environment he shares with his partner, thus finding "new leaves, fresh flowers" in "what looked dead," its debt to the common themes of gay male class fetishism is obvious. We know nothing about the two painters other than what they look like, but we do know that they are workers, that the narrator has hired them and considers them available for use—for their literal labor as house painters, as fantasy objects, and as a restorative tonic for a timeworn relationship—and that the narrator instinctively understands the power dynamics inherent in the painters' state of subjection to the owner of their labor; however briefly and semi-seriously, he contemplates denying the workers' appeal for a more agreeable working environment, for example. Such a refusal is conceivable, first, because his role as employer gives him the power to dictate the conditions of employment, even if workers find them unpleasant; and, second, because it would be permissible—in the classed economies of gay male (literary) interaction—to place his and his partner's desire to erotically enjoy the painters' shirtless bodies above their request for physical comfort as they work. Even in what is meant to be a serious piece of literary fiction and not erotica, workers can only be seen as sexy ciphers.

Because most people who write are readers first, and because reading so often leads directly to writing, there's little mystery here. Fiction writers, particularly when they're starting out, tend to copy what they see being published, and queer fiction that is commercially rewarded with publication (which is, to be fair, very little of it), often demonstrates, as Larry Kramer famously argued, that "the goals of gay fiction (are) so small" (1997: 60). The one growth industry in gay fiction, in fact, is the surprisingly successful subgenre—though I'm apparently the only one who's surprised—that unashamedly characterizes itself as "beach reading" and whose entire point is to publicize the fabulous lives and fabulous romances of fabulously young, assimilated, and consumer-very-friendly gay men. Literature is, after all, the propaganda of a culture, and working-class queer men are often propagandized right out of the picture.

Up until the end of the first decade of the new millennium or thereabouts, that fact could easily have been blamed on the way books were made: Queer lit overwhelmingly reproduced bourgeois perspectives and voices because the vast majority of it was the product of a bourgeois institution: the mainstream publishing industry. Access to the whole circuit of writing programs, behind-the-scenes recommendations, personal contacts, helpful blurbs, and lunches with agents and editors depended less upon talent than upon social capital, which working-class people tend to lack. As a generalization, but one with several grains of truth in it, traditional publishing was a plutocracy and not a meritocracy. That hasn't really changed.

But there's a new reality in town. The explosion of self-publishing, micro-editors, and print-on-demand services, for better though often for worse, has been extremely democratizing: Writers have almost total control over the production process, their overheads are very low in comparison to traditional publishing, and the self-publisher can operate on tiny profit margins.[39] (Though reliable statistics are hard to

---

[39] According to *Publishers Weekly*, self-published titles outstripped traditional publishing for the first time in 2009, accounting for nearly 73% of all published books. In that explosion, the genre categories of erotica, romance, and "speculative" fiction (scifi, horror, fantasy, etc.) published for queer audiences have resoundingly trounced all others, while the number of self-published titles that qualify as literary fiction remains insignificant. Moreover, given that self-published books are sold almost exclusively online, as Steve Berman (2014) notes, "the sheer number of titles has ballooned to an imbroglio no matter what the genre…. [Online] your chances of finding that book you overheard friends talking about is like a pricking yourself while rolling in a haystack…. Oh, and during your online hunt, you'll be forced to look at so many lurid covers—because isn't gay publishing about sex, sex, sex?—that searching for a book has become, at times, not-safe-for-work." In fairness, as Berman also makes clear, it isn't as though mainstream brick-and-mortar bookstores were ever all that friendly to queer books or gave shelf space to very many of them, which is why gay bookstores—now dying like the dinosaurs—played such an important role in the diffusion of queer lit during the post-Stonewall, pre-Amazon era.

come by, the vast majority of self-published titles appear to sell very few copies—between an average of 40 and 150, according to some sources—but even very low sales can be enough to break even.) This new boom in gay and lesbian publishing, however—in which writers can increasingly liberate themselves from market imperatives and old-boy networks and in which working-class themes could, at least theoretically, circumvent the class-privileged cold shoulder—has produced a body of work that is more bourgeois, venal, and vacuous than ever. Whether that's a defect or a feature remains to be seen.

Meanwhile, you won't do much better with nonfiction. Visit the HQ section at your local library (or the 305-306s, if they're on the Dewey system) and glance at the tables of contents and indices of the scores of books on LGBTQ "culture," "politics," and "studies"—books with titles like *Ethnic and Cultural Diversity among Gay Men and Lesbians*; *The Culture of Queers*; *Inside the Academy & Out: Lesbian/Gay/Queer Studies & Social Action*; and *Rhetorical Secrets: Mapping Gay Identity and Queer Resistance in Contemporary America.*

You will not find in these books any discussion of class, nor are you likely to find much analysis of the subject in the billions of words published in recent decades on the dissection of homosexual "culture." David Bergman, in his otherwise excellent study, *Gaiety Transfigured: Gay Self-Representation in American Literature* (1991), includes chapters on camp, race, AIDS, family formation, and gender, but cannot manage to wrap an analysis around the way that gay male self-representation in literature is *classed*. Suzanna Danuta Walters, in her *All the Rage: The Story of Gay Visibility in America* (2001), devotes two chapters ("Consuming Queers" and "If It's Pink We'll Sell It") to a consideration of gay wealth and entrepreneurship—but brings herself to use the word "class" once, on the last page of the last chapter, without a word of comment.

In *"You Can Tell Just By Looking": And 20 Other Myths about LGBT Life and People*, authors Michael Bronski, Ann Pellegrini, and Michael Amico set out to identify the twenty-one "most persistent and pernicious contemporary myths about LGBT people" (2013: xv) in order to "dispel harmful, often hostile … stereotypes, and false assumptions," including "the claims that LGBT people make about themselves" and "the myths … they believe about their own lives and culture" (ix). In so doing, the authors say they intend to "grapple with the complexities of what it means to be LGBT in the broadest social, emotional, psychological, political, cultural, and personal sense" (xiv), in full awareness that "myths uphold existing social roles and expectations" (xvi) and "tap into preconceived notions of what is good or bad, just or unjust, pleasurable or disgusting" (xvii). With all of that as premise in the book's Introduction alone, any reader would expect the myths of gay wealth and high disposable income to be featured, perhaps in the section entitled "Struggling in the World"? If so, any reader would be disappointed.

Instead, writers like Barbara Smith, Audre Lorde, and Gloria Anzaldúa are briefly mentioned for their "passionate and brilliant" writing about racism in the LGBT movement and homophobia in "various communities of color" (101) but not for writing about class. Socioeconomic status, meanwhile, gets a quick nod in "Myth 18: Coming Out Is Easier Now Than Ever Before":

> [T]he belief that gay celebrities are positive role models and examples for how things can and do get better only grows stronger the more difficult coming out is for everyone else. This is especially true for LGB people who live at the socioeconomic margins, disproportionately young queers of color." (147)

There are two separate assertions here, but let's take them in reverse order. The second is that queer people "at the socioeconomic margins" are more likely to be young and people of color. Though there's no question that "queers of color" are *disproportionately* represented among poor and working-class queers (just as people of color are disproportionately represented among the poor in general), it is misleading to imply that the *majority* of queer people "on the socioeconomic margins" are young or nonwhite. "Disproportionate" doesn't mean "most," but a sloppy use of language leaves that impression and reinforces the comforting notion that economic struggle doesn't have all that much to do with white queers.

The first assertion, however—that coming out is more difficult for people "at the socioeconomic margins"—is highly questionable. Moreover, it betrays a whiff of class bias along the lines of those beloved bromides about how working-class people or people of color are more homophobic. If "coming out" means nothing more than traveling to a gay urban area and engaging in high-end consumption, there might be some truth to the claim that "coming out" is harder for poor and working people. But one hopes that isn't what the authors meant.

Still, there is reason to be suspicious. Writing several years earlier in *The Pleasure Principle*: *Sex, Backlash, and the Struggle for Gay Freedom*, Bronski had congratulated popular culture for creating the space in which gay and lesbian liberation could finally succeed, sidestepping entirely the *classed* nature of pop culture's idioms. "The politics of popular culture," Bronski wrote, "is the politics of pleasure and personal freedom" (36).

On the contrary. American commodity culture—a more accurate name for it—is diametrically opposed to personal freedom (except as that freedom is expressed in consumption), discourages the unfettered expression of pleasure by valorizing heterosexual or quasi-heterosexual monogamous coupling above all other forms, and actively corrodes human(e) interaction by insisting that only those able to meet unreasonable standards of beauty, youth, and wealth are eligible to participate. Pop culture does not—cannot—exist outside of economics, nor does gay (male) participation in it. Here again, however, discourse on the nature of queer life cannot admit of class.

Bronski is absolutely correct that pop culture and the gay "community" can barely keep their hands off each other, but to confuse liberation from oppression with "open, celebratory displays of gay sexuality and the gay body" (108) is simply sinister (not to mention misogynist, racist, and ageist, since that "celebratory" body is nearly invariably male, white, and young). To assert, finally, that "because gay and lesbian identity is defined by sexual attraction to members of the same gender, sexuality is, necessarily, at the heart of gay culture" (54) is to land in a tangled tautology. Moreover, it iterates the presumption that individual concerns are only pertinent to gay cultural membership if they result from the gender of one's sexual partners. To the extent that class (or race or gender or any one of a number of other affiliations, or perhaps all of them together) lies closer to *my* heart, am I admissible then only to the queer auxiliary?

And then it sometimes happens that we disappear even when we appear. In 2001, Alyson published Dan Woog's *Gay Men, Straight Jobs*, a collection of interviews with gay men who work in what Woog identified as "'heterosexual jobs,' as most people—gay as well as straight—would call them" (vii). Leaving aside the curious process by which Woog operationally defined occupations like judge, public relations executive, investment banker, and doctor as "heterosexual jobs," I turn to more vexing questions.

First, more than half of the men Woog interviewed are employed in *working-class* occupations (prison guard, oil rig mechanic, trucker, forklift driver, mason, lumberyard man), though he never engages with that fact. Second, the sole job-related issue that interested Woog in his interviews was whether or not the man was "out" at work:

> [A]ll out gay men—no matter what profession or job— share certain experiences that straight men never can. These experiences revolve around overcoming homophobia, be it subtle or overt, in the workplace.... Some of the men I talked with ... are not out, or are semi-out at work and way out at home; for them, every day is a demanding, energy-draining balancing act (viii).

A "demanding, energy-draining balancing act" because of "homophobia," but presumably not, for Woog's working-class informants, because of the nature of their jobs, their lack of control over their time and their work, or the stress of financial insecurity. I scarcely need to add that the cover of the book is decorated with a handsome, hunky guy wearing a sweaty undershirt and a hard hat. One wonders whether he is the straight man emblematic of the "heterosexual job" or the "heterosexually-employed" gay man who holds one; he is, in any case, visually (if stereotypically) marked as working-class, a juxtaposition that conflates the categories of "working class" and "heterosexual" in a way that Andrew Holleran's Sutherland and Malone would have grasped instantly.

Over the last decade and a half, meanwhile, what I would call "fiction written for television"—otherwise known as TV dramas and sitcoms—has shown a willingness to explore non-privileged queer lives in much more interesting ways than has published fiction. Before getting down to cases, however, I want to acknowledge a debt to the work and ideas of American studies scholar and professor Lisa Henderson, author of *Love and Money: Queers, Class, and Cultural Production* (2013) as well as a number of articles on the same subject.

In a 2004 lecture entitled "Queer Visibility and Social Class," for example, Henderson encouraged cultural and media critics to resist "the familiar critical idea that U.S. media culture contained no popular discourse about social class" (and, by extension, that such discourse was also absent regarding queers and social class). Rather, Henderson noted, a consideration of class and class difference was often "richly present" in media but could only be discerned through the use of more subtle instruments. As Henderson put it, the "high profile of queerness" was often eclipsed by the "low profile of class difference."

As a practical matter—and this is true in literature as well as in visual media, which are Henderson's subject—writers appear to have an easier time "signifying" or "marking" queerness than class. That was certainly the case with the short-lived 2000 sitcom, *Normal, Ohio*, in which writers attempted to place a gay man (played by John Goodman) in the context of his middle-middle/occasionally working-class-appearing family in small-town Ohio. In the sitcom's back story, Goodman's character, William Gamble (nicknamed, either brilliantly or ham-handedly, "Butch"), has come out during a long-term heterosexual marriage, "run away" to Los Angeles, and returned home two years later.

What became painfully obvious in the seven episodes that were aired (six others were made but not shown on TV) was the extent to which the writers and actors struggled in vain to find a convincing way to depict Butch's sexual orientation, his social class, and his blue-collar masculinity (Butch is a beer-drinking, foot-ball loving "Bear"; in one episode he plays pool with a gang of bikers, a doo rag around his head). Rather, placed in an almost exclusively heterosexual context (there are no other gay characters in the seven episodes that aired, though Butch has a brief fling in the unaired Episode 12), Butch can only "appear gay" by singing show tunes, quoting *The Wizard of Oz*, admitting a simpering attraction for a straight car salesman, or making camp references to himself (when his sister experiences a moment of doubt about whether he is really gay, Butch reassures her: "No, I'm a big girl!").

At the same time, although Butch is largely indistinguishable from Dan Connor, the working-class character Goodman portrayed for nine seasons on *Roseanne*, the actual class position of the Gamble family is extremely confusing. Though the physical setting (the houses and neighborhood) seems solidly middle-class, Butch's father, as a young man, worked as a kill bolt operator in a slaughterhouse before starting his own, apparently successful business; Butch's sister, meanwhile, studies to become a licensed beautician and briefly considers working as a stripper to supplement her income from a nail salon. In contrast, Butch apparently does not work at all, though he has no difficulty paying cash for a used (but not new) car when his son needs one. The humor also betrays anxiety about being seen as low-class: in one episode a character's plan to keep a junk car in the yard elicits the comment, "Why not just put him on the porch with a banjo?" and, in the last episode that Fox aired, elaborate Christmas decorations are said to have turned the house into "white trash Vegas."

But if the gay humor was clichéd and stale and the class-based humor seemed more derogatory than participatory, *Normal, Ohio* remains instructive for the very issues that caused it to fail: its creators and writers seemed overwhelmed by the difficulty of locating a gay man in a "nongay" context and by the effort of creating a character whose "normalcy" relied so heavily, if maladroitly, upon a highly classed "Joe Sixpack" stereotype of American maleness. What is funny about an openly gay man in a blue-collar town, after all, if he insists on fitting in there?

Shameless and *Queer as Folk*, on the other hand—both produced for American pay TV and both remakes of British series—have enjoyed much greater popularity and created more nuanced opportunities to examine queers and class in popular media.

In its Showtime reincarnation, *Shameless* premiered in 2011 and, as this book went to press, had concluded its fourth season. Among the main characters is Ian Gallagher, a teenager and the third-oldest child of a large, substantially parent-less family living in a working-class-verging-on-poverty milieu in Canaryville on Chicago's South Side. Ian initially has both female and male partners but, in the first season, begins an ongoing sexual relationship with Mickey Milkovic, a deeply closeted thug and the brother of the young woman who has agreed to act as Ian's sham girlfriend in order to help him fend off questions about his sexuality. Both Ian and Mickey show a traditional, carefully curated masculine face to the world (exaggeratedly so in the case of Mickey, whose fear of being identified as gay, at least until the end of the fourth season when he undergoes a dramatic but anti-climactic coming out, borders on the psychotic), and both engage in behaviors that might be called stereotypically working-class: Mickey is a juvenile delinquent, an ex-con, and a thief; when his homosexual panic is high, he sleeps with women and, in fact, is forced by his father to marry a prostitute he has impregnated. Ian is politically conservative and describes himself as "a patriot." He participates in JROTC at his high school and is more than eager to engage in fistfights; following a vicious beating by Mickey on the eve of the latter's wedding, he falsifies papers that allow him to join the Army before he has turned eighteen.

Because both characters are approximately the same age, come from the same social conditions, and are both white, however, disparities of class, age, or race do not figure into their obvious sexual and emotional connection. They are, in that sense, peers, which does not discount the possibility that they find each other attractive for the very same motives that might cause non-working-class men to find them attractive, fetishistically or not.

Notably, these stereotypes of working-class masculinity are repeatedly troubled not solely by queerness but by the fact that Mickey, who is the more violent, more homophobic, more closeted and, arguably, the more "butch" character, is also a sexual bottom. His desire for penetration, in fact, doubtless adds to his ambivalence over his sexual desires, but his "dilemma" is also the source of wry humor for the series' writers. To an extent, Mickey's heterosexual behavior and his willingness to engage in all the mannerisms of homophobia (including going so far as to plan the murder of Ian's father after the latter catches the boys having sex) give him power over Ian, whom he can cast as the "punk" in their relationship, but Mickey's private sexual desires—along with his inability to express his emotional attachment to Ian, something that Ian is free to name and therefore does not fear—draw them toward parity. The psychological and physical violence in the relationship, all of which is directed at Ian, is disturbing; still, although Ian is hurt, he never considers himself a victim.

At a superficial level, *Shameless* appears to raise the usual gay vs. working-class dilemma: In such a hostile, homophobic environment, can Ian and Mickey live as a "normal" couple— normal meaning, in this case, as normal as any of the series' dating or married heterosexual couples which are, with one important exception, fairly seriously dysfunctional. In reality, however, the world that Ian and Mickey inhabit isn't especially hostile; Ian's coming out to his family was unremarkable and, while his neighbors and acquaintances possess no particularly sophisticated understanding of homosexuality, they are far from antagonistic. At the same time, neither Ian nor Mickey has or desires any connection to a "gay community." Quite to the contrary. Although Ian uses gay bars as a venue in which to meet men for sex, and for a time, works in one as a cocktail waiter and go-go boy, both he and Mickey view Chicago's

Boystown with contempt; they neither aspire to be part of "gay life" nor experience the slightest sense of being "out of place" in their natal culture. The result, as Henderson anticipates, is that what initially seems "high profile" about Ian and Mickey is their sexuality, while their social class and circumstances serve as landscape. In fact, however, they may well be among the "queerest" gay characters on television. Their relationship troubles neither their working-class loyalties nor their connections to place and family, and their socioeconomic milieu, far from attempting to force them out, is a source of support and tactical advantage. To say it another way, they are aligned more closely to other members of their shared "underclass" than they are to any gay "tribe."

In the American-Canadian co-production of *Queer As Folk*, by contrast, which aired from 2000-2005, class-inflected tensions were frequently present between the show's characters from working-class origins and those who came from—or were scrambling toward—other class positions. I would argue, in fact, that the friction created by working-class versus privileged-class values, behaviors, and aspirations was one of two principal dichotomies that *Queer As Folk*'s writers explored, with varying degrees of success and sensitivity, during the five-year run of the show.

The other, of course, was the tension between sexuality as alliance and sexuality as pleasure, which is to say between the polarities of gay and queer. The first position was represented largely by the stable, long-term relationship of the lesbian characters, Lindsay and Melanie and, later, by Michael's marriage to Ben; in the attempts at and clearly expressed longing for committed coupledom on the part of most of the male characters; and in depictions of gayness as the impetus for community-formation and political solidarity over issues such as AIDS, gay bashing, and civil rights.

The standard-bearer for sexuality as pleasure was the complex character of Brian Kinney whose militant queerness was marked by his hostility to same-sex couples (which he described as "ersatz heterosexuals"), his allergy to politics, his antipathy for the image-conscious "good gays" of the Gay & Lesbian Center and, especially, by the legions of men with whom he had sex, including in ways that disrupted the binaries of friend/lover, public/private, and coercive/consensual and even occasionally threatened his own safety and livelihood. When asked to describe his ongoing "non-boyfriend" relationship with Justin, for example,

Brian quipped, "That's a difficult question to answer given the limitations of the language, and the conventionality of most people's thinking.... Let's just say he's the guy I've fucked more than once." After Brian was fired from his job as an advertising executive (he was the only male character who could be described as resolutely upwardly mobile), he decided to open his own ad agency, choosing to renovate a derelict gay bathhouse for his company's headquarters and placing his private office in the former steamroom.[40]

The final episodes of Season 3 made this gay vs. queer distinction visually clear in two parallel scenes of shared celebration. In the first ("Poster May Lead to the Truth," Ep. 11), Brian used a sledgehammer to destroy the lock on the door to the backroom at the local disco, reopening the sex area that had been shuttered during a mayoral candidate's anti-smut campaign. To a shower of confetti, the bar patrons whooped and waved their arms in triumph as they streamed through the door. In the second ("The Election," Ep. 14), Liberty Avenue revelers bearing rainbow flags danced in the street when it became clear that votes from their gay district had caused the electoral defeat of the same anti-gay candidate.

There's no question that gayness was "high profile" in *Queer As Folk*, but the "low profile" of class difference was often well in view. In story line after story line, for example, the series' writers explored such issues as Michael's struggle to "fit in" with the social world of his lover in Season 1, Dr. David Cameron, a wealthy chiropractor, who literally could not find room in his designer apartment for Michael's low-brow collection of comic-book paraphernalia and who, by paying for everything and managing all the material details of their life, robbed Michael of agency. Toward the end of Season 2 and for the rest of the series, Michael was involved with Ben Bruckner, a college professor, and the two of them began a fitful climb toward marriage and the middle class—accompanied at every step by

---

[40] The oversexed queer vs. the nice-guy-who-wants-to-settle-down—which many writers seem to imagine as a sort of immutable blue state/red state divide—is hardly a new theme in post-Stonewall gay writing. Larry Kramer got off the opening salvo with his 1978 *Faggots*, but Wayne Hoffman's 2006 *Hard*—whether an homage to or plagiarism of Kramer's works is in the eye of the beholder—mines identical territory.

Brian's bitter commentary: Michael was a "defector," a sell-out, and a middle-class conformist.

Another subplot involved Ted Schmidt who, after being fired from his job as an accountant, created a popular porn site and briefly imagined (wrongly) that his success would earn him access to the echelons of the city's A-gays. When his friend (and, briefly, lover), Emmett, began to thrive in his event-planning and catering business for an upper-crust clientele, Ted lashed out at him from within their shared class shame:

> You think because you put a piece of cheese on a cracker [and] you pawn it off as chic, that somehow you're better than everyone. Well, let me tell you something. No matter how many fancy parties you give or how much money they give you to give them, you'll always be a piece of trash from Hazlehurst, Mississippi.

"I don't need you to tell me that," Emmett responded, "because I tell myself that every day."

"Money troubles," in addition, were a recurring theme in the series—meaning both the limitations imposed by a lack of financial resources and the dilemmas characters repeatedly faced in which lack of money was an obstacle or, more frequently, in which access to money was posited as a Faustian bargain requiring moral compromise: Justin's inability to afford his art-school tuition when his father cut him off; Ethan's decision to busker in the streets rather than accept a recording contract that would have required him to go back in the closet (he ultimately did accept, ending his relationship with Justin); Ted and Emmett's loss of their home when Ted faced legal troubles; Emmett's brief relationship with George Schickle, a multimillionaire entrepreneur who died suddenly, leaving Emmett a $10 million inheritance, all of which Emmett ultimately renounced when George's family contested the will and insisted that Emmett deny his relationship with George.

Let's be clear: *Queer As Folk* was no psalm to proletariat solidarity. None of the recurring characters was close to being poor, and the series traded heavily in the middle-class fantasy that is a cornerstone of American television—the idea that money is always available from *somewhere* (a loan, friends' largesse, a sudden windfall) when it is genuinely needed. (Still, one might argue that the acknowledgement that money is *even temporarily* a problem is unusual in American television; for gay characters, it is unheard of.)

From the beginning, moreover, the American-Canadian incarnation of the series discarded the UK version's explicitly working-class ambience and muddied working-class vs. middle-class distinctions, playing into the American mythology that "everyone is middle-class" and rendering its characters' socioeconomic context difficult to read. Particularly in its fifth and final season, finally, whose approach I would argue departed from the previous seventy episodes, the writers largely abandoned questions of class difference in order to work out happy, coupled endings for all of the main characters—with the important exception of Brian and Justin (Brian remained the "queer" in a sea of gays).

On the other hand, neither did the main characters (once again excluding Brian) accumulate significant wealth or property: they spent when they had it, scrimped when they didn't, worked when they could (several characters faced unemployment), had jobs but rarely careers and, for the most part, related to money and labor in ways that were tinged with working-class knowledge. They tended to have, in short, little more than the wage-worker's due which, in that far-off time in which the series is set, still included the possibility of such things as home ownership and at least a modest disposable income.[41]

Both *Shameless* and *Queer As Folk*, but especially the latter, are also innovative in depicting gay characters in the context of work—in many cases in *Queer As Folk* they were wage earners who had to hustle to find paying jobs and who were subject to firing and exploitation by bosses: Justin worked as a waiter at a diner and later as a go-go dancer in a gay bar; before he began work as an event planner, Emmett was a sex worker on Ted's porn site and a clerk in a clothing store; in the early seasons, Michael was an assistant manager at a Walmart-like supercenter and later took over a struggling comic-book store; on the side, Michael and Justin attempted to make a go of a gay-themed comic and were briefly dazzled by Hollywood fantasies that ultimately came to nothing. In *Shameless*, Ian

---

[41] There was also a wink to Harry Hay in Season 4, Episode 2 when Michael and Emmett attended a Radical Faerie gathering and Hay appeared to Emmett as a guiding spirit. Discerning viewers might have recognized Hay, who died in 2000, as a devoted Marxist, left-wing labor activist, anti-capitalist, and anti-assimilationist, but *Queer As Folk*'s writers limited Hay and Emmett's conversation to a discussion of how adversities in Emmett's life had dimmed his "fairy flame."

works in a convenience store or as a waiter and is briefly a soldier; Mickey has no formal employment, though in recent seasons has established himself as a pimp.

Finally, both series accomplish something unusual in successfully presenting working-class gay characters as people with a history that has neither been "left behind" nor "overcome" but which is joined to their lived present. Several of *Queer As Folk*'s main characters were born and remained in Pittsburgh (a fictional Pittsburgh, to be sure, but the point remains), and *Shameless*'s Ian and Mickey show no desire to leave their neighborhood, never mind Chicago. In a media and literary context in which gay characters so often seem to arise *ex nihilo* in a constructed present whose connection to a life before their rebirth is either absent or highly tenuous, that fact deserves emphasis. It stands in marked contrast to gay-Diaspora narratives and to attempts to rinse queer media and literary characters of a (working) classed past before setting them down in the successful careers, middle-class aspirations, and trendy hyper-commercialism of scores of by-now-familiar portrayals.

VIII.

"Excuse for saying so but isn't gay and working-class kind of a contradiction in terms?"
(*Posted to the Working Class Academics listserv in response to the* Everything I Have Is Blue *call for submissions, 22 November 2002*)

"There's no such thing as a working-class gay man."
(*Ethan Mordden, telephone conversation, 28 April 2003*)

"The great thing about gay is that it erases class."
(*Ethan Mordden, same conversation*)

Perhaps comments like the three above help explain why it is so hard to find legitimate contemporary American queer fiction—meaning the kind that appears in those semiannual "best" anthologies or which is recognized with publication by mainstream houses (including mainstream gay houses)—in which the boys in question aren't spending the fall at a villa in Tuscany (or summering in Provincetown, or taking a three-month excursion through the "ruins" of Mexico); aren't decorating their lofts in SoHo (or their getaway home in Vermont or their Victorian in Pacific Heights); aren't pulling out credit cards to pay for first-class flights to Bangkok (or a new set of Baccarat bibelots or dinner at Elaine's); don't have cleaning ladies (or real-estate agents or personal trainers). They are white-collar professionals—or, if they aren't, they either don't need to work or are working their way up. They have taste and culture and subscriptions to *Architectural Digest*, but they have no politics (or would have no politics were it not for AIDS and marriage). They are products of the queer Diaspora, and they have come to the urban centers where "we" are presumed to thrive and (significantly) to prosper.

I'm exaggerating, but not as much as you might think. These giddy descriptions by publishers and reviewers of recent gay men's fiction tell the story:

- The son of an upper-crust clothing designer....

- Gabe Richards is a wealthy businessman....

- After winning millions in a settlement from the church....

- A life of wealth and privilege doesn't equal happiness— just ask Eric Courtland....

- Rusty Baker is a blond, rich, entitled football player in a high school full of them....

- ... repressed and expressed sexualities clash on the sedate campus of a modern-day boys' prep school in upstate New York...

- Nathaniel Rice is a technical genius, a company executive and the son of a very powerful person....

- ... four young, image-conscious New York gay men ... attempt to recalibrate their out-of-whack love lives while looking their best in the latest designer fashions ...

- ... a young posse of preppy Upper East Siders with a taste for high fashion, top-shelf liquor and other men ...

- Will Spencer used and discarded lovers as easily as he made his Wall Street stock trades....

- Ben Walsh is well on his way to becoming one of Manhattan's top litigators, with a gorgeous boyfriend and friends on the A-list.

- Braxton Todd's LA PR firm was flourishing.... When a pair of A-type individuals find working with each other a breeze [will they jump] into each other's arms?

- ... a younger, prettier set who spend their time at resorts with names like Babylon and clubs with names like Universe....
- In a world of gas lighting and horse-drawn carriages, Rex is fixing up an old mansion to host a Christmas party for his wealthy family's business....
- Lloyd ... adopt[s] a peaceful, celibate Provincetown lifestyle.... Lurking in the background [is] the independently wealthy Anthony....
- ... bittersweet romance in Provincetown with Eduardo, twenty-two and a vision of gorgeous, wide-eyed youth ...
- Nigel Adams and cynical, aristocratic Nicky Borja ... are accidentally thrown together in a Tuscany villa ...
- As soon as they're settled in their new home on the French Riviera....
- When Reed Kensington—ruthless attorney, self-made millionaire and handsome playboy—returns from abroad....

Such a skewing of perspective, in fact, has an important corollary, which is that privileged-class gay writers are often entirely incapable of identifying the classed nature of their and their colleagues' production. One example can stand for many. In a 2008 interview with the literary journal *Gulf Coast*, writer Robert Leleux described his then-forthcoming novel, *The Memoirs of a Beautiful Boy*, as "the first very bourgeoise [sic] gay love story" (280).

In light of the admittedly tongue-in-cheek list above, but much more seriously in light of the realities of the literary representations of gay men's lives from the 1980s onward, there's something both comic and alarming in Leleux's claim that no other "bourgeoise gay love story" had been written prior to 2009, when his *Memoirs* appeared. On the contrary, one might easily have formed the impression that gay writers at the time were writing virtually nothing else.[42]

---

[42] It's not a novel, but the first example that comes to mind is Terrence McNally's Tony Award-winning Broadway play (and 1997 film) *Love! Valour! Compassion!*, in which eight well turned-out gay male friends—gym-toned business consultants, Volvo-driving yuppies, "successful" artists, and urban sophisticates—spend the summer at a large, secluded nineteenth-century home in Dutchess County, New York.

At the same time, Lisa Henderson's work has attempted to chart a course beyond the obviously untenable critical strategy of deriding media for its "lack of so-called realism relative to an empirical universe" and then pronouncing that media corrupt for its failure to reproduce empirical realities (2004, n.p.). Henderson's objective, as she emphasizes in *Love and Money*, is neither to replace definitions of class "historically defined through labor-capital analysis (in the Marxist tradition) or empirically defined by occupation, income, and formal education (in the liberal one)" nor to "imagine class as fundamentally or primarily a cultural form" (5), but rather to place a "cultural study of queer-class conjuncture" alongside political and economic analyses.

One way to frame the "queer-class conjuncture" is to describe it in terms of cultural products and artifacts, as did novelist and activist John Weir in "Going In" (1997):

> The true division in the gay community is between the entrenched, privileged, politically active urban and suburban trend-setters and policy makers, and the mass of people with homosexual urges who feel represented more by *Reader's Digest* and *Soldier of Fortune* magazine than by *The Advocate* or *10 Percent* or *Frontiers* or *Deneuve* or *On Our Backs* or *Out*. If indeed they have ever heard of them. (32-33)

John Lauritsen makes a similar argument quite a bit more pointedly in his "Political-Economic Construction of Gay Male Clone Identity," noting that "Many features of the gay clone lifestyle were not created by or in the interests of gay men at all, but instead were economically constructed. The gay subculture largely evolved according to the profit-logic of an expanding sex industry." He continues

> Over a dozen years ago, the sidewalks of my neighborhood, New York City's Lower East Side, were spray painted with the slogan, "CLONES GO HOME!" This was not an act of antigay bigotry. Gay men themselves had done the spray painting. Living in the Lower East Side-New York's traditional "melting pot," these men had

---

Love affairs, shopping, and drag Follies ensue. Kensington Publishing Corporation's "Gay Romance" category, meanwhile, has published virtually nothing but bourgeois gay love stories since about 1999.

a way of life they wished to preserve from the encroachment of the "Gay Clone" lifestyle. Gay Lower East Siders considered themselves part of a diverse and vital community. They looked upon the newly emerging Gay Clone lifestyle as the product of a ghettoized mentality, an embodiment of commercialism, conformism, and vacuity.

Granted, the specific phenomenon Lauritsen describes—the much copied and widely parodied clone as he existed more than two decades ago—is no more, but the impulse that created the clone has never once dimmed. Rather, the clone has simply been replaced by later generations of consumer objects and fashion symbols, emblems of the enduring urge to belong and no less the embodiment of conformity and consumerism as a badge of gay identity.

This is what Ethan Mordden meant when he said, in our 2003 interview, "The great thing about gay is that it erases class." Mordden's comment assumed, first, that the "erasure of class" was necessarily a desirable outcome (especially to the extent that "erasure," in this context, was a euphemism for "escape from the underclass") and, second, implied not the creation of a class-free "community" (in which class distinctions were genuinely "erased") but rather the fusion of "gay identity" with middle- and privileged-class status markers in a Pygmalion-like atmosphere of homophily and "gay-positive" institutions, services, and the *dernier cri* tokens of pop culture. In other words, being gay— belonging to the "gay community" or pursuing a "gay lifestyle"— far from being the great leveler that the phrase "erases class" suggests, "erased" class by creating a social class all its own.

In one of the smarmiest articles ever to appear in the pages of *Details* magazine, Mike Albo called that class by name in his 2008 encomium to the notion that the rich are better than us, "The Rise of the A-Gay." A-gays "transcend gayness in much the same way that Barack Obama is said to have transcended race," Albo wrote, quoting lemondrop.com's Laura Gilbert on the way in which "A-gays mark measurable societal progress." He continued:

> Moneyed, successful, educated, and comfortable in their own skin, they're fast becoming the new archetype of cosmopolitan masculinity.... They don't own yappy miniature dogs or time-shares in Fort Lauderdale; they own Labradors and four-bedroom summer homes in Sag Harbor. Instead of cruising in gay clubs, they jet to

Gstaad or the TED conference, and party at Sundance with Zooey Deschanel.... Their Saville Row suits are impeccable ... and they furnish their homes with collectible pieces by designers like Claude Lalanne. They drive to Krav Maga class in Lexus hybrids and read four newspapers a day, including the *Wall Street Journal*, because they're bosses and entrepreneurs, not employees.... For the most part, they have opted out of the gay scene and its social networks and eschew the theme parties and bathhouses of the lower castes.

To suggest that the accumulation of wealth by a restricted elite represents "societal progress" is nothing short of malevolent, but the same class tensions to which Mordden's comment alludes and which Albo makes the subject of fawning praise were reflected thirty years before in *Dancer from the Dance* (though even Holleran's most arriviste characters would surely have been numbered among the "lower castes" of time-sharers and people who had to work for a living). They can, in fact, be read even earlier in Mart Crowley's ground-breaking play, *The Boys in the Band*, which opened in 1968. Gay-community participation is already marked in *Boys in the Band* by correct shopping and stylish consumption and, though the majority of the play's characters are identifiable as working-class, gayness is manifestly positioned as antagonistic to class—is, indeed, a dye adopted deliberately for the masking of working-class roots.

The success or failure of that disguise, of course, is the subject of no small anxiety among the characters, and they verbally skewer each other for (among many other things) the menial nature of their employment, their dress and grooming, and their inability to support their shopping habits without incurring debt. When Emory refers to Alan as "that piss-elegant kooze," his insult seeks to assault both Alan's masculinity and his middle-class pretensions.

In that connection, John Champagne's discussion of Liberace in the context of working-class gay men's styles of self-presentation is fascinating. Noting Liberace's origins in the economically depressed mill town of West Allis, Wisconsin, Champagne writes:

Having grown up a short distance from Liberace's birthplace, I can attest to the working-class character of his "natal" community.... I read Liberace's style as emblematic of the desires of a man from a working-class "natal" culture to erase all visible traces of that culture from his adult homosexual body. The adoption of Liberace's brand of "piss" elegance is one strategy whereby working-class gay men attempt to distance themselves from their background. (1993: 164)

Indeed, Liberace, like another gay man from an immigrant and working-class background, Andy Warhol, is rarely located within his original class context (with regard to Warhol, Deborah Bright's excellent 2001 article, "Shopping the Leftovers" is the only example of which I am aware), nor—in either man's case—is his construction of an adult presentation generally considered in light of the way both class experiences and exposure to and participation in urban gay life may have shaped his aesthetic choices.[43]

In any case, Warhol's and Liberace's shared focus on camp, kitsch, trash art, and drag—albeit in markedly different deployments—is a stylistics for which gay men from the working classes deserve more credit than they've gotten. In fact, both men were at the vanguard of a mode of expression famously classified by their rough contemporary, Susan Sontag, in her 1964 "Notes on Camp":

> Aristocracy is a position vis-à-vis culture (as well as vis-à-vis power)..... But since no authentic aristocrats in the old sense exist today to sponsor special tastes, who is the bearer of this taste? Answer: an improvised self-elected class, mainly homosexuals, who constitute themselves as aristocrats of taste.... Homosexuals have pinned their integration into society on promoting the aesthetic sense. Camp is a solvent of morality. It neutralizes moral indignation, sponsors playfulness. (290)

What Sontag doesn't quite do is make the obvious connection: to the extent that "aesthetic taste" is constituted as an "aristocratic" feature and a heightened appreciation of beauty is

---

[43] In *Liberace: An Autobiography* (New York: G. P. Putnam's Sons, 1973), Liberace writes, "Perhaps it was my humble beginnings that gave me my penchant for expensive, exciting stage clothes. Maybe it was an eagerness to eliminate in some way those drab surroundings of my youth and the dull clothing that was all we had. In my act I jokingly refer to the days when I had to wear my brother George's hand-me-downs, which isn't really a joke because they weren't really hand-me-downs. He was also wearing them. We took turns"(161).

considered innate to the patriciate, its improvised, "self-selected" exercise among homosexuals necessarily requires a presentation that is *also* marked as haute bourgeois. In other words, the bearer of "the aesthetic sense" must be *recognized* as authoritatively aristocratic (including in the "old sense") or his directives will be ignored as posturing. That in turn, implies class masquerade— eternally in danger of being exposed as "piss elegance." In consequence, Sontag overlooks an important reality: camp isn't the only solvent of morality and sponsor of integration. As Albo makes clear in his way and Kushner in his, so is money.

As if to put the finest possible point on these concepts, a letter sent to gay businesses in 2000 by the Millennium March On Washington's Millennium Festival Street Fair Committee read in part:

> Marketers worldwide are increasingly recognizing the importance and spending power of the gay community as a dynamic, fast growing economic force in the business world today. As a result of their unique lifestyles, gay men and women are by definition intensely brand loyal, and hyper acquisitive. They for the most part enjoy joint earnings, yielding them high disposable incomes.

Now, I would propose that most of us are well aware (and would even acknowledge if pressed) that—*in real life*—the majority of queer people aren't really "hyper-acquisitive" and don't really enjoy "high disposable incomes." In fact, the extent and power of the gay über-consumer (largely but not exclusively male) has been magnified far beyond what sociological and economic data can support, and recent studies suggest that LGBTQ people may actually be more vulnerable to being poor. A 2013 Pew Research Center study, *A Survey of LGBT Americans: Attitudes, Experiences, and Values in Changing Times*, found not only that the LBGT adults in their sample more frequently reported—compared to all U.S. adults—incomes of less than $30K annually (39% vs. 28%), but less often reported incomes of $75K or more (20% vs. 34%).

Badgett, Durso and Schneebaum (2013) concluded that "LGB people who are young, [who are] from communities of color, who have children, [or] who identify as bisexual," along with those in rural settings, were at highest income risk (25), and Gates' 2014 study indicated that lesbians and gay men were nearly twice as likely to experience "food insecurity" (that is, did not have enough money to feed themselves or their families) in comparison to heterosexuals: 16% vs. 29%.

According to a 2012 review by the market-research firm, Richard K. Miller & Associates, meanwhile, "Although past studies have portrayed the GLBT community as an affluent subgroup, more recent findings suggest they are probably no better off than heterosexual consumers" (Miller & Washington, 2012: 278). The authors include this pithy quote from Bob Witeck, founder and CEO of the Washington, DC-based PR and marketing firm, Witeck Communications: "No one should infer that same-sex households are more affluent than others—this is little more than a stereotype, considering the economic evidence available" (278).[44]

But the myth is slow to die, and studies will doubtless continue to be done even if they ultimately serve only to confirm what seems intuitively to be the case. If most Americans are working-class or poor (and they are), then so are most LGBTQ Americans, a point that feminist critic and scholar Barbara Smith made in a 1997 interview:

> Our economic system has the most implications for lesbians and gay men when their class position makes them vulnerable to that economic system.... It's not that in general being lesbian and gay puts you into a critical relationship to capitalism, it's that a large proportion of lesbians and gay men are poor and working class, but of course they're completely invisible the way the movement's politics are defined now.[45]

But if the frenzy to shift gay men and women into the middle class (or beyond)—to see Weir's "privileged, politically active

---

[44] See also the "occasional series" which began in February 2014 in the *Washington Blade*. The *Blade*'s "Special Report: Poverty in the LGBT Community" (Chibbaro, 2014; Wolf, 2014a & b) draws on the same data that Badgett et al. examined, but takes a more "local" approach in pulling together findings from other sources that reveal an alarmingly high rate of poverty and homelessness among transgender people and an LGBTQ homelessness rate of nearly 30% in San Francisco where gentrification has caused housing costs to skyrocket and led to unprecedented numbers of evictions.

[45] Quoted in Bell, David & Binnie, Jon (2000). The Love that Dares Not Forget its Brand Name. In *The Sexual Citizen: Queer Politics and Beyond*. Cambridge, England: The Polity Press: 96-107: 99.

urban and suburban trend-setters and policy makers" and the Millennium March's "brand loyal, hyper acquisitive, high-disposable-income gay men and women" as the majority if not the entirety of the demographic—has been underway for decades, it would seem difficult to dismiss as mere coincidence the fact that the markedly reduced visibility of nonurban, nonmiddle-class, unfabulous, and unwaxed queers in "our" fiction so closely parallels the absence of such images in the agendas of "our" national political organizations, in journalistic coverage of "our" community, and in the breathless PR packets disseminated to those who hope to entice "our" business. On the contrary, two sets of constructs have emerged and converged— those created for the purposes of story-telling and those created for the purposes of marketing—and both are fictional.

Nonetheless, by the late 1970s and early 1980s, the playful practitioners of camp found themselves seaborne upon the extremely serious—because extremely profitable—waters of gay liberation. Complicit in this (con)fusion of "community" with "lifestyle," of social progress with capitalist participation, of a sense of shared comradeship and sodality with the exterior display of "taste," "style," and purchasing power were the new gay and lesbian media, which quickly began to reinterpret and disseminate the notion of community through a consumer-driven, celebrity-studded lens.

The moment in 1982 when *The Advocate* landed Absolut as the first major national advertiser in the gay press,[46] for example, was publicly heralded not as a victory for the newspaper's balance sheet but as an exemplar of the success of *gay liberation*. The publishers of the New York-based *Out* magazine, similarly, which began life a decade later as a self-styled edgy outsider whose scrappy, hard-hitting approach was intended to set it apart from "mainstream" media like *The Advocate*, had always privately intended to sell what they claimed was its wealthier, better educated reader base to Madison Avenue advertisers such as Benetton, Banana Republic, Calvin Klein, Virgin Atlantic Airlines, and a variety of record labels.

In fact, that's precisely what *Out* did, and with great success, an achievement that *Out*'s president and editor-in-chief, Michael Goff, chalked up to the fact that the magazine had come along

---

[46] See, e.g., Haggerty, George (1999). Advocate. *Encyclopedia of Gay Histories and Cultures: Volume 2. New* York: Routledge, 13.

"at just the right time ... [at a moment in which] what we are experiencing is a mainstreaming of the gay community."[47] Thus, the putative "radical" ultimately became, in its late-stage avatar, another mechanism for the metamorphosis of social, relational, and political "community" into an acquisition- and social-status-based "lifestyle."[48] Numerous "community" magazines followed a similar model of "commercialism, conformism, and vacuity," including *Genre*, which targeted "alternative lifestyles" in a succession of frantic makeovers before succumbing in 2009, and several publications designed for women (*Curve* and Australia's *LOTL*, for example).

To be sure, "gay community" can be defined in many ways, and I don't intend to pretend otherwise. But it is fair to make a distinction between "community" in the sense of a congregation of interconnected concerns, common cultural values, and shared goals (in which membership revolves around more-or-less durable commonalities) and a sort of cafeteria-style "community" that encompasses a select few geographical locations (the usual "gay-friendly" cities and neighborhoods), the consumers of "gay lifestyle" products and services (from apps to resorts to T-shirts to novels), and the participants in "gay and lesbian community events" such as pride rides, womyn's festivals, and softball leagues (in which membership can be conferred through temporary physical presence or a single economic transaction). Where many people say "community," in other words, it might be more accurate to say "club."

This is the point that Miranda Joseph raises in her *Against The Romance of Community*: that community membership tends to

---

[47] Cone, Tracie (1993, 16 April). Gay Magazine Profits by Going All Out to Attract Mainstream Advertisers. *Chicago Tribune*: n.p. Web: http://articles.chicagotribune.com/1993-04-16/news/9304170034 _1_gay-community-periodical-magazine.

[48] One enormous—and almost entirely overlooked—irony is that these highly successful media outlets have historically been and continue to be notorious for paying their staffs and writers miserably. By extension, the institutions—within which the newly "mainstreamed gay community" was presumably consuming—functioned only because they created a class of gay service workers—waiters, busboys, porters, baristas, janitors and custodians, clerks and attendants, go-go dancers and sex workers, among many others. Arguably, the lack of access these workers have to the "lifestyles" they make possible aligns them much more closely with the wage-earning underclass than it does with other gay people.

have meaning only to the extent it can be "performed." Because that performance almost always requires some act of consumption, community is complicit in capitalism—or, to put it as she does, involvement in a "community" makes individuals available as "raw material" that can be transformed into the "subjects of ... capital" (2002: 28). In that transaction, a "community" must reproduce the same social and class hierarchies that capitalism requires for its existence.

Placed in such a context, Goff's phrase—the "mainstreaming of the gay community"—becomes ominous for what it so blithely assumes, overlooks, and fails to define. At the same time, as the discussion above suggests, the term "gay community" is evoked almost exclusively as the unambiguously positive expression of such high ideals as comradeship, mutual regard, and political solidarity—in denial of community's embrace of the very inequalities of class and access upon which capitalism depends. To be sure, there is ambiguity here and, as Joseph herself notes, communities "may be or may become sites of resistance to the flow of capital" (29). They *may* become, but doing so is by no means inevitable or even likely.

And so the intriguing question remains: When so much of what we are offered to read (and to watch and to consume) is founded on this mirage of community, on a kind of sleight-of-hand that turns materialistic motivations into moral ones, of what material is the connection forged between our socioeconomic mythomyopia and our literary/cultural one?

IX.

"Don't I wish this were a story about closets and how you find your way out of them?" (Judith K. Witherow, "Not Just Merely Queer")

In *Brown*, the third and final installment of his memoirs, Richard Rodriguez writes that

American bookshelves of the twenty-first century describe fractiousness, reduction, hurt. Books are isolated from one another, like gardenias or peaches, lest they bruise or become bruised, or, worse, consort, confuse. If a man in a wheelchair writes his life, his book will be parked in a blue-crossed zone: "Self-Help" or "Health." There is no shelf for bitterness. No shelf for redemption. The professor of Romance languages at Dresden, a convert to Protestantism, was tortured by the Nazis as a Jew—only that—a Jew. His book, published sixty years after the events it recounts, is shelved in my neighborhood bookstore as "Judaica." There is no shelf for irony. (11-12)

Because writing continues to be ghettoized in book sales—whether because of placement on physical shelves in brick-and-mortar stores or of keyword choices in online sources[49]—what Rodriguez is talking about are first and foremost *marketing* categories, which is not an imperative that anyone is forced to obey except, well, marketers. And yet we often do obey them which, if you think about it, is a metaphor for capitalism itself.

In any case, questions of category and genre seem inevitable in conversations about writing, whether those take place in published reviews or formal criticism, in classrooms, among writers, or informally between friends who like to read. Our job, when we encounter phrases like "speculative fiction," "southern writers," "African American literature," or "postmodernism" is to develop the suspicion that such terms are both less precise and more complex than they appear—or than it might be convenient for them to be. Which, of course, is exactly the case.

The categories of "gay and lesbian literature" or "queer literature" are no different. What is "gay literature," after all? What makes a novel a "lesbian novel"? The author? The theme?

---

[49] Paradoxically, queer writing has become more deeply hidden as book selling has moved online. If you search for a specific title by a specific author in the listings of major online booksellers like Amazon, you'll find it easily. If you simply want to see what's new in gay literary fiction, conversely, an arduous journey awaits you. Chronological listings are haphazard, randomly mixing new work with reprints, reissues, and multiple editions of the same title; "fiction" is a single category that merges the work of established authors with self-published potboilers, genre books, and porn (the "Gay Paranormal Werewolf Erotic Romance Stories" series, e.g., or "Gay Transgender Holiday Romance Novelettes"); keywords are applied so haphazardly that nonfiction often shows up in the list alongside the occasional DVD or foreign-language title. Amazon's "citizen reviews" may provide some help in deciding what merits attention, but the would-be reader must wade through hundreds of them. In short, a worthy new gay book—unless a reader already know that it exists—is virtually guaranteed to drown in this sea.

The intended or presumed audience?[50] Can we speak of gay literature when the author is not lesbian or gay (J. K. Rowling's character, Albus Dumbledore, for example) or when the author *is* gay or lesbian but does not write plainly about the topic (in 1966, critic Stanley Kaufmann, writing in the *New York Times*, railed against the "disguised homosexual influence" in American theater as practiced by more-or-less closeted playwrights Edward Albee, Tennessee Williams, and William Inge)?[51]

And consider the complications that arise when same-sex themes are deliberately hidden (such as in Harlem Renaissance writer Richard Bruce Nugent's widely anthologized "Smoke, Lilies and Jade"), unintended, or even unconscious (doesn't Philip Core, the protagonist of Somerset Maugham's *Of Human Bondage,* seem somehow more coherent if we understand him as a self-denying homosexual?). Do we really go too far beyond the text if we acknowledge, as Leslie Fiedler did (along with many later critics), the "homosexual-pastoral nature" of the "buddy tradition" in American fiction and recognize the homoerotic or homoromantic subtext in the marriage and honeymoon of Ishmael and Queequeg in *Moby-Dick* or in the friendship of Huck and Jim in *Huckleberry Finn*?

To be sure, as Stuart Kellogg wrote in "The Uses of Homosexuality in Literature," "gay readers are especially quick to discover allusions to homosexuality and to crack coded references to it, sometimes so quick that they hear a thump where no apple fell" (3), but there are very good reasons for the search. In an erudite and panoramic 1999 essay-review of

---

[50] Katherine V. Forrest, writing in 2009 on behalf of the Board of Trustees of the Lambda Literary Foundation, which awards the Lambda Literary Awards each year, issued a statement intended to "clarify" the Foundation's nominations process. The statement entirely sidesteps the issue of genre definitions, invoking instead what Forrest called an "LGBT family of writers" that included "those who support our writers, those in all the allied areas of our literature: our readers, publishers, booksellers, publicists, agents ... and straight allies of every kind." She concluded, "As to what defines LGBT? That is not up to anyone at Lambda Literary Foundation to decide.... Sexuality today is fluid and we welcome and cherish this freedom. We take the nomination of any book at face value: if the book is nominated as LGBT, then the author is self-identifying as part of our LGBT family of writers, and that is all that is required." Web: tinyurl.com/nwrxvk5.

[51] Kaufmann doesn't specifically name Albee, Williams, and Inge, but the references to them are unmistakable.

Gregory Woods' *A History of Gay Literature: The Male Tradition*, for example, Colm Tóibín confronts that very issue: Why does finding "evidence of homosexuality" in literature matter at all?

> It matters because as gay readers and writers become more visible and confident, and gay politics more settled and serious, gay history becomes a vital element in gay identity, just as Irish history does in Ireland, or Jewish history among Jewish people. It is not simply a question of finding obscure traces of a gay presence in the past ... but of including writers ... who were clearly and explicitly gay, and whose homosexuality, ignored by most critics and teachers, has a considerable bearing on their work.... The gay past in writing is sometimes explicit and sometimes hidden, while the gay present is, for the most part, only explicit. (n.p.)

The intersection of LGBTQ writing with the comparatively more recent (recent at least in academia) category of "working class literature,"[52] meanwhile, raises new versions of these familiar concerns. Defining "the working class" is no simple task, even if we restrict ourselves to contemporary history and to a single country. Defining "working-class literature" or "working-class authors," then, is necessarily no easier. Meanwhile, just as Rodriguez reminds us, while we can readily find the work of writers such as James Baldwin, Audre Lorde, John Rechy, and Dorothy Allison shelved and indexed as African American literature (Baldwin, Lorde), feminist literature (Lorde, Allison), Chicano literature (Rechy), or gay and lesbian literature (all four), it is rarely identified with its other, obvious constituency: working-class literature.

All of that said, I'm not anxious to try to box in either the terminology or the concepts I have used here, and there are two very good reasons why. First, and simply as an objective matter, because universally accepted definitions of constructs such as "working-class" or "gay" (not to mention "literature") simply do not exist. Attempting to define them, at best, provides the opportunity to appear reductive and categorical about aspects of human existence that are necessarily continuous and, at worst, is an invitation to attack—either from what I might call

---

[52] Writing produced by, for, and about working-class people is, of course, not new, but what is new is the notion of a literary movement or genre worthy of preservation and study.

the "traditionalist" working-class organizing/labor studies camp, which sees the working-class as nearly exclusively blue-collar and views any "oppression" that is not determined specifically and solely by economic relations as bourgeois "identity politics"; or from the bourgeois identity politicians who see discussions of class as antediluvian, irrelevant, and sectarian in the context of the LBGTQ civil-rights "agenda."

The second reason is simply that I, like many of today's writers and thinkers, am one who has Deconstructed Too Much. We are living in an eternal post-structuralist hangover in which meaning itself has become suspect. As a writer, what that creates is the following problem. If I begin a sentence with the words "working-class gay men," I am already hip deep in terms that require copious footnoting. My "subjectivities" need explaining; the history of the social configuration of each of those three categories necessitates painstaking review.

The result of all that is that it becomes difficult to say anything—or, at least, to say anything coherent. (Which explains a great deal of queer theory.) If I ask for a ham on rye at my favorite deli, what I don't need is to explain that I want the ham between two slices of bread (which a priori excludes the possibility of the open-faced sandwich and enforces a binary view that restricts human agency to create a three-slice sandwich or, indeed, to envision a meal called "ham sandwich" in which neither "bread" nor "ham" figures at all); to acknowledge that "ham" is a culturally laden and inexact term that appears to describe a single "essence" but which, in fact, is a social and, indeed, religious construction that may refer to any one of scores of comestibles known in some form in many major Christian civilizations over the last thousand years; to specify that I'd like it on a plate (a culture-bound requirement that unreasonably privileges Western food-service techniques); or to engage in a discourse about the power relations that have enabled me to enter the institution called "restaurant" and command a perfect stranger to prepare and deliver food, solely because I am able to legitimize and enforce my hegemonic demand for service via the proffer of money. Whatever we mean by service. Or money. Or the.

Frankly, I just don't have that kind of time.

My decision, then, has been to write phrases like "working-class queers," along with similarly freighted terms, having negotiated a personal truce with two realities: 1) that such shorthand is (like all language) necessarily a wink at the reader—

you get the gist of what I mean; and 2) that complex cultural and social constructs always require examination, a notion that isn't actually lost on all that many people. In other words, while it is no capital crime to use such terms, it is at least an intellectual crime to act as if they were objective fact itself rather than signposts scattered along a vast and complex landscape.

"When *I* use a word," Humpty Dumpty tells Alice scornfully, "it means just what I choose it to mean—neither more nor less."

Well, not quite. But it is important to engage some of the "big ideas" (and when we're talking about class and sex, the ideas are big, indeed) that are relevant to my topic and even to express my own doubts about them, and the only tool I have is language. So let's dive right in. What, in the end, do class and (homo)sexuality actually have to do with one another and, more to the point, what do they have to do with writing?

At a superficial level, LGBTQ and working-class literature share two important characteristics: Historically speaking, both types of writing are likely to have been unintentionally overlooked, casually lost, randomly misinterpreted, or deliberately suppressed—albeit for different motives—and both may need to be reclaimed or recontextualized in order to bring their broadest implications to light.

We know that, in much the same way as sexual orientation or same-sex relationships, social class can also be camouflaged or misrepresented, with greater or lesser success—both in life and in literature. Unlike so-called biological sex (in most cases) and race or ethnicity (ditto), what sexual orientation and class share, then, is that they may not be immediately, visually discernible at first glance. Here, of course, the issue is tremendously complicated by what I mean by sexual orientation (although, it might be argued, the same is true regarding what I mean by "race/ethnicity" or "biological sex," but let's at least try to get to the end of the thought). Certainly, clothing and personal adornment may provide clues, but not in the same way as do skin color, the presence or absence of an epicanthic fold (to give one example), or facial features that code as "male" or "female" (and which, evidence suggests, we learn to categorize in infancy).[53]

---

[53] See, e.g., Leinbach, M. D. & Fagot, B. I. (1993). Categorical Habituation to Male and Female Faces: Gender Schematic Processing in Infancy. *Infant Behavior and Development 16*(3), 317–332; and Ramsey, Jennifer L., Langlois, Judith H. & Marti, Nathan C. (2005). Infant Categorization of Faces: Ladies First. *Developmental Review 25*, 212–246.

That poses a problem for the writer who has to figure out what pins to drop, so to speak, to ensure that the reader identifies characters according to her intentions (or cannot identify them, if that's the goal). It also raises the issue of who has the right to write or, in less polemical terms, whose work can fairly be said to come from an "insider" vs. a "colonialist" perspective.[54] As Dorothy Allison observes in her essay "A Question of Class," for example:

> Everything in our culture—books, television, movies, school, fashion—is presented as if it is being seen by one pair of eyes, shaped by one set of hands, heard by one pair of ears. Even if you know you are not part of that imaginary creature—if you like country music not symphonies, read books cynically, listen to the news unbelievingly, are lesbian not heterosexual ... you are still shaped by that hegemony, or your resistance to it. (16-17)

Analyzing who gazes and upon whom the writer invites the reader to gaze, by the way, happens to be a powerful tool for evaluating literature because it raises the question of the writer's values and presumptions. If the purpose of examining "gaze" is to play a game of literary gotcha, then it becomes a deadly, self-congratulatory bore; on the other hand, a thoughtful consideration of gaze can open a text up in unexpected ways.

No surprise, then, as Renny Christopher and Carolyn Whitson point out in their article, "Toward a Theory of Working Class Literature," that "[i]f working-class literature is defined as work by an author with origins in the working class, then authorial biography is integral to literary criticism" (72). In other words, in looking at whether writing is or is not "working class," we may also spend time researching or debating the class background (or class present) of the writer as we do on the writing itself. But this is something else that working-class literature shares with LGBTQ literature, in which unearthing, interpreting, or speculating upon the sexual and affectional history of writers

---

[54] An excellent discussion of who has the power to create and disseminate images in popular media—and of the ability of mishandled representations to create significant damage—can be found in the 2009 documentary, *Reel Injun* (written and directed by Catherine Bainbridge, Neil Diamond, and Jeremiah Hayes; produced by the National Film Board of Canada/Rezolution Pictures).

becomes essential to the project of attempting to catch firmly hold of the intent and significance of the work.

At a slightly deeper level, writing that foregrounds lesbian and gay perspectives, ethics, and consciousness can "queer" assumptions about a heterosexual universe and about the "proper" deployment of sex roles, physical sexual behavior, and gender just as working-class writing can "queer" certitudes about class mobility, the nature of work and opportunity, and the dream of liberty and justice for all. They are both—or they can be—subversive. I'm always surprised, for example, that there's not more working-class queer cultural production on the theme of class revenge. I can think of Joe Orton's play *Entertaining Mr. Sloane*, Gregg Araki's film *The Living End*, and a few novels (*Fixer Chao* by Han Ong, Patricia Highsmith's *The Talented Mr. Ripley*, and Charles Gorham's *McCaffery*, and not many others). But I digress.

In the first house I shared when I moved to San Francisco in 1981, I found a poster on the wall of our living room. "Class consciousness is knowing what side of the fence you're on," it read. "Class analysis is figuring out who's there with you."

Arguably, figuring out who is there with you is the whole point of life, and one of the ways we go about doing that is by interacting with art, media, literature, and the other products of the culture(s) in which we live.

This project, which has been part of my life in one form or another for more than a decade, came about because I am still working out my analysis. It answers my need for a response—not so much to silence, but to noise and lies, a reminder of the experiences that are elided, obscured, overlooked, manipulated, disdained, misunderstood, or simply out-shouted.

As Stanley Kunitz wrote in his poem, "The Layers":

> Oh, I have made myself a tribe
> out of my true affections,
> and my tribe is scattered!

I, too, am scattered.

I like the part of me that gets about as excited by a demolition derby as I do by the Tony Awards, that likes both fancy cheese and Spam. Drag queens feel like home to me because they were there in the bars I came out in, but non-cross-dressing gay boys with tweezed eyebrows and shaved chests make about as much sense to me as a screen door on a submarine (as my mom used to say).

With all due respect to the many gay pride parades I've happily attended, I have experienced my most profound moments of bonding with other men when I have worked in prisons and jails in Texas, New Mexico, and San Francisco, places where poor and working-class men are not the majority, they are quite simply the whole.

Nobody better say a word against Tammy Wynette or Randy Travis in my presence, yet I suspect I might have learned to like opera more if you didn't have to pay a day's wages to get into one. I'm proud of being the first in my family to earn a college degree, and I'm just as demoralized by ignorance as I am by the attempts of the right to make formal education seem "elitist" and un-American. At the same time, some of the most decent, intellectually astute, and politically committed people I've ever known hated school and got out as fast as they could.

I can't help feeling that "my" culture has been validated when Harvey Fierstein and Billy Porter take home prizes for *Kinky Boots*, a story about a working-class sissy who also happens to be a marketing genius, or when Ellen DeGeneres at the Oscars pretends to mistake Liza Minnelli for a female impersonator, just as I can't help recognizing the extent to which I am being dissed in politicians' newfound love for the "middle class," their slimy, calculated effort to make poor and working-class people invisible all over again. As if those who aren't participating fully in American capitalism just aren't pulling their weight.

I'm not sure where all of that leaves me. But I do know I don't want to be told I'm not queer enough, and I don't want to be told I'm not working class enough. I'd never claim that my experience of either one should be anyone else's, but I do say that the issue of "realness" ought to be left to drag contests, where it still makes some sense.

"How many points determine a line?" a dear old friend used to exclaim in frustration whenever he argued with someone who refused to concede the obvious.

The answer, as it turns out, is a lot of them.

References

About *Butt* (2014). *BUTT Magazine*. Web: www.buttmagazine.com/ information.

Albo, Mike (2008, November). The Rise of the A-Gay. *Details*. Web: details.com/culture-trends/critical-eye/200811/the-rise-of-the-a-gay.

Alexander, Shana (1973, 22 January). The Silence of The Louds. *Newsweek*: 28.

Allison, Dorothy (1994). A Question of Class. In *Skin: Talking about Sex, Class & Literature*. Ithaca, NY: Firebrand Books, 13-36.

Allison, Dorothy (2002/1988). Introduction: Stubborn Girls and Mean Stories. *Trash*. New York: Plume.

Andriette, Bill (1999, November). Fuck the Elite (Interview with Yaroslav Mogutin). *The Guide*. Web: tinyurl.com/pdzr5l5.

Anzaldúa, Gloria (1991). To(o) Queer the Writer: *Loca, Escritora y Chicana*. In Betsy Warland, Ed., *InVersions: Writings by Dykes, Queers, and Lesbians*. Vancouver: Press Gang, 249-263.

Aptheker, Bettina (2008, Summer). Keeping the Communist Party Straight, 1940s-1980s. *New Politics*: 22-27.

Badgett, M.V. Lee, Durso, Laura E., & Schneebaum, Alyssa (2013, June). *New Patterns of Poverty in the Lesbian, Gay, and Bisexual Community*. Los Angeles: The Williams Institute. Web: williamsinstitute.law.ucla.edu/wp-content/uploads/LGB-Poverty-Update-Jun-2013.pdf.

Bain, H. William (2008, 29 January). Andy Warhol's Pittsburgh: The Working-Class Background of the Iconic Queer Artist. *The Advocate*: 44-45.

Barnard, Ian (1996). Fuck Community, or Why I Support Gay-Bashing. In Renée R. Curry & Terry L. Allison, Eds., *States of Rage: Emotional Eruption, Violence, and Social Change*. New York: New York University Press, 74-88.

Berman, Steve (2014, 4 May). The Slow, Tragic Death of the LGBT Publishing Industry. *Salon.com*. Web: tinyurl.com/mvgv7sb.

Billow, John (2011, 24 March). Openly Gay NASCAR Driver Evan Darling. *Rage Monthly/edge on the Net*. Web: tinyurl.com/l5c32sb.

Blue-Collar Brawn (1999, November). *Men's Health 14*(9): 118-119.

Brennan, Debbie (2010, Summer/Autumn). A Militant Queer Movement Can Win Same-Sex Marriage Rights and Full Equality! *Feminist Socialist Bulletin: Australian Voice of Revolutionary Feminism*. Web: www.socialism.com/drupal-6.8/node/1249.

Brewis, Joanna & Jack, Gavin (2010, April). Consuming Chavs: The Ambiguous Politics of Gay Chavinism. *Sociology 44*: 251-268.

Bright, Deborah (2001, April). Shopping the Leftovers: Warhol's Collecting Strategies in *Raid the Icebox I. Art History 24*(2): 278-291.

Bronski, Michael (1998). *The Pleasure Principle: Sex, Backlash, and the Struggle for Gay Freedom*. New York: St. Martin's.

Bronski, Michael, Pellegrini, Ann & Amico, Michael (2013). *"You Can Tell Just By Looking": And 20 Other Myths about LGBT Life and People.* Boston: Beacon Press.

Brown, Rita Mae (1988/1973). *Rubyfruit Jungle.* New York: Bantam Books.

Bulkin, Elly (1981). Introduction: A Look at Lesbian Short Fiction. In *Lesbian Fiction: An Anthology.* Watertown, MA: Persephone Press, xi-xxxviii.

Caffey, John (1982). *The Coming Out Party.* New York: Pinnacle Books.

Champagne, John (1993). Seven Speculations on Queers and Class. *Journal of Homosexuality 26*(1): 159-174.

Chibbaro, Lou (2014, 12 February). Poverty in the LGBT Community. *Washington Blade.* Web: www.washingtonblade.com/2014/02/12/special-report-poverty-lgbt-community.

Cho, Margaret (2005, 17 March). Mullet Fantasies of Neighborhood Gays. *Buzzflash.com.* Web: tinyurl.com/nsmw3qc.

Christopher, Renny & Whitson, Carolyn (1999) Toward a Theory of Working Class Literature. *The NEA Higher Education Journal 15*: 71-81.

Clarkson, Jay (2006). "Everyday Joe" versus "Pissy, Bitchy, Queens": Gay Masculinity on StraightActing.com. *The Journal of Men's Studies 14*(2): 191-207.

Conrad, Ryan (Ed.) (2014). *Against Equality: Queer Revolution, Not Mere Inclusion.* Oakland, CA: AK Press.

Davidson, Alex J. (2013, 24 October). Why Are So Many LGBT Families Living in Hostile Territory? *The Advocate.* Web: advocate.com/parenting/2013/10/24/why-are-so-many-lgbt-families-living-hostile-territory.

Duberman, Martin (2001, 9 July). In Defense of Identity Politics. *In These Times.* Web: inthesetimes.com/issue/25/16/duberman2516.html.

Duggan, Lisa (1995/2006). Crossing the Line: The Brandon Teena Case and the Social Psychology of Working-Class Resentment. In Lisa Duggan and Nan D. Hunter, Eds., *Sex Wars: Sexual Dissent and Political Culture.* New York: Routledge, 213-220.

Eror, Aleks (2014, 17 March). Scally Lads. *VICE.* Web: vice.com/en_uk/read/scally-lads-v21n2.

Escoffier, Jeffrey (2008, Summer). Left-Wing Homosexuality Emancipation, Sexual Liberation, and Identity Politics. *New Politics*: 38-43.

Faderman, Lillian (1991). *Odd Girls and Twilight Lovers: A History of Lesbian Life in Twentieth-Century America.* New York: Columbia University Press.

Fiedler, Leslie (1998/1960). *Love and Death in the American Novel.* Champaign, IL: Dalkey Archive Press.

Forster, E. M. (1971/1993). *Maurice.* New York: W. W. Norton & Company.

Gates, Gary J. (2013, February) (a). *LGBT Parenting in the United States.* Web: williamsinstitute.law.ucla.edu/wp-content/uploads/LGBT-Parenting.pdf.

Gates, Gary J. (2013, February) (b). *Same Sex and Different Sex Couples in the American Community Survey: 2005-2011.* Web: williamsinstitute.law.ucla.edu/wp-content/uploads/ACS-2013.pdf.

Gates, Gary J. (2014, February). *Food Insecurity and SNAP (Food Stamps) Participation in LGBT Communities.* Los Angeles: The Williams Institute. Web: williamsinstitute.law.ucla.edu/wp-content/uploads/Food-Insecurity-in-LGBT-Communities.pdf.

Goldstein, Richard (2000, 15 February). Cease fire! *The Advocate 805*: 36-40.

Grosskurth, Phyllis (Ed.) (1984). *The Memoirs of John Addington Symonds.* London: Hutchinson and Company.

Halberstam, Jack (2014, 5 July). You Are Triggering Me! The Neo-Liberal Rhetoric of Harm, Danger and Trauma. *Bully Bloggers.* Web: bullybloggers.wordpress.com/2014/07/05/you-are-triggering-me-the-neo-liberal-rhetoric-of-harm-danger-and-trauma.

Henderson, Lisa (2004, 2 April). "Queer Visibility and Social Class," presentation at the symposium "Media/Queered: Visibility and its Discontents," University of Massachusetts at Amherst. Web: http://tigger.uic.edu/~kgbcomm/mq/Lisa_Henderson.html.

Henderson, Lisa (2013). *Love and Money: Queers, Class, and Cultural Production.* New York: New York University Press.

Hennen, Peter (2005, February). Bear Bodies, Bear Masculinity: Recuperation, Resistance, or Retreat? *Gender and Society 19*(1): 25-43.

Holleran, Andrew (1978). *Dancer from the Dance.* New York: William Morrow and Company.

Hoofatt, Laniaya Alesia (2011, June). Where The Bois Are. *Curve:* 50-51. Web: http://somaresearch.files.wordpress.com/2013/05/brown-boi-project.pdf.

hooks, bell (1992). Is Paris Burning? In *Black Looks: Race and Representation.* Boston: South End Press, 145-156.

hooks, bell (2000). Feminist Class Struggle. In *Feminism is for Everybody: Passionate Politics.* Cambridge, MA: South End Press, 37-43.

Johnson, Paul (2008). "Rude Boys": The Homosexual Eroticization of Class. *Sociology 42*(1): 65-82.

Jones, G. B. & LaBruce, Bruce (1989, February). "Don't Be Gay, or How I Learned to Stop Worrying and Fuck Punk in the Ass. *Maximum RockNRoll, 69*, n.p.

Joseph, Miranda (2002). *Against the Romance of Community.* Minneapolis: University of Minnesota Press.

Kastanis, Angeliki & Wilson, Bianca D. M. (2014, February). *Race/Ethnicity, Gender and Socioeconomic Wellbeing of Individuals in Same-sex Couples.* Web: williamsinstitute.law.ucla.edu/wp-content/uploads/Census-Compare-Feb-2014.pdf.

Kauffman, Stanley (1966, 23 January). "Homosexual Drama and its Disguises." *The New York Times,* II:1.

Kellogg, Stuart (1983). Introduction: The Uses of Homosexuality in Literature. In Stuart Kellogg, Ed., *Literary Visions of Homosexuality.* New York: The Haworth Press, 1-12.

Killian, Kevin (2011, 12 August). Tom the Carpenter is Good with Wood and Likes Men Who Work with Their Hands. *BUTT Magazine.* Web: www.buttmagazine.com/magazine/interviews/tom-the-carpenter-is-good-with-wood-and-likes-men-who-work-with-their-hands.

Kirsch, Max H. (2000). From Culture to Action. In Max H. Kirsch, Ed., *Queer Theory and Social Change.* London and New York: Routledge, 97-112.

Kramer, Larry (1997, 27 May). Sex and Sensibility. *The Advocate, 734*: 59+.

Kushner, Tony (1993). *Angels in America: A Gay Fantasia on National Themes. Part One—Millennium Approaches.* New York: Theater Communications Group.

Kushner, Tony (1994, 4 July). A Socialism of the Skin. *The Nation*: 9-14.

Lauritsen, John (1993). Political-Economic Construction of Gay Male Clone Identity. *Journal of Homosexuality 24*(3-4): 221-232.

Leleux, Robert & Jones, Mike (2008, Summer/Fall). "The First Very Bourgeoise Gay Love Story": An Interview with Robert Leleux and Mike Jones. *Gulf Coast: A Journal of Literature and Fine Arts*: 278-285.

Mann, Jeff (2014, 12 June). The Painters. *Chelsea Station.* Web: www.chelseastationmagazine.com/2014/06/the-painters.html.

Martin, Robert (1983). Edward Carpenter and the Double Structure of *Maurice.* In Stuart Kellogg, Ed., *Literary Visions of Homosexuality.* New York: The Haworth Press, 35-46.

McKenzie, Mia (2013, 28 March). 6 Things That Happened While Y'all Were Preoccupied With Gay Marriage. *Black Girl Dangerous.* Web: blackgirldangerous.org/2013/03/20133276-things-that-happened-while-yall-were-pre-occupied-with-gay-marriage.

Melville, Herman (1902/1851) *Moby-Dick or, The Whale.* New York: Charles Scribner's Sons.

Miller, Richard K. and Washington, Kelli (2012). Gay and Lesbian Consumers. In *Consumer Behavior*, 8th Ed. Loganville, GA: Richard K. Miller & Associates, 277-281.

Monteagudo, Jesse G. (1991). Miami, Florida. In John Preston, Ed., *Hometowns: Gay Men Write about Where They Belong.* New York: Dutton, 11-20.

Nava, Michael (1991). Gardenland, Sacramento, California. In John Preston, Ed., *Hometowns: Gay Men Write about Where They Belong.* New York: Dutton, 21-29.

Newton, Esther (1993). Just One of the Boys: Lesbians in Cherry Grove, 1960-1988. In Henry Abelove, Michèle Aina Barale, and David M. Halperin, Eds., *The Lesbian and Gay Studies Reader.* New York: Routledge, 528-541.

Preston, John (Ed.) (1991). Introduction. In John Preston (Ed.), *Hometowns: Gay Men Write about Where They Belong.* New York: Dutton, xi-xiv.

Read, Kirk (2001). *How I Learned to Snap: A Small-Town Coming-Out and Coming-of-Age Story*. Athens, GA: Hill Street Press.

Rechy, John (1967) *Numbers*. New York: Grove Press.

Resolution on the Queer Struggle (2013, 1 May). Adopted by the Founding Congress of the New Communist Party. Web: ncpocinfo.wordpress.com/2013/05/05/resolution-on-the-queer-struggle.

Rist, Darrell Yates (1992). *Heartlands: A Gay Man's Odyssey across America*. New York: Dutton.

Rodriguez, Richard (2002). *Brown: The Last Discovery of America*. New York: Viking.

Simon, John (1995). Edward Carpenter, Whitman and the Radical Aesthetic. In Christopher Parker, Ed., *Gender Roles and Sexuality in Victorian Literature*. Hants, England: Scolar Press, 115-127.

Sontag, Susan (2001). Notes on 'Camp.' In *Against Interpretation and Other Essays*. New York: Farrar, Straus & Giroux, 275-292.

Swan, Rachel (2014, 25 June). Pride of Place: As the Nation's Gay Districts Grow More Affluent, Lesbians Are Migrating to the 'Burbs. *SF Weekly*. Web: www.sfweekly.com/2014-06-25/news/bernal-heights-wild-side-west-oakland.

Sycamore, Mattilda Bernstein (2013, 15 October). A Movement That's a Little More Radical. *New York Times* "Room for Debate." Web: nytimes.com/roomfordebate/2013/10/15/are-trans-rights-and-gay-rights-still-allies/an-lgbt-movement-should-be-more-radical.

Taylor, Yvette (2005). The Gap and How to Mind It: Intersections of Class and Sexuality (Research Note). *Sociological Research Online 10*(3). Web: socresonline.org.uk/10/3/taylor.html.

Taylor, Yvette (2008, October). 'That's Not Really My Scene': Working-Class Lesbians In (and Out of) Place. *Sexualities 11*(5): 523-546.

Taylor, Yvette and Addison, Michelle (2013). Queer Presences and Absences: An Introduction. In Y. Taylor and M. Addison, Eds., *Queer Presences and Absences*. New York: Palgrave Macmillan, 1-10.

Thane, David (2014, May-June). Blink and You've Missed him. *The Gay & Lesbian Review/Worldwide*: 26-29.

Tóibín, Colm (1999, 21 January). Roaming the Greenwood. *London Review of Books 21*(2): 12-16.

Urban Institute (2004). *Fact Sheet: Where Do Gay and Lesbian Couples Live.* Washington, DC: The Urban Institute. Web: www.urban.org/UploadedPDF/900695_GL_FactSheet.pdf.

Uttal, Lynne (1990). Inclusion without Influence: The Continued Tokenism of Women of Color. In Gloria Anzaldúa, Ed., *Making Face/Making Soul: Creative and Critical Perspectives by Feminists of Color*. San Francisco: Aunt Lute Books, 42-45.

Walters, Suzanna Danuta (2014, 19 May). An Incomplete Rainbow: Queer Freedom and the Tolerance Trap. *Chronicle of Higher Education*. Web: chronicle.com/article/An-Incomplete-Rainbow/146555.

Warner, Michael (1993). Introduction. In *Fear of a Queer Planet: Queer Politics and Social Theory.* Minneapolis, MN: University of Minnesota Press, vii-xxxi.

Warner, Michael (1999). *The Trouble with Normal: Sex, Politics, and the Ethics of Queer Life.* New York: The Free Press.

Weir, John (1997). Going In. In Mark Simpson, Ed., *Anti-Gay.* New York & London: Freedom Editions/Cassell, 26-34.

Wilde, Oscar (1983/1891) The Soul of Man Under Socialism. In *The Complete Works of Oscar Wilde.* London: The Hamlyn Publishing Group, 915-936.

Wolf, Kathi (2014, 20 March). (a) "You Can't Let Adversity Get You Down." *Washington Blade.* Web: www.washingtonblade.com/2014/03/20/special-report-cant-let-adversity-get.

Wolf, Kathi (2014, 27 March). (b) In Their Own Words: Elders Facing Poverty, Ageism. Washington Blade. Web: washingtonblade.com/2014/03/27/special-report-words-elders-facing-poverty-ageism.

Woog, Dan (2001). *Gay Men, Straight Jobs.* Los Angeles: Alyson Books.

Wright, Les (1991). Clinton, New York. In John Preston, Ed., *Hometowns: Gay Men Write about Where They Belong.* New York: Dutton, 137-151.

A Blue Study

The Reader's, Writer's, and Scholar's Guide to

Blue, Too: More Writing by (for or about) Working-Class Queers

by Wendell Ricketts

CLASSING QUEER AND QUEERING CLASS: READING CLASS IN *BLUE, TOO*

Wendell Ricketts

Janet Zandy's "In the Skin of a Worker; or, What Makes a Text Working Class?," her indispensable chapter from *Hands: Physical Labor, Class, and Cultural Work*, tackles the issue of defining and categorizing working-class literature in this way: "If we focus on process rather than category," she writes, "it is possible to move from the static 'what is a working-class text?' to the more dynamic and active 'what makes a text working class?'"

Such a "dynamic," process-driven approach works equally well for reading and studying LGBTQ literature and especially for looking at literature in which two (or more) categories are wound together. The ten-point schema below is developed directly from Zandy's much more evolved discussion in *Hands*.*

1.   Working-class writing may or may not have an overt political consciousness, but it does have a recognition of class disparities—understanding class not as an abstraction but as a set of lived human relationships shaped by economic forces and ... [a] relationship to work at particular historical moments (86-87). A working-class text centers the lived, material experiences of working-class people.... We see the (thinking) body at work ... and the effects of work on the human body.... Working-class

---

*See Zandy, Janet (2004). "In the Skin of a Worker; or, What Makes a Text Working Class?" From *Hands: Physical Labor, Class, And Cultural Work*. New Brunswick, NJ: Rutgers University Press: 84-93. The notes below are developed from pp. 86-92. I am indebted to Janet Zandy for her kind permission to quote at length from her book.

texts contest the dehumanization of the working mind/body (90).

2. The writer of working-class literature (who may be living a middle-class life) creates imaginatively or realistically ... a space for working-class people to represent themselves.... Working-class representation usually includes the idioms, dialects, syntax, curses, blessings, and direct tones of working-class speech in particular regions and accented by ethnic and racial identities. Perhaps this is the most challenging aspect of writing the working class (90).

3. Working-class literature is not a ... solitary act. This is not so much collective writing, but rather communal sensibility. The writer is conscious of his or her ghosts, of the multiple competing, contradictory, and demanding voices that inhabit the "we" inside the individual writer's "I" (90).

4. Readers who are of the working class have the opportunity to recognize themselves in working-class writing, a rarity in an economy that uses working people and simultaneously erases and denies their existence as cultural citizens. Published writing by workers not only affirms working-class experience, but also gives permission for working-class readers to become writers of their own experience.... On the other hand, the class-privileged reader who ordinarily sees himself reflected in (written texts) is displaced and de-centered in working-class writing and is challenged to make an imaginative leap into another class world (91).

5. Working-class texts give language to human suffering and grief.... Working-class writers are particularly attentive to the physicality of suffering. This is a validation of the physical conditions that separate working-class life from bourgeois existence (91).

6. Conversely, working-class humor, wit, and language play have to be decoded in working-class texts. [W]orking-class voices ... sometimes ... have "smart mouths" at the expense of the dominant culture. Working-class humor often takes the form of in-your-face sarcasm, ridicule, and irony (91).

7. Pride rather than shame is a characteristic of some working-class writing. It is an insistence on human

dignity despite economic hardship.... Many (working-class) texts present the formation of consciousness, the coming into class knowledge.... Class oppression is evident ... in the background landscape of an economic system of exploited labor, and in the more foregrounded subjective landscape of working-class ... (voices) as they interact with others inside or outside their own class.... Many working-class writers, especially those writing in more pronounced historical moments of class struggle, take sides (92).

8.   Working-class writing is not "White" writing. Many texts ordinarily categorized as ethnic or African American can also be read as working-class texts. This is not a privileging of class over race or gender or sexual identities, but rather an insistence that any analysis of race, gender, sexuality, even disability, cannot be complete if class is excluded. (91).

9.   Working-class texts are intended to be useful, to have agency in the world ... not to be mere decorations or aesthetic commodities (91-92).

10.   Working-class texts are less concerned with postmodern linguistic play for its own ends (although they may be deeply inventive, lyrical, and funny).... Working-class texts question and challenge dominant assumptions about aesthetics, [insisting upon] the complexities of local knowledge and other circumstances (92).

To these indispensable points of departure for the serious consideration of working-class writing, I would add these reflections upon Zandy's discussion:

11.   In addition to dealing with work, many working-class texts directly consider economic costs and resources (or the basic needs that such resources provide, such as housing or food), family income or the lack thereof, and material deprivations (or the fear of such deprivation) as an ongoing force in characters' lives. Working-class texts, that is, talk openly about money.

12.   Working-class texts are conscious of how class-privileged characters see or judge working-class lives. Similarly, because working-class people tend to be more keen observers of people "above" them than are members of the privileged classes with respect to those "below" them, working-class characters may trade on the special

knowledge they gain through astute surveillance or may exploit the tendency of class-privileged characters to see them as interchangeable, "representative," or unfaceted. (Analogously, queer people may also be more attentive to the rituals, imperatives, and protocols of heterosexuality than are straight people themselves, just as members of any historically disenfranchised group often are with respect to the "majority.")

13.   Working-class writing often argues for the utility and heroism of values that the texts specifically identify as particular to the working-class: perseverance; practicality and pragmatism; survival; cleverness or inventiveness in working around "systems" whose rules or policies are oppressive to or ignorant of the working class; satisfaction with little; and respect for the dignity of "honest work," though the work may be acknowledged as "menial." Working-class texts may thus valorize characters' resistance against social or economic systems of power, even when such resistance may seem futile.

14.   The view of life and its possibilities in working-class writing may seem superficially pessimistic but actually demonstrates an approach to the "negative" aspects of human existence—thwarted expectations, reduced resources, violence, setback and loss, illness and tragedy, imprisonment, alcoholism, and depression—that is flexible and highly adaptive. Ever conscious of the likelihood of trouble and the possibility of failure, working-class characters are not necessarily undone when such events come to pass. Intimacy with tragedy, the ability to accommodate it when it comes, and stolidness in its wake may be seen to hold intrinsic value quite apart from any consideration of the effects of the misfortune itself.

15.   In working-class texts, working-class characters "speak" in their own voices, defining and interpreting their realities in their own terms as opposed to being observed, described, or "consumed" from a position within a privileged-class milieu. Standing alone, that is, the mere presence of identifiably working-class characters or of working-class settings does not make a working-class text. Careful assessment of the author's "gaze" and of the narrator's voice, then, is an essential practice in working-class textual analysis.

You'll find these fifteen aspects of working-class literature illustrated throughout the writing in *Blue, Too*. Not all of them appear in each and every piece, naturally, but this list provides ample opportunities to consider wider contexts in reading.

Reading, of course, tends to be wonderfully anarchic, obedient above all to personal taste. No one wants to approach books armed with dissecting scissors and forceps, intent on teasing out the narrowest constituent strands, but the more perspectives we can bring to our reading, the more breadth and depth we will find there. While there is great value in approaching literature as scholars, armed with our intellects and with the tools we've developed through reading and study, it is no less important to approach literature as people with personal histories, with lived experience, and with hearts, who read not passively but always with the question in mind: *How am I connected to or implicated in what this writer has to say?*

A note about the term "literature": Rumor has it that the word is anathema to working-class people and can barely be spoken among us. Accordingly, researchers and commentators in working-class studies tend to avoid references to "literature" when they can favor terms such as "texts." In part I concur. I appreciate the postmodern inclusiveness of "texts," for example, which is elastic enough to embrace songs, movies, folk sayings, television commercials, and restroom graffiti, for that matter. But I mourn the loss of "literature," especially if its disappearance is motivated by some obscure concurrence with the notion that working-class people don't like books, object to formal learning, and would be both insulted and disoriented by references to "literature." That "working class" and "intellectual" are often conceived of as oppositional terms strikes me as the worst kind of insult—the insult that pretends to pay you a compliment.

Literature is nothing more than the verbal representation of cultural values and experiences. As distinct from ordinary, everyday utterances, literature has a purpose, which is to convey or to reinforce shared knowledge or background—it is, as I've suggested, the propaganda of a culture. Literature means to embody something larger than itself, to instruct, to be passed along. That's why a shopping list is (probably) not literature but a working-class joke about the general thick-headedness of bosses (probably) is.

Working-class people and LGBTQ people have cultures, we are *literate* in those cultures, and we make *literature* about them. If we reject the term, we tacitly participate in the structures whose goal is to hold literature and learning over our heads and out of our reach. We can—and should—always discuss the merits of the texts we encounter: their scope and breadth; the sharpness of their attack; their richness of language; the use of symbol, metaphor, or allegory; their ability to evoke, provoke, or inspire; their authors' success or failure in getting their points across. But all of that is distinct from the question of whether they are *literature*.

The writing in *Blue, Too* means to be queer literature and it means to be working-class literature, but it is of necessity more than that. This is writing that represents literatures of nationality, of chronological age and of gender, of politics and region, of modern stylistics and literary fashion, and of the new millennium itself. For purposes of creating an anthology and, later, of creating a study guide for that anthology, I wrestled them into a category, but from the very start I have felt them struggling to get out. As you read, you will undo what I have done, and that is as it should be.

How to Use This Guide

The *Reader's, Writer's, and Scholar's Guide* pairs each of the pieces in *Blue, Too* with specific study and discussion materials, beginning with a series of prompts suitable for consideration of the book project as a whole. From that point on, each guide is divided into:

— a brief *Synopsis* of each of the contributions in *Blue, Too*;

— a list of possible *Discussion Questions*, suitable for small-group or classroom conversation as well as for short written responses or brief essays; and

— prompts for *Writing and Other Directions* that are intended to encourage writing and to provide a focus for group activities and research projects.

The discussion questions and prompts in the *Reader's, Writer's, and Scholar's Guide* presume a reasonable degree of sensibility to the (sub)cultural and political aspects of LGBTQ and working-class life and literature. As a result, they may not be ideal for readers encountering these issues for the very first time. Introductory materials are, however, widely available for those who want to explore these questions more fully. In the Annotated Bibliography below, you might start with the categories "LGBTQ Literature: A Few Basics" and "Working-Class Studies: Places to Start."

A Word about Trigger Warnings

I respectfully ask educators not to use trigger warnings for the materials in this book, and I do so for three reasons. First, trigger warnings are infantilizing by definition; encouraging students to determine beforehand (and without guidance) what they should or should not be exposed to tells them we value lack of experience over intellectual literacy. Second, trigger warnings are no substitute for open, frank discussions guided by well-trained, competent instructors; if you're not at ease with the material or the reactions it might provoke, don't present it, but don't try to gloss over lack of preparation with a trigger warning. Finally, it has become all too common to "warn" readers automatically whenever LGBTQ lives are under consideration, regardless of specific content, on the apparent theory that our mere existence is upsetting. Consider that there are likely lesbian, gay, queer, and transgender people in your group; for them, these materials may pose no challenge at all. Warning other group members about them, on the other hand, suggests that there is something intrinsically disturbing about LGBTQ people and that catering to the presumed discomfort of others is a worthy educational goal.

If you feel you must provide a "heads up," here's an all-purpose statement that gets the job done:

> The materials in this volume may run contrary to some readers' beliefs and values. I am not advocating, nor am I asking you to adopt or embrace any of the points of view found in these readings. You should understand, however, that presenting you with this material is intended to expand your knowledge and exercise your intellectual muscles. That requires asking you to examine issues you may not previously have considered, that you may disapprove of, or that you may find unsettling. The material in this book is intended for adults ready to engage in intelligent and mature discussion—the key words are "intelligent" and "mature." That said, no topic is "off limits," and you're not on your own. I am always here to help.

Blue, Too: Overall Themes

If you are not from a working-class background or don't identify as an LGBTQ person (or both), how should you talk about working-class life and writing or LGBTQ life and writing?

First, take a deep breath. There is nothing here that you cannot understand. Recall, in fact, Walt Whitman's rapturous claim: "I am large—I contain multitudes." And so does each one of us. Like Whitman, we can aspire to be "no stander above men and women, or apart from them."

In fact, the main tools that are required for comprehension of LGBTQ and working-class lives and perspectives (or any experience that might happen to be different from yours) are good will and a curious mind.

Along those lines, don't be afraid to talk or write honestly about your own experience, to ask questions, and to receive feedback. But above all, don't be afraid of silence—both the silence that accompanies listening (to the authors in this anthology and to your classmates, peers, colleagues, and friends) and the silence that provides the opportunity for reflection.

And here's a special note to readers who *are* from working-class backgrounds or who *do* identify as LGBTQ—or possibly both: At times, discussing our lives with "outsiders" can be fraught. We may feel marginalized or misunderstood, or—perhaps worse—may worry that we will be on display as "specimens" and spokespeople for categories that others find troubling, foreign, or exotic.

Never forget that you have a choice about what you reveal and what you participate in. If you do not feel safe, trust that feeling, but I hope you will take some risks. You have absolutely no obligation to serve as an example or to educate people who haven't done their homework; at the same time, consider how useful honesty can be in making the kinds of interpersonal connections that can potentially change lives.

Finally, remember that you are not alone. The writers in this anthology were writing with you in mind. They knew that their experiences as writers from the working-classes, as queer people, were worthy and valuable and deserved to be heard. And so are yours.

Blue, Too: General Discussion Questions

- Among the many elements that go into making up what we call our "personalities," "selves," or "identities," social class, very much like sexual orientation, is often superficially invisible. For the fiction writer who wants to create fully fleshed working-class characters, then, the "signaling" of social class also becomes a technical matter. Class, that is, must somehow be indicated to the reader—"performed," to use a word that has become common in postmodern criticism. If that is the case, we can explore the means by which the authors of these texts show the class status of their characters to the reader, how they portray working-class milieux, and what assumptions they make about readers' ability to "read" the clues they leave along the way. How, then, are characters in *Blue, Too* identified as gay and/or working class? What "markings" do you recognize? Are some signals more effective than others?

- Notice that the two terms that might appear to be most important in defining the work in the *Blue, Too* anthology— "working class" and "gay"—appear relatively rarely in the writing in these pages. What might be some reasons for that?

- In Janet Zandy's *Hands: Physical Labor, Class, and Cultural Work* (2004), as we've already mentioned, Zandy argues that working-class writing is grounded in the lived experiences of workers—that it is, in effect, quite often about work itself. Review the stories in *Blue, Too* that seem to have the greatest focus on work ("The Lowest of the Low," "Walls," "Men Without Bliss," "Austin," "Middle-Class Drag," and "Hooters, Tooters, and The Big Dog," e.g.). Do these pieces fit Zandy's characterization of working-class writing? What aspects of working-class perspectives on work do they reveal?

- Using the writing in *Blue, Too*, discuss stereotypes of "traditional working-class masculinity." Specifically, consider the narrator's violence, both literal and imagined, in "Financial Aid"; the family violence that Dean struggles with in "Saving" or that John Gilgun describes in "Fragments from an Autobiography"; Dan's violence toward Joe in "Bleeding Toy Boys"; and Rat's toward Crow in "Skins." What observations can you make about the authors' views regarding working-class masculinity and queerness, or working-class men and intimacy? What might they be suggesting about working-class men and violence?

- In materials created to accompany his book, *The Working Class Majority: America's Best Kept Secret* (The Center for Study of Working Class Life, Stony Brook University, www.stonybrook.edu/commcms/workingclass/books-wcm-studyguide.html), Michael Zweig writes that "[p]ower can be visible, as when a supervisor has authority over a workforce. But power can also be invisible, when it operates through the 'rules of the game' that we take for granted and obey because 'that's the way it is.' Invisible power is transmitted in the culture, in the education system, and in the occasional visible application of power to discipline people who think or act in ways that challenge the rules." How do the writers in *Blue, Too* show and comment on power? Pick three of the stories you find most interesting and discuss who holds power in them. What is the characters' relationship to that power? Consider whether the nature of the power is economic or something else.

- Define your own class position as precisely as possible. Begin by making a complete list of your class attributes (or those of your parents or others who believe are important in making you who you are). Include all the aspects of social class you can think of—and don't forget things like taste in music, food, or clothing; attitudes toward authority, work, or education; and life goals or plans alongside the class-related indicators that come most easily to mind (income, occupation, and education level, e.g.). Summarize what each attribute tells you about your class position. Who else in your workplace, classroom, community, state, or nation is in roughly the same class as you?

- Using the list you created above, consider who holds power over you. How is it expressed? Over whom do you have power? Does income alone entirely explain these distinctions? What does this tell you about the implications of thinking about class in terms of what might be called "power relations" as opposed to thinking about it in other ways?

- Using the writing in *Blue, Too*, discuss whether working class is an identity. Are there times when the characters in these pieces see themselves as having more in common with—or feel more solidarity with—other members of their class than they do with others who share their sexual orientation? What might make that so? In your own case, have there been (or might there be) times in which your basic differences from others (gender, race, sexual orientation) are less important when compared to the similarities you share because of your social class? What kinds of issues would tend to make you feel more connected to people whose class or sexual or gender identity is different from yours?

- Regardless of our social class, we tend to acknowledge "identities" based on race, gender, ethnicity, sexual orientation, and other attributes. From the civil rights movements of the 1950s and 1960s to the present, calls for "power" or "pride" based upon these many strands of identity have been responsible for extending basic rights to millions of Americans. At the same time, the rise of "identity politics" has coincided with a decline in class politics, labor movements, union organizing, calls for economic justice, and so forth. What do you make of that observation? Does a focus on redressing racism, sexism, or homophobia necessarily mean less attention to economic enfranchisement and disenfranchisement in society? Conversely, has awareness of so-called "civil rights" issues led to a better understanding of interdependencies and a recognition of the need for cooperation between class and "identity" politics? What conflicts do you imagine might arise along the "borderlands" between these two broad categories?

- Expand your consideration of power and class to include race, biological sex (or assigned gender), gender identity, and sexual orientation. How do these attributes affect power, either singly or in combinations? Let's assume for example, that a supervisor at a job site has more power than the employees. He or she can hire, fire, or promote them; their use of their time and the duties they perform are not under their control. What happens if that supervisor is a woman of color and the employees are largely male and white? What happens if the employees and the supervisor are all mostly of color, but the supervisor is open about being a gay man? Does power potentially shift and, if so, why? Does the category of job change your answer? If so, how?

Writing and Other Directions

- Watch individual episodes of three or four different American television sitcoms from the last four decades, presuming they are available to you (many can be found on YouTube). You can do this either as a class activity or on your own. You might watch *Roseanne*, *All in the Family*, *Married with ... Children*, *Will and Grace*, *Modern Family*,

Sanford and Son, Arrested Development, The New Normal, Friends, Good Times, Home Improvement, Seinfeld, Sex and the City, or any others that interest you. As you watch, take notes, paying particular attention to these three aspects:

> a) How is characters' sexual identity or preference indicated? That is, even though it may not be stated directly, what signs or hints are provided in jokes, offhand comments, cultural references, clothing, etc. How often is a character's sexual preference simply made clear without specific comment? What differences are there in the way the sexuality of straight and gay characters is "signaled" or identified for the viewer?

> b) How is characters' class position indicated? Look for clues in their jobs, income levels, purchasing habits, homes and furnishings, leisure activities, travel, and comments they make about money or spending.

> c) To what extent does the humor comment on or make reference to the economic or class position of the characters?

When you've finished watching and note-taking, discuss what you've observed and see what conclusions, if any, you can draw about representations of class and sexuality. To what extent do characters in these sitcoms "accept" or consider "natural" the divisions of power and influence that exist in their lives? In other words, who holds power, according to the characters? To what extent is that power economic? In what ways, if at all, do the characters question or challenge (or reinforce and approve of) these "lines of power"?

- If you have time and interest, pair that viewing with the 2005 documentary *Class Dismissed: How TV Frames the Working Class*, sections of which are available on YouTube. What insights and ideas can you borrow from *Class Dismissed* to inform your own analysis?

- Our characters, histories, and personalities include a wide variety of memberships and allegiances in addition to social class—race and ethnicity, regional or national origins, biological sex and gender identity, sexual preference, age, native language, and relationship to an immigrant past or present, to name a few. In addition, we all have personal interests (such as cooking or baseball or jazz) that place us in what we might call "communities," as well as closely or loosely held religious or political beliefs. These many different facets of our lives are more important at some points in our existence than at others, and any given characteristic may seem more-or-less important in terms of all the others (taking your life as a whole, for example, you may consider your race more important than your fascination with astronomy, or being a cancer survivor may strike you as more important than being a southerner). Make as complete a list as possible of each of your "identities," "communities," "allegiances," or "facets." When you are done, use your list to create a graphic representation of your entire "identity," using color, shapes, images cut out from magazines, or any method you choose to indicate visually the relative importance of each aspect of your identities and the ways in which those aspects intersect, overlap, complement one another, or come into conflict.

- One of the realities of our lives, though not one we often think about, is that we are almost always in someone's workplace as we move through our days. Keep a log of all the different occupations or job classifications that exist in the workplaces you pass through in the course of a normal week (at school or your worksite, at the bank or grocery store, on the bus or the highway, in your neighborhood, and so on). Which of these jobs is working class? Which are middle class? How many people are top-level executives? What does this suggest about the class composition of the labor force around you?

- Write a short story in which you invent a character who lives in a society that marginalizes and stigmatizes some characteristic, behavior, or identity that is considered unremarkable or even desirable in the world we actually live in. For example, it might be a society in which being young or having an athletic body is frowned upon, where being rich could cause one to be turned down for a job or excluded from a social opportunity, or where some churches consider pet ownership to be sinful or even sick. What attitudes does your character adopt regarding his or her difference and the views of the "mainstream"? Does your character reject "normalcy" or does she or he try to blend in? Does your character form an "identity" based on his or her difference? How does your character see power? Where does your character make alliances and find support?

"Flowers, Flames"
by C. Bard Cole

Synopsis

Among the beauties of "Flowers, Flames" is C. Bard Cole's skill with understatement. The relationship between David Florian and Frankie falls outside of categories (of sexuality and race, to name the most prominent), though it might be more accurate to say that it simply floats within them. The temptation is to describe "Flowers, Flames" as the story of an unusual relationship, but it is, in fact, a story that describes the most usual kind of relationship of all—one in which rules are being written, boundaries are being established, and contexts are being renegotiated from moment to moment, in which the partners' needs and desires are subject to change, and in which virtually none of this is explicitly discussed.

Discussion Questions

- Describe the differences you perceive between the language David Florian and Frankie use with each other and the language they use with others. How might you imagine David speaking with the people who are his clients—at Rhino Records, for instance, or at the restaurant whose menu he is designing? Notice how even the narrator's language shifts at different moments of the story. What does such linguistic "switching" reflect, in your view? Why do the changes come when they do?
- Revisit the scenes in the story in which David struggles over whether or not his relationship with Frankie needs defining. After they eat pork chops and yellow rice and are relaxing on the couch, Frankie puts his arm around David, and David thinks to himself, "Well, if I was less of a fag I wouldn't be afraid and we would kiss and make love and we'd never have to say that it meant anything in particular except we love each other." Nearer the end of the story, as David struggles to express himself, Frankie challenges him to "tell me your words for it." Cole adds, "(Frankie) almost understands but the words you choose for things matter and he wants to hear it." Discuss these and other scenes in terms of the question of

whether human relationships can exist without definitions, without clarification. Consider David's desire to know what his closeness with Frankie "means." What parallels exist in opposite-sex relationships?

- In the "bookend" scenes at the beginning and ending of the story, take note of what Frankie does not say to Raj—or what he says by not saying it. Compare the deliberate vagueness of their communication to what goes on between Frankie and David. What do you make of such differences? Would David and Frankie be better off if they communicated more like Frankie and Raj?

- What is David Florian's social class? What evidence do you have for your position? What does Frankie indicate by calling David "Flores" instead of "Florian"? Does Frankie think much about his social class, his ethnicity, or about what other "groups" he belongs to? Does he think about it as much as David? Explain your answers.

- Of all the emotions David might have when telling Frankie about his feelings for him, what is the one that causes David to "hate himself," wishing he "could die or something and get it over with"? Is his self-hatred related to his sexuality, his class, or something else?

Writing and Other Directions

- Explore the concept of the queer "homeboy." You might start with James Earl Hardy's *B-Boy Blues: A Seriously Sexy, Fiercely Funny, Black-On-Black Love Story* (Alyson, 1994) or other of his "B-Boy" novels or with Charles Rice-González's 2011 novel, *Chulito*. Alternately, locate and read one of the following articles: Touré's "Gay Rappers: Too Real for Hip-Hop?" (*New York Times*, 20 April 2003); Malcolm Venable's controversial, "A Question of Identity" (*VIBE*, July 2001: 98-106); Guy Trebay's piece on the gay hip-hop scene in Bronx, New York ("Homo Thugz Blow Up the Spot," *Village Voice*, 1 February 2000; villagevoice.com/news/0005,trebay,12230,1.html); or Richard Rodríguez's "Queering the Homeboy Aesthetic" (*Aztlan: A Journal of Chicano Studies 31*(2), Fall 2006: 127-137).

- Check out some of the "gay hip-hop nation" sites or artists on the web: Rainbow Noise, Tori Fixx, Juba Kalamka (tinyurl.com/ktj7n4c), Karter (getkarter.com), and others, or check out the documentary *Pick Up the Mic* (pickupthemic.com/Pick_Up_The_Mic). What criticisms are leveled in these sources against gay "culture" as it is commonly construed and understood? Consider the comment of a gay hip-hop clubgoer, as reported in Trebay's article: "You can walk through projects and be gay ... but you can't walk through the projects and be a faggot." What difference is being described?

- At the end of the story, have David and Frankie stopped being friends? Or has their relationship changed in some other way? What happens once Frankie gets up from the stoop? Take on the author's perspective and write the sequel or ending that you consider most likely. Be prepared to speak or to journal about what motivated your choices.

Synopsis

In describing "My Blue Midnights," Rane Arroyo wrote, "I came out in Boys Town (Chicago's gay district), after many years as a lost soul: choosing religion, trying on non-Latino names, getting engaged to a woman, falling in love with straight men. I wanted to capture the confusion of those years when I met men who should have been my perfect lovers, but only became friends. I didn't realize then what treasures friends were and are." "My Blue Midnights" deliberately reflects, both in its plot developments and specifically in its language, the unanchored, questing spirit that Arroyo was alluding to. The story lightly traces the relationship between the narrator, Ricky, and Pablo, a bartender whom Ricky meets at a family gathering and briefly dates. Arroyo touches on the murder of Pablo's later lover, Chino; on the envy Ricky evidently feels for the passion Pablo experienced for Chino; and on Ricky's own "lost soul."

Discussion Questions

- Consider the line that comes near the beginning of the story: "I see lots of businessmen eyeing unemployed (or unemployable, as my friend Linc insists) men in cowboy suits. How has the gay world become so full of uniforms?" How do choices of clothing and costume signify both genuine class differences and the "performance" of class? You will certainly think of other examples, but you might start with deliberate "dressing down" by college students in order to appear bohemian or countercultural, "hip hop" fashions that reference prison clothing (sagging, e.g.) and have been widely adopted by suburban white adolescents, the "tacky" (read: working class) drag that is a purposeful part of some male-to-female cross dressing, or the notion that dressing like a manual laborer increases one's sexual attractiveness (and not solely in a gay-male context).

The Guide for "My Blue Midnights" was prepared with the kind contributions of the author, Rane Arroyo.

- Arroyo wrote, "I didn't know I was working-class even though I worked at a factory at the age of fourteen. I wasn't a blue-collar white man." Discuss his comment in terms of this story. Do Pablo or Ricky consider themselves to be "working class"? How do you know? Is it possible to be working class and not know it? Is "working class" an identity? For what reasons might a person of color who was working class be less willing to locate her- or himself in the working class?
- Is "My Blue Midnights" a story more about race than about class (or the reverse)? What makes you hold one view or another? What does "My Blue Midnights" suggest about the intersections of race/ethnicity and class?
- Latinos (and the more hotly contested word, "Hispanics") are now the largest "minority" group in America, and Spanish and Spanglish have become necessary languages for Latino writers to describe their lives. Consider the use of Spanish and Spanglish in this story and, in particular, the significance of Ricky's observation that "Pablo talks in his sleep. He talks in Spanish." Locate some examples in the story of what is sometimes called "code switching" (moving naturally back and forth between two languages). What are some of the possible uses and meanings of this verbal crossing of linguistic and cultural borders?
- Ricky seems to believe that he is destined to live alone and lonely ("My mother and father are sleeping in each other's arms and why can't I have the same refuge?"). Pablo, meanwhile, at least in the midst of his mourning, insists that he is in some way cursed—that Chino was "taken from (him)" because "(Chino) was special" and because Pablo loved him. Would you describe these somewhat pessimistic worldviews as "typically" working class? Is loneliness or alienation a gay experience? A working-class experience? What evidence from your own life can you bring to the discussion?
- "My Blue Midnights" includes a number of pop-cultural references (film, music, etc.), but their inclusion is complicated by the fact that many of them are deliberately inaccurate. "Misreading" can be a powerful means of resisting dominant discourses—consider the simple act of changing the gender pronouns in a song to make it fit your situation or, more radically, of watching a romantic movie involving a heterosexual couple and "translating" that experience via an act of imagination into one that fits a same-sex situation. What

experiences do Ricky, Pablo, or other characters "misread," "translate," or change in "My Blue Midnights"? What similar acts do you perform in your own life?

- Revisit the opening scene at the party and consider how working-class families may be different from the families of other classes. Along those lines, discuss the significance of Ricky's line, "In our family, sometimes we had celebrations to celebrate the fact that nothing bad had happened in a long time"?

Writing and Other Directions

- Make a list of as many examples as you can remember of your family's private language—perhaps it was literally a language other than English, perhaps it was simply your family's "secret" words for things, or perhaps it was the encoded references to events or to private jokes that you shared but which "outsiders" couldn't understand. What memories do the words and phrases on your list conjure up for you?

- The last line of the story is: "I spite the gods by dreaming about reality." Think about how dreams can be revolutionary. What are some of your dreams that tempt fate—ones that might not "spite the gods," but that would perhaps seem unusual or even upsetting to your family, your friends, your partner(s)? Write about one of those dreams— or give the dream to a character you create and see what he or she can do with it.

"There Are No Pretty Girls at the Tabernacle"

by Marcel Devon

Synopsis

Scotty returns home at the end of his first year at the University of Houston with a friend in tow, his college "roommate," Terry. Scotty's mother prepares sandwiches for the boys, and, as they eat, Terry is treated to a demonstration of the bizarre and exaggerated goings-on in Scotty's family: his mother's religious fixations and obsessions with race-mixing, immorality, and the neighbors' sins; his father's sloth, vulgarity, and violence. Scotty's ironic internal dialogue betrays a comic and sometimes astringent sense of superiority, and the story lets us wonder whether the clever and condescending Scotty will keep the true nature of his relationship with Terry a secret and, indeed, whether he will keep Terry at all.

Discussion Questions

- Although "There Are No Pretty Girls at the Tabernacle" is written as humor, some of its underlying tones and themes are quite serious. Imagine a version of this story written without the humor. How would the story be different? What "serious" topics does the author broach via humor?

- What does Scotty appear to believe that a college education will do for him? In what way does attending college seem to have affected how he views his background and his family? Working-class parents sometimes warn their children with some version of the phrase "Don't get above your raising!" What do you understand that term to mean? Is Scotty someone who has "gotten above his raising"?

- What is the significance of Pa's beating the dogs? What phenomenon is the author referencing or what comment is he making, perhaps through exaggeration, in this scene?

- What clues does Scotty give regarding his ambivalence toward the environment and social class he grew up in? Given that ambivalence, how is it that he seems completely unashamed to have Terry witness them as they are? How do you feel about the way Scotty treats his mother and father?

Knowing how Scotty's parents would probably react if they knew about Scotty's relationship with Terry, would you say Scotty is justified in his attitudes or is he more critical than necessary?

- What do you make of Ma's obsession with her neighbors and their behavior? How can she be so observant and so suspicious and yet not understand Scotty's relationship with Terry? Here again, see if you can identify the wider commentary in the author's setting of this scene.
- Is Terry gay? Is Scotty? Are your answers different for the two boys? What leads Scotty to tell Terry, "There are no pretty girls at the Tabernacle"? Is he suggesting that he (like Terry?) notices the pretty girls, is he expressing jealousy, or something else? What clues do you pick up from the story that prompt you to answer one way or the other? Why do you think the author never uses the word "gay"?
- Talk about the concept of "white trash," which could perhaps be used to describe Scotty's family. What does the term mean? Is it always offensive? Consider the "reclaimed" use of the term by working-class people, which is related to the in-group use of terms like "queer" or "nigger." Marcel Devon has said, "I can write this way because it's what I come from." Discuss the freedoms and limitations of the notion of "criticizing one's own."

Writing and Other Directions

- Using the style of the story, write a humorous scene in which Scotty finally comes out to his parents.
- Pick a group that you belong to and, thus, feel free to criticize. Write several paragraphs in which you make your criticisms clear, either directly in expository writing or in humorous or some other form. Now, pick a group you'd like to criticize but don't feel quite so "safe" talking about. Outline your criticisms in the same format you used in the first exercise. Be prepared to discuss what you found different about the two writing experiences.
- Find other examples of short stories in which an author uses humor or satire to lodge more serious and pointed criticisms. You might start with the work of British writer Saki ("Mrs. Packletide's Tiger," for example), Edith Wharton's "Xingu," or Martin Amis's "Straight Fiction," but there are many examples. What do you think about such a technique? What keeps the writers in question from

choosing to express their complaints or criticisms plainly? What benefits does a humorous or satirical approach bring?

- Who do you know that you could never bring home to your parents? Perhaps, instead, it's someone you could never introduce to the people at work, take to church, or invite to your sister's wedding. And now imagine that you were to do just that. Write the scene for television or the stage. Is it humorous or serious? Keep in mind that humor may be easier, though it threatens to be superficial. Seriousness, on the other hand, could mean having to describe genuinely unpleasant interactions. See which direction your characters pull you in.

"Skins"
by Rick Laurent Feely

Synopsis

The main characters of "Skins" are Rat and Crow, two young men who live on the street and have sex-for-pay in order to support their drug habits and meet basic survival needs. We see them in the midst of an interpersonal relationship that they both (at one point or another) describe as "love." Rat provides for Crow's material needs (he arranges dates, gets them clean works, defends against danger), and Crow provides escapism (he sings, tells stories, and interprets their dreams). They also interact with gay activists from a local social-service agency. Although the activists appear to want to help Rat, they can't accept him as he is, and Rat in turn experiences them as "alien." When Crow is attacked by a gay-basher, their existence together unravels.

Discussion Questions

- Discuss the concept of "skins" as Feely uses it. What literal and metaphorical "skins" can you identify in the story?
- In the story's opening scene, Crow never finishes the sentence that begins, "But Rat...." How might Crow have completed the sentence if he were speaking for himself? Note that Crow has very little direct speech in the story. Discuss Feely's purpose in writing a nearly silent Crow.
- Rat is attracted to Crow, but he also appears to believe that Crow deserves punishment for being flamboyant and androgynous ("my first thought was that he had it coming")—or perhaps that they both should be punished just for being together. Discuss this observation in terms of what you know about "acceptance" of LGBTQ people. What does "acceptance" mean? To what degree is there an expectation, spoken or not, that people who are "accepted" ought to behave in particular ways? Discuss the American concept of "life, liberty, and the pursuit of happiness" in terms of queer visibility and "outrageous" or flamboyant

---

The Guide for "Skins" was prepared with the kind contributions of the author, Rick Laurent Feely.

public (sexual) behavior. Discuss the concept in terms of the realities of people living in poverty.

- Have you ever been told that you were dressed "inappropriately"? What did it mean? Who writes the "codes" that dictate what is meant by certain kinds of clothing? Where do such rules come from? What keeps them in place and what causes them to change?
- How does wearing a set of mechanic's overalls or a fast-food-restaurant uniform, for example, identify the wearer's class? How does such clothing prevent or complicate the wearer's access to certain environments? What differences in access might wearing a suit create? What do we know about the class of a man wearing a suit?
- In Rat's view, the gay men doing social-service work have hidden their "raw" sexuality behind a façade of middle-class civility, which is signaled (largely but not only) in the way they dress. Rat, in contrast, wears his outsider status in plain view. Beginning with that premise, discuss how middle-class and working-class or poverty-class expressions of male and gay "identities" may be different.
- Rat maintains a strict code of behavior: unemotional, unattached, practical, and both physically and sexually aggressive, even abusive. He is, however, also fascinated and impressed by (and sometimes envious of) the way Crow "wears" his own sexuality—the fact that Crow is more androgynous, "feminine" or "queer." Still, Crow's lipstick and feathers and his "flinging gestures" put them in danger on the street. Discuss what holds Rat and Crow together as well as the ambivalence they may experience toward one another.
- Why does Crow accept being sexually hurt by Rat in their first encounter? Why does he not react with anger or violence when Rat hits him after Crow is gay bashed?
- After the bashing, Crow makes the conscious decision to escape permanently from his existence. Discuss his suicide—what were his reasons for doing what he did? What other options did he have? To what extent is Rat responsible for Crow's suicide?

Writing and Other Directions

- Being a drug addict, being homeless, being poor, or working as a prostitute—all might be considered "shameful" realities. Choose (or invent) an experience you have lived or an element of your identity that you normally keep more-or-less secret. Write—in any genre—from the point of view of someone "performing" that secret publicly or making it visible to strangers. Imagine the conflicts you/your character might encounter; imagine the responses.

- Recall that Rat wears Crow's beads over his leathers when he goes to the Center for Civil Rights at the end of the story—a highly symbolic action. Write a story or a poem in which an article of clothing takes on important symbolic value.

- Rick Feely writes, "There are some stories out there about folks on the street, usually non-queer. I find most of them offensive because they are obviously written by middle-class people who don't really know the reality they are describing: The authors can't really describe what it's like to be hungry or hopeless; they don't realize what it's like to believe THIS IS ALL THERE IS. The relationship between a person's self and poverty is complex and hard. But magic is always possible in spite of the starkness. It graces it, gives it depth and beauty, though reality always has the last word. So that is my challenge: to be honest and ruthless. Not to ignore the beauty, the magic, because it is there, too." Write something in which you meet Feely's challenge to describe a hard reality in ways that are "honest, ruthless, and beautiful."

- Research homeless queer youth, male street prostitution, or suicide among LGBTQ teenagers and young people. What role does homophobia (internal or external) play in suicide? In what ways are queer and trans youth exposed to greater danger in the world (including in school or in public settings)? Report, orally or in writing, on your findings.

- Read *The Onion*'s parody "Gay-Pride Parade Sets Mainstream Acceptance of Gays Back 50 Years" (theonion.com/articles/gaypride-parade-sets-mainstream-acceptance-of-gays,351). What, specifically, is the target of the satire? Write a similar satire focusing on a different group of people, preferably one to which you belong. You might try people at the park on a Sunday afternoon, teenagers at the mall, sports fans at a football game, young hipsters at a trendy club, the crowd at a St. Patrick's or Fourth of July parade. Pay particular attention to your process—that is, what must you do to turn the people you see into negative stereotypes or parody them as outrageous, shocking, or distasteful?

```
┌─────────────────────────────────────────┐
│ ┌───────────────────────────────────────┐ │
│ │                                       │ │
│ │         "Financial Aid"               │ │
│ │      by Wendell Ricketts              │ │
│ │                                       │ │
│ └───────────────────────────────────────┘ │
└─────────────────────────────────────────┘
```

Synopsis

"Financial Aid" takes place over a short span of time in the administrative offices of an unnamed university. On one level, it describes the kind of bureaucratic conflict that many of us have experienced at one time or another. At another, "Financial Aid" is steeped in a less typically acknowledged kind of "class struggle": the conflict between someone who is entitled to institutional or government help and the person responsible for providing it—but who also has the power to withhold that help or to require the recipient to "jump through hoops." In his frustration, the protagonist responds with anger.

Discussion Questions

- Name some of the markers of class differences between the narrator of this story and the financial-aid officer, Sean Owens. Describe how each of them interprets differently the events that take place (you'll have to imagine much of Owens' point of view). What role does social class play in their ways of seeing the world?
- People sometimes say that "working class people are always so angry." Discuss the sense of narrator's rage. Would you consider such rage justified? What accounts for it—his sense of need, his sexuality, his social class, something else?
- The narrator seems particularly incensed that Owens is gay but refuses to help him. If Owens were straight, would the narrator have used the same device to get his check? If they were both women? Play with changing the characters' race, gender, sexuality, or class and discuss what you think might have been different, if anything, in their brief encounter.
- There are two points in the story at which a check passes into or from the narrator's hands. What do these brief interactions have in common? What views toward money and its literal and symbolic power can you discern in them?
- The narrator decides not to make his underlying situation clear to Owens ("Why should I give him the satisfaction of hearing me explain my life?" Do you agree with the strategy?

Might Owens have relented if he had known more about the narrator? What would the narrator have risked by explaining? In terms of the subtle (or not) power dynamics at play in situations like the one described in "Financial Aid," how is the person who explains in a different position from the person who can accept or reject the explanation?

- Use the story to discuss the concept of "social capital," which the narrator appears to lack. Imagine, for instance, that it is Sean Owens who needs something from a bureaucracy (a bank, a real estate agency, his insurance company) but his request is denied for petty "procedural" reasons. What strategies might Owens use to get what he needs? Does he potentially have more resources or options at his disposal (a lawyer in the family, a friend at the bank, a university administrator who could vouch for him?) Might his personal appearance and dress also be an example of social capital?

Writing and Other Directions

- Write about an experience from your past in which your living situation or well-being were threatened because of trouble with money. (If you've never had such an experience, write about that.)
- Imagine what happens after the story ends. Assume that Sean Owens has called the police after all. Write a scene in which the narrator explains to an officer why he did what he did. In your scenario, is the officer convinced? Include a resolution to the situation.
- Rewrite the initial scenes of the story from Owens' point of view. Make him sympathetic or not. The narrator suggests that his need for the check is particularly pressing, though Owens doesn't know the salient facts. Include in your scene what the narrator might not know about Owens.
- Imagine that you are a mediator called in to resolve the conflict between the two men. Act the encounter out in a role play with others in your group. In what way to class differences "get in the way" of a solution?
- If you are a university student, or if there is a university near you, research students who receive need-based financial aid (not loans). What are the income parameters? How much is a typical award? How many students receive such aid? In your school or area, how many students work full- or part-time while also attending college? Compared to national figures?

Synopsis

The relationship between Andrés and his father, Rafael, in "Men Without Bliss" is decidedly peculiar. Though Andrés is devoted to caring and providing for his father, the two men seem to dwell in a world of half-misunderstood communications and parallel but rarely intersecting orbits. After Andrés is fired from his job as a language tutor, he finds a new job as a residential counselor in a home for developmentally disabled adults. During Andrés' moments at home, his father begins talking about a mysterious "woman in a red hat" whom he claims to have seen on the day Andrés was born. The memory sets off a powerful desire in Andrés to track down the truth of this mystery and, in so doing, to trace his history.

Discussion Questions

- What do you make of the way that Andrés and his father, Rafael, interact? If you had to choose one or two words to describe the nature of their relationship, what would they be? Can you imagine a time when their relationship was different? What emotional function do you suppose Andrés' mother fulfilled in their family before she died?
- What is represented by Andrés search for the woman in the red hat? Why does Rafael drag the story out, giving his son only a small snippet at a time? Is it possible that there never was any woman in a red hat? Suppose Andrés finds the movie poster in the book he buys. What will he have learned or established?
- What allows Andrés to take medication and food from the facility so easily and apparently without guilt? If he feels justified in "stealing," what contributes to that feeling? Do you approve or disapprove?
- How does the author show his characters' race or ethnicity? When and how do the characters themselves talk about race?

The Guide for "Men Without Bliss" was prepared with the kind contributions of the author, Rigoberto González.

- What kind of environment is the home for developmentally disabled adults? How does the author introduce issues of mental and physical health? Comment on the way Andrés deals with the residents at the home for developmentally disabled adults. Why does Rafael refer to them as "retards"?
- What does Andrés' visit to the bookstore, and his apparently familiar relationship with the woman who works there, tell you about him? Think about books and their significance, both as physical objects and in their subject matter? What can you say about how a relationship to books and reading may be influenced by social class?
- Is Andrés gay? Would you describe him as part of a "gay community?" Why or why not? Why does Andrés seem so little preoccupied with the question of "gay identity"? What kinds of issues do preoccupy him and why?
- Though there is no particular indication in the story that Andrés' father "knows" he is about to die, it is still possible to talk about the way the story of the woman in the red hat is something that he bequeaths to his son, almost as if he is aware that the mystery will energize Andrés in a way that other aspects of his life (apparently) do not. Discuss that idea, including the larger issue of how mythologies and mysteries sometimes play vital roles in enlivening our lives. Don't forget that the woman in the red hat is, in essence, a story within a story, a fiction (perhaps) within a fiction.
- How do you explain Andrés' reaction to his father's death? After "those few moments of panic [that seemed to be] all he had to offer," what is his state of mind? What, in his way of reacting to unfortunate events—being fired from his tutoring job, for example—reflects a working-class worldview? Is Andrés simply indifferent? What else might account for his way of moving through the world with such apparent detachment?
- Comment on the word "Bliss" in the title? What does bliss mean and what does it refer to in the story? Who are the men without bliss?

Writing and Other Directions

- Search the classifieds in your local paper for job advertisements for home healthcare workers, residential counselors, nurses' aides, elder- and child-care workers, hospital orderlies, and the like. Try to find a wide variety of listings (use online classifieds in other cities if that yields more results). Report on what you learn about the requirements and the pay for such jobs. What do you make of anecdotal evidence that such jobs are often performed by gay men? Using the classifieds again, compare the first set of salaries you found with those offered for jobs such as nursing home administrators, doctors and nurses, or so-called "skilled" health care staff. Draw some conclusions based on what you find.

- Write about the books you had at home when you were growing up—or their absence. What was the attitude where you grew up toward books and reading? Alone or with a group of other researchers, interview others about the role of books in their childhood homes. Be creative about the questions you ask, and take note of your interviewees' demographic information: age, gender, race/ethnicity, social class, region, and so forth. Finally, analyze the results of your data. What do your findings about books and reading suggest?

"Middle-Class Drag: A Performance Piece"
by Renny Christopher

Synopsis

"Middle-Class Drag" is the autobiographical story of the narrator's multi-level journey: from childhood (or "working-class boyhood," as Christopher puts it) to adulthood; from home through a series of moves to and from far-off cities, universities, and workplaces; through various attempts to negotiate "being told what I wasn't and should be"; and from working-class laborer to "middle-class woman trying to invent a gendered and classed identity that spans boundaries." Christopher is outspoken, ironic, and humorous in discussing a lifetime spent "resisting or eluding social control" and in whose resistance gender and sexuality play a significant role.

Discussion Questions

- Christopher says "I'm not really transgender or transsexual. I'm something else. Just genderqueer, like I'm class-queer." What does she mean by "genderqueer" and "class-queer"? Beyond the common current meanings of "queer," how does Christopher intend the word? What does it mean, for example, "to queer class" or "to queer gender"?
- In what way is "gender ... the new frontier: the place to rebel, to create new individuality and uniqueness, to defy old, tired outdated social norms"?
- Compare "Middle-Class Drag," in which Christopher speaks specifically about articles of clothing and personal appearance as "drag," with Judy Grahn's story, "Boys at the Rodeo," which also touches on issues of gender-as-performance. Christopher seems to be agreeing with queer theoretician and cultural philosopher Judith Butler who suggests that, even if we cannot consciously choose whether or not to perform gender, we can take some control over the form that performance will take. What does Christopher gain or achieve through "drag"? What keeps her from simply "fitting in"?

- In the closing poem, "So Arrest Me," Christopher asks "What, exactly, is 'women's clothing,' anyway?" If you're in a group, have members write their answers down anonymously on paper and then compile the results. Discuss what you find out.
- What important event in American history took place on May 4, 1970? What is it that the narrator "sees" through the television "window"? What "revolution" does she contemplate? When she says that "Kids from my town became the soldiers, / never the students," what is she suggesting about class and the U.S. military?
- Consider the other pieces in this volume that suggest, in one way or another, that a kind of border-crossing takes place between working-class origins and a university education: "Austin," "Bleeding Toy Boys," "Fragments from an Autobiography," "Red vs. Blue," and even "There Are No Pretty Girls at the Tabernacle." What impact does higher education have on class status? Consider Tara Hardy's statement: "I am a slim generation away from not being able to decipher my own ballot." How does putting "Dr." in front of her name help Christopher hide "not only my sex, but the truth of my origin"? How much is the supposed relationship between class and education a truism vs. observable fact (see what statistics tell you about class and educational level)? Does university education reliably move working-class people out of the working class?

Writing and Other Directions

- Write a scene in which you invent a character whose actions are in some way dictated by codes of clothing and costume. Think about the circumstances that might bring a janitor to put on a business suit, for example. Imagine a character who, dressed in an orange jail jumpsuit, is visited by his or her relatives. Or else a style-conscious adolescent who puts on a plaid polyester uniform in order to hold down a job at a fast-food restaurant. Let their clothing—and their changes of clothing—give you ideas about what motivates your characters and about what happens to them.
- Alternately, write and perform a scene in which you make use of physical props that indicate your transition between the roles and worlds that you inhabit. Choose clothing or other items that symbolically represent your "transitions." If you'd rather not perform, create a visual collage of the same concept using images that you draw or find.

360 I A Blue Study: The Reader's, Writer's, and Scholar's Guide

- Research working-class people in "academia," either as students or teachers. You might start with books like *This Fine Place So Far from Home: Voices of Academics from the Working Class* (C. L. Barney Dews and Carolyn Leste Law, Temple University Press, 1995), or with articles like Stacy Torian's "Breaking through the Class Ceiling" (inthefray.org/ 2005/03/breaking-through-the-class-ceiling) or Sherry Linkon's "Should Working-Class People Go to College" (workingclassstudies.wordpress.com/2011/04/18/should-working-class-people-go-to-college). Prepare a presentation on some of the realities that working-class people face as students in colleges and universities, and feel free to discuss your own experiences if they are relevant.
- Read about why the issue of employing "adjuncts" as professors in American universities has become controversial. (Adjuncts are part time, untenured teachers who typically work without job security on semester-to-semester contracts and without employment benefits, including health insurance.) Are these people "middle-class" because they teach in colleges and universities and are called "professor"? Is adjuncting a "white-collar" profession? What is a "white-collar profession"? Learn about adjunct salaries and working conditions and respond to these questions in a presentation to your group, or in writing. Be sure to discuss how adjuncts "trouble" easy distinctions between working-class and middle-class work. Some places to start:

   The Adjunct Project (a service of the *Chronicle of Higher Education*): adjunct.chronicle.com. Provides specific information on adjunct salaries by zip code. The "Get Advice" section contains many useful articles and commentaries.

   Fruscione, Joseph (2014, 25 July). When a College Contracts 'Adjunctivitis,' It's the Students Who Lose. *PBS Newshour.* Web: pbs.org/newshour/making-sense/when-a-college-contracts-adjunctivitis-its-the-students-who-lose.

   Kilgannon, Corey (2014, 27 March). Without Tenure or a Home. *New York Times.* Web: nytimes.com/2014/03/30/nyregion/without-tenure-or-a-home.html.

   Segran, Elizabeth (2014, 28 April). The Adjunct Revolt: How Poor Professors Are Fighting Back. *The Atlantic.* Web: theatlantic.com/business/archive/2014/04/the-adjunct-professor-crisis/361336.

"Anyway, It's Not Like Things Could Get Much Worse"

by Andrej Longo

Synopsis

In Naples, Italy, Samantha has taken a room on the top floor of a hotel, intending to commit suicide. She is spending a final few minutes, thinking and looking out at the city, before jumping from a high ledge. When a firefighter comes to her rescue, she is at first distrustful, and then his simple acts of kindness convince her to speak to him honestly. By the end of their brief encounter, they seem to have found a common language, and Samantha has begun to consider other options.

Discussion Questions

- One way to read the story might be to link Samantha's despair to the fact that she is both transgendered and a prostitute. In her view, however, neither of those issues is "really the problem." What, then, does lead to Samantha's decision to commit suicide? To what extent do we tend to see others' differences (gender, sexual orientation, religion, language, immigration or economic status) as a "problem" for them? What might Longo be suggesting about the way people who are "different" experience their lives?
- To what degree is Samantha's situation a consequence of her social class? Her goals for herself (to "decide what she wants to do with her life: be a whore or a hairdresser, or maybe start studying and get a diploma") seem quite basic. How do economic realities get in her way? Would she face the same roadblocks—severe enough to make her contemplate suicide—if she were middle-class or wealthy? If not, what problems might she face?
- At the end of the story, Samantha contemplates "giving herself the gift of a dream" and imagines that "things might even go the other way" in her life. What argument can you make for or against the likelihood of such change?
- Imagine that Samantha gets on that train for "Paris or Madrid." What happens next? Consider that Samantha has no job, few marketable skills, no place to live, and limited

prospects. She would be leaving the culture she knew; she would face language barriers and might find doors closed to her because of her gender. Would it be courageous or foolish for her to "slam the door" on her life and leave?

Writing and Other Directions

- Just "getting on a train and changing my life" may be a romantic escape fantasy, but see if you can design a realistic plan for Samantha to get out of her situation and create a new life. Focus on the six months immediately following the end of the story. Feel free to invent details.

- Do some reading about so-called "white slavery" and discover why it is considered a major international human rights concern (see, e.g., the Convention for the Suppression of the Traffic in Persons and of the Exploitation of the Prostitution of Others, a resolution of the UN General Assembly). Report your findings.

- Though the story mentions this only in passing ("maybe it had something to do with all those firemen who died in America trying to save people"), it is part of a collection of stories set in Naples, Italy, in the hours following the September 11, 2001 attacks on the United States. Do some research about the first responders on 9/11. How many of them were working class? Is heroism of that kind—risking one's physical safety for others—a working-class virtue? Continue your research to include the volunteers who have joined the U.S. armed forces since 9/11. They, too, are often described as heroes. What can you find out about their social class?

- When Samantha says "You got no idea what the police are like, right?" and explains that she "belongs to some piece-a-shit boss," what reality is she describing? To answer the question more deeply, read at least a few chapters of Roberto Saviano's *Gomorrah: A Personal Journey into the Violent International Empire of Naples' Organized Crime System* (New York: Picador, 2008; if the book isn't in your local library, excerpts are available on the *New York Times* website and elsewhere). What is the relationship between the Italian mafia (called the Camorra in Naples) and women? Though organized crime certainly makes a few people very rich, it depends to a great extent upon the participation of poor and working-class people and on the erosion of the economic and social power of the middle-class. To what extent is that also true of criminal gangs in the U.S.? Divide the tasks up among several researchers and report on your findings.

Synopsis

"Heaven" takes place in an industrial English Midlands that is, to say the least, economically and socially depressed, and is told from the point of view of a young resident, Enoch Jones. Enoch is a month away from entering "reform school," the result of his apparently incorrigible delinquency. As he waits for his sentence to begin, Enoch becomes the special mission of the local vicar, who lays out a program of church attendance and compulsory choir practice for the "wayward" boy. Enoch, however, acutely feels his and his family's difference in their community, and he refuses to cooperate in the effort to fit him more neatly into the wasted lives he observes around him. Enoch's wild and desperate project of resistance—his "acting out"—is, paradoxically, an effort to save himself. Enoch is a reminder that recognizing what one cannot bear is often easier than knowing how to change it.

Discussion Questions

- Some argue that "delinquency" is a necessary means for young people to find their place in the world. Depending upon the social setting, however, the "antisocial" behavior of boys more than girls, and of whites more than of people of color, can be met either with an amused sense of tolerance or with a grim desire to impose punishment and control: "boys will be boys" vs. "they must learn their limits"; "they're good kids just letting off a little steam" vs. "we must nip this behavior in the bud." Significantly, Enoch's transgressions are not likely ever to be seen as simply "letting off steam" or as the acceptable boundary-testing of a normal boy. What limits do we impose on the kinds of behavior depicted in "Heaven"? What role do class and color play in the way the "criminal" behavior of young people is viewed (or, more specifically, in how the behavior of young people is criminalized)?
- "Heaven" can be seen as a tale in which a young man comes face to face with an important self-discovery. In what ways, if

---

The Guide for "Heaven" was prepared with the kind contributions of the author, Royston Tester.

any, might young gay men's journeys of self-discovery be different from those of their heterosexual contemporaries? What about the journeys of working-class boys?

- In what ways does Enoch's homosexual "practice" stand in for (or combine with) other symbols of difference and alienation? Notice that Mr. Ketland, even in the midst of his physical encounter with Enoch, reminds Enoch that he and his family are "bad news," that they were "trouble" from the moment they came to town. How does Enoch's "seduction" of Mr. Ketland become a symptom of the kind of "trouble" the older man believes Enoch to represent?
- Consider the above question from Enoch's point of view. How is his homosexual "practice" or his stealing a form of resistance? And to what? In the last line of the story, what causes his "optimism" about reform school?
- Analyze Enoch's contention that "The way you discover things about yourself—Nancy-boy? Trash? Bog whore?—is when you're not expecting to. Even the worst sounding places—and people—can turn you right around." Using your own experience, evaluate the truth of Enoch's philosophy.
- What is the nature of "trailer trash"? Note the ways in which the poor or working-class are sometimes viewed as detached from the mores of "normal" society and therefore as "free" (and, similarly, as "depraved," an attribution that contains a clear sexual element).
- Think about the working-class snobbery that Tester weaves into "Heaven": the differences between the "skilled" Austin workers and the others in Longbridge ("a cut above"); the ways that Enoch and his family are considered "trash" even among other solidly working-class people. For her part, Enoch's mother expresses a similar conviction of superiority over the local people. What is the source of such conflict and competition among people who appear to share difficult economic circumstances?

Writing and Other Directions

- Enoch Jones comes from England's "Black Country," described by Theodore Dalrymple as one of the world's "most depressing areas of urban devastation." Locate the region, investigate its not insignificant industrial and cultural heritage, and compare it with similar areas closer to home. You might want to look into the history of the Austin Motor Works and compare that to the rise and collapse of the auto industry in America (see, e.g., Michael Moore's 1989 film, *Roger & Me*). Present your findings and decide whether Dalrymple's opinion is just.

- Men's washrooms and locker-rooms seem to play a crucial role (as reality or fantasy) in the cultural and psychosexual self-awareness of men who have sex with men. Examples from literature cross disciplines, including Renaud Camus' *Tricks* and the early novels of John Rechy; the diary of the late British playwright, Joe Orton; the controversial 1976 study, *Tearoom Trade* by Laud Humphreys; William Leap's edited volume of scholarly essays, *Public Sex/Gay Space,* or references in gay men's "coming out" novels to self-recognition achieved in the high-school changing room. In short, washrooms, locker-rooms, and rest-stop bathrooms have historically been sexualized spaces for gay and gay-behaving men. Delve into this topic and see what you can find out, then present your findings. Investigate some of the moral and "public image" questions the issue presents; consider the fact that some of the very first modern gay "civil rights" legislation concerned the entrapment and harassment of men who went looking for sex in public lavatories. Why does no related phenomenon exist for women who have sex with women?

- Jane Austen once commented, "One has not great hopes from Birmingham. I always say there is something direful in the sound." How would you define the spirit of this industrial city as reflected in the characters and events of "Heaven"? Imagine "Heaven" were a movie. Write the tagline that would appear in a television advertisement for the movie or on a poster, "summing up" in a few dramatic words the story's content and themes. Design the movie poster or perform your commercials out loud in front of your group.

```
┌─────────────────────────────────────────────┐
│  ┌───────────────────────────────────────┐  │
│  │                                       │  │
│  │             "Austin"                  │  │
│  │          by Robby Nadler              │  │
│  │                                       │  │
│  └───────────────────────────────────────┘  │
└─────────────────────────────────────────────┘
```

Synopsis

In language that may strike the reader as fractured, poetic, stream-of-consciousness, or at moments perhaps even deliberately unintelligible, "Austin" is largely a description of work—in this particular case, of the sweaty, dangerous, exhausting work of sandwich-delivery boys in the financial district of Austin, Texas. "Austin" celebrates and solemnizes the camaraderie and solidarity of the "boys at the shop" (the other delivery riders whose experience of the city is shaped, as is the narrator's, by the work they do) even as it serves as a nostalgic valediction on the part of the narrator who is about to leave a milieu that has profoundly shaped his life.

Discussion Questions

- The most immediately striking aspect of "Austin" is its language. Do you consider the writer's use of language to be "authentic"? What is problematic about saying that "Austin" is or is not "authentic"? In other words, on what basis do we establish the criteria we use to judge "authenticity" here?
- "In the Skin of a Worker; or, What Makes a Text Working Class?," Janet Zandy writes that "working-class texts are less concerned with postmodern linguistic play for its own ends" but may "question and challenge dominant assumptions about aesthetics" even as they insist upon "the complexities of local knowledge." Discuss "Austin" in these terms.
- Race, ethnicity, class, gender, etc., all have an impact on the language(s) we use in daily life. Based on the language of this piece, how do you imagine the race, ethnicity, class, etc. of the author? Would it surprise you to learn he was raised in an Orthodox Jewish household in Beverly Hills, California, has been privileged to study abroad and to earn several advanced degrees, and is now a doctoral student in creative writing? Given those facts, do you think he has the "credibility" to tell this story (or to tell it in the way he does)? Don't forget how

The Guide for "Austin" was prepared with the kind contributions of the author, Robby Nadler.

common it is for writers to co-opt or appropriate other people's cultures, including at the level of language. Does Nadler "steal" anything that isn't his to tell?

- The author may no longer be a boy in Beverly Hills but he is also no longer a young man who sweats on a bike to deliver sandwiches in the Texas heat for a thousand dollars a month. Which of his class lives is "real"? Is he bound to the class life he is born into? Are we? Does the author romanticize the "daily grind" of the sandwich-delivery rider? How might someone who is still living the existence described in the story and who cannot leave it write about the experience?
- The drivers in Nadler's story are closely attuned to how other people treat them. In commenting on the men who flirt with him at the "glitter bars," the narrator says, "One of the first rules of driving is never give your digits to a tie-man if he isn't kind to you with the uniform on." What would make that one of the first rules?
- Discuss the narrator's comment, "We got called lazy 'cause we are in lots of ways." To what extent do you agree that workers should always be "giving 100%" or trying to please the boss? One way to look at "laziness" is as a form of resistance that workers can engage in. If that is so, what might it be resistance against? Do only so-called "low-level workers" engage in such resistance? What is your "work ethic"?
- In the last section, the narrator has left his job as a delivery boy to enter graduate school. He returns briefly for a party thrown for him by his former co-workers. What does the narrator mean when he says, "Looking back is water"? Consider the final line, "Honestly, I had never been as happy," which follows his observation that, when the party was over, he would be "'college boy' again and lose the language that bound us." What is the source of the narrator's happiness? What emotions might he be experiencing about leaving Austin for the place "up north [that] was the jump off"? When he says "language," what lies beyond the literal sense of the word?

Writing and Other Directions

- There has long been controversy about what "standard English" is and whether or not it is a completely arbitrary, even oppressive construct. To speak (or write) "incorrectly" is to fail to adhere to a set of rules, and rule-breaking speakers are sometimes penalized—they may be denied employment opportunities, thought of as stupid, flunk courses, or be ridiculed even when their language is steeped in rich community ties. At the same time, "non-standard" dialects, accents, or slangs may at times be expected because they identify speakers as "insiders." Language, in other words, also functions as a gatekeeper. Keep a log of the different "Englishes" you encounter over the next few days. Include what you can observe about the speakers'/writers' age, class, gender, and ethnicity and a description of what you notice about their language. Include what you read in written materials from any source, including posters and graffiti; encounter in music or online; and hear on television and in conversations, whether you participate in them or overhear them. When your logs are complete, compare them with those of others in the group. What conclusions can you draw from your observations? In which cases did you notice negative or positive reactions (including your own) to particular ways of using language? What do those reactions suggest?

- "Hidden" workers surround us. They may not be literally invisible (though some are), but they often fade into the background. For example, if you eat in a restaurant, you will certainly be aware of your waiter, but perhaps not of the person who drives the food to the restaurant, stacks it in the refrigerator, washes the dishes, carries away the garbage, or launders the napkins. The sandwich-delivery boys in "Austin" might be considered "semi-hidden" workers, but others who are more invisible include the men and women who fill the paper-towel dispensers in the bathrooms at the mall, the people who package the food you buy at the supermarket, the mechanics who keep busses and subways running, the workers who sort your recycling, the people who sweep up popcorn and soda cups at the movie theater. If you've ever held such a job, write about how others see you in your work role—or about what it is like *not* to be seen. If you haven't, imagine such a situation, perhaps based on the workers you encounter or know of in your daily life. You may decide that fiction, nonfiction, drama, or poetry is most appropriate for the voice you want to create, but pay particular attention to how you use the language of your real or imagined workplace. Note: You may find it useful to consult Studs Terkel's *Working: People Talk About What They Do All Day and How They Feel About What They Do* (originally published in 1974, but much reprinted).

Synopsis

"Hooters, Tooters, and The Big Dog" might be described as a picaresque, a story of adventurers and rogues on the highways of life—literal highways, in Anderson's case. The trucker known for most of the story as "High Mountain" (but whose real CB handle is "Northern Exposure") is hauling a load of fertilizer west toward California when he finds himself drawn into an unusual competition. Anderson steeps his true-life account in the terminology and daily realities of the trucker's life, as well as in a sly, bawdy wit that gives his characters a particular vibrancy. Northern Exposure's "secret," which the reader may guess but which the other truckers don't know, adds an additional layer to the comedy.

Discussion Questions

- What makes "Northern Exposure" so reluctant to reveal his CB handle to most of the other truckers? Talk about how the theme of "exposure" runs through the story in different ways.
- Notice, as with many of the pieces in this anthology, that the word "gay" is never mentioned. Note, too, that Northern Exposure's possible hookup with the "cowboy with a big, dark, bushy mustache and a straw Stetson hat" is managed in a kind of code in which nothing is explicitly stated. Discuss that ambiguity in terms of issues like honesty, openness, self-disclosure, and "coming out." Is what is unsaid also uncommunicated?
- One of the interesting features of "Hooters, Tooters, and The Big Dog" is the highly "gendered" world that Anderson depicts. Take note of scenes and descriptions in the story in which Anderson seems to comment specifically on the behavior, speech, and attitudes of men vs. women. Notice, for example, that In Between sports "long, painted nails" and expects to be treated "like a lady," though she earns her living as a trucker, is verbally and sexually aggressive, and instigates the "hooters contest." What is Anderson saying about gender and gender roles? What might he be saying

about the way that working-class work (truck driving, in this case) interacts with gender? Argue for or against the notion that Anderson's view of gender in this story is a specifically working-class one. Does Northern Exposure's presence as a (hidden) gay man "queer" expectations of gender and of sexual orientation in the story and, if so, how?

- The "hooters contest" could simply be viewed as sexist, but see if you can develop a discussion that invites a more complex view. Were In Between and Go Figure objectified by their would-be admirers? Is it possible they were being exploited without being aware of it? What about "wet T-shirt contests" in the real world? Consider, too, the largely working-class occupation of stripper. How does the issue of choice—as both gender and economics affect it—enter into your thinking? We often hear the argument that women have the right to choose abortion because they have final control over their bodies. Do we agree that women also control their bodies if they want to use them for prostitution, stripping, surrogate parenting—or just for their own amusement?

- When Northern Exposure participates in the "hooters contest," he exploits, in a certain sense, the heterosexual presumption—that is, the general attitude that everyone is heterosexual. Northern Exposure knows he isn't involved in the contest in the same way as the other presumably male, presumably heterosexual truckers who genuinely want to see In Between's and Go Figure's "hooters," and he tries to bow out of judging the contest as gracefully as possible. Still, the other drivers insist—In Between says she'd be offended if he didn't want to see her topless—and so he goes along, allowing others to think what they want. There may be both drawbacks and advantages to permitting a certain level of "murkiness" in our interactions with others, but are there good reasons to allow others to "presume" you are straight if you are not? (What about safety, for example?) Disadvantages? Consider the argument that being gay or lesbian is "private" and no one else's business. Is that all there is to it?

Writing and Other Directions

- Browse Anderson's highmountainranch.com website. Check out, in particular, the sections called "Tales from the Road" and "Witnesses from the Circle." In the latter, Anderson celebrates the medium of personal story telling, noting how the tradition of the "story circle" revitalizes lost connections and brings strangers together. He writes, "[S]tory circles eventually became places where sequestered gay men and women came out, told their stories and even found acceptance." What do you notice in the writing on Anderson's site that surprises or challenges you? Notice his use of the word "sequestered" instead of the more common "closeted." What does Anderson's word choice suggest? Report back on what you discover.

- Conduct a media survey of the heterosexual presumption in advertising. Print or broadcast advertisements that depict heterosexual relationships or mother-and-father families as "typical" or "universal," for example, often trade in the heterosexual presumption (as well as presumptions about so-called "intact families," gender roles, race, and so on), but gay-inclusive advertising makes use of gender and sexual-orientation presumptions as well. Here are some places to start if you need them, but materials are widely available on the internet and YouTube:

  ~ Amazon Kindle: youtu.be/S-7IA54-tmE
  ~ Levis: youtu.be/rB1hxyFHi3Q
  ~ Renault Twingo: youtu.be/1pwN-yiho4M
  ~ Pepsi: youtu.be/tIG0kB9lOxo
  ~ Toyota: youtu.be/3lkjBmsdJvU
  ~ Dolce & Gabbana: youtu.be/-wa40b1C_jc
  ~ "A Barneys Campaign Embraces a Gender Identity Issue" (nytimes.com/2014/01/30/fashion/Barneys-Bruce-Weber-transgender-models.html; thewindow.barneys.com/brothers-sisters-sons-daughters)

Discuss how these examples play off/with the presumption that everyone is heterosexual or that an individual's apparent gender is the same as the one she or he was assigned at birth. Why is there sometimes such a violent reaction to advertisements that challenge heterosexual or gender presumptions? (See, e.g., "Nabisco's Gay-Inclusive Honey Maid/Teddy Grahams Commercial Slammed By One Million Moms" (tinyurl.com/lybw2yo; youtu.be/3UMMn6oVtOc.)

Synopsis

John Gilgun's "Fragments from an Autobiography" is exactly what the title suggests: sections of an autobiography that the author is completing. In a nonfiction context, "Fragments" reflects the themes that Gilgun has explored in his writing throughout his career ("Cream" in *Everything I Have Is Blue,* "Cannon Fodder," in the *Harrington Gay Men's Fiction Quarterly*) as well as in his own books (see the Annotated Bibliography)— life in Irish working-class Boston in mid-twentieth-century America, sexual difference, and intellectual achievement as a "way out" of dead-end work and mental suffocation. In "Fragments," Gilgun, who will be eighty in 2015, describes both a youthful struggle to uncover family secrets and, perhaps in some ways, an adult one to put old hurts to rest.

Discussion Questions

- Why does Gilgun speak so much about work? What was the source of his resistance to being put to work in his family's business? What did it represent to him?
- In Oscar Wilde's 1891 *The Soul of Man Under Socialism*, Wilde wrote, "I cannot help saying that a great deal of nonsense is being written and talked nowadays about the dignity of manual labour. There is nothing necessarily dignified about manual labour at all, and most of it is absolutely degrading. It is mentally and morally injurious to man to do anything in which he does not find pleasure." What does Wilde mean by "degrading"? Would Gilgun agree with Wilde? Do you?
- Gilgun has strong words for his parents and grandparents ("I'd have killed the son of a bitch," he says of his father) as well for the "good old family business" and for religion ("God made you to work your ass off at coolie labor for a dollar a day, six days a week. Sunday you have off so you can spend it in church with me"). How do you interpret such comments? Do you imagine Gilgun as someone who is bitter or as someone who has cleanly amputated an uninhabitable past?

On what do you base your answer? To what end does Gilgun present his memories in such strong terms and with such blunt language?

- Reflect on the dining-room scene in Fragment I between Charles and May. What do you imagine—or what do you think Gilgun imagines—to be the motivation behind May's behavior? What larger drama does this interaction represent?

- What did Gilgun see as his way out of the limited and limiting possibilities he saw around him—either the lives of members of his own generation or those of his parents and grandparents? What choices did he face? What role did being gay play in his consciousness that life at Gilgun's Milk wasn't for him? How about his desire, even as a young man, to become a writer?

- Janet Zandy writes that one characteristic of working-class writing is that working-class writers "take sides" regarding class struggle. (See "Classing Queer and Queering Class: Reading Class in *Blue, Too*" for a fuller discussion of Zandy's take on working-class writing.) Discuss the "sides" that Gilgun takes for or against the people he mentions in his autobiography. Whose side is he on? Against whom? Who is on his side?

- "Every time you laugh at something I write here, I get a day off in Purgatory," Gilgun writes, suggesting that he clearly sees humor in "Fragments." Do you? What is humorous? If you find no humor in "Fragments," what do you see in its place? How effective is Gilgun's voice?

Writing and Other Directions

- The Irish-Catholic working-class milieu of Boston, Massachusetts and nearby neighborhoods and suburbs plays an almost mythic role in the history of American class and race relations. Malden, for example, where "Fragments" is set, is about six miles north of the center of Boston. Alone or in a group, see what you can learn about this area. You might start with the films *Good Will Hunting* or *Mystic River* (note that the actual Mystic River flows just south of Malden and meets the Malden River on its way to Boston Harbor). Alternately, read Michael Patrick MacDonald's memoirs *All Souls: A Family Story from Southie* or *Easter Rising: A Memoir of Roots and Rebellion*; J. G. Hayes' short-story collection, *This Thing Called Courage: South Boston Stories* or his second collection, *Now Batting For Boston*; Richard Marinick's detective novel, *Boyos*; or Dennis Lehane's novel, *Mystic River*, on which the movie is based. Alternately, find other representations of Irish-Catholic working-class life in Boston during the twentieth century. Compare and contrast "Fragments" with the work you have reviewed. Orally or in writing, present what you have learned regarding working-class issues and the Boston Irish.

- Returning to Wilde's and Gilgun's reflections on the nature of manual work, "family business," and so forth, begin to make a list—either alone or with others—of the work you observe being performed around you (or which you or someone in your family performs or has performed) that is "absolutely degrading" and devoid of pleasure. Write or talk to the group about whether such work is "necessary" in America today. Briefly research Marx's concept of "alienated labor" and, in light of the kinds of work you have identified, discuss (or ask the group to discuss) the possible consequences of an expanding labor force in which the worker does not direct his own actions and is seen wholly or largely as an cog in a wheel that produces profit for others.

- Choose one of the other characters in "Fragments" and write a "fragment" of her or his autobiography. Have your character reshape or reinterpret some of the events that Gilgun describes. You can make your narrator sympathetic, villainous, funny, remorseful, or anything you choose.

- Consider Gilgun's short poem, "What Work Is":

> Work is letting someone
> pound your thumb
> with a hammer
> because it feels so good when they stop.
> Only they don't
> stop.

Write a very short poem of your own that begins "Work is...."

Synopsis

An air of worry or of tragedy, but also of a sort of amiable resignation, infuses "Lowest of the Low," a story about chaotic lives, ill-defined relationships, and low-end existences. The narrator, Dwayne, is contemplating the end of a three-month relationship when a teenaged neighbor, Tiffany, knocks on his door and asks for his help. Her arrival initiates a new, unexpected set of circumstances in Dwayne's life, and he adapts with what might either be considered passivity or viewed as a well-honed ability to make the best of what life throws his way.

Discussion Questions

- The question of "identification" comes up often in discussions of fiction. Some readers believe that one of the writer's jobs is to give the reader a reason to like a character, to "relate to" the character, to "pull for" him or her, or to "care about" his or her ultimate fate. What does it mean to "relate to" a character? In your reading of stories, how important is it to your appreciation of the story to "relate" to the characters? Discuss the issue of "identification" in this story. How does Banner create connection between the reader and Dwayne despite everything?
- Tiffany says that Kyle is the "lowest of the low" when he is depressed. Who belongs in the category of "the low," however? When Banner chose that phrase for the title of the story, was he referring to Kyle, to himself, to a group of people in general? Support your position with quotes from the story.
- What does Dwayne mean when he says that his love for Tiffany and Kyle is "lazy and good-for-nothing, even possibly illegal"? Contrast his relationship with Barney: Dwayne loves Barney as well, he says, but adds that he understands "how (Barney) can just leave without one thought about me and pick up where he left off." In this instances in which Dwayne directly declares his love for another character, what do you imagine "love" means for him?

- By now, to speak or write about "self-destructive behavior" or "low self-esteem" is nearly a cliché. Banner seems to suggest, however, that Dwayne's existence is more complicated than the all-too-familiar narratives we may be tempted to impose upon it: a wasted life, a man engaged in self-sabotage, and so on. Discuss Dwayne from his own point of view. How does he feel about the life is he living?
- "Hell I don't know" both begins and ends the story and some version of "I don't know" appears several other times. What doesn't Dwayne know when he says it? How does he feel about not knowing? What are some of the many meanings we intend when we say "I don't know"?
- In one way or another, all of the main characters in the story—Dwayne, Kyle, Tiffany—are leading lives they might prefer to leave. Or, in any case, they might be better off if they did. Why don't they?
- In creating the physical environment of the story and setting the scene, Banner employs what might be called "class markers"—products, clothing, food, etc. Which, if any, of these identify the characters are "low class"? Are there such things as "low class" or "high class" tastes in TV programs, food, entertainment, and so forth? How are such distinctions created or maintained?

Writing and Other Directions

- Alone or with a partner, become an anthropological field researcher and visit some of the sites in Banner's story—a convenience store like United Dairy Farmers, a public laundromat in a strip mall, a Walmart store. Observe the people who work there or who are customers. Take notes. Report back (or write about) the impressions you have about their lives or about the interactions you witnessed. Are they like you or different from you? How?
- Find or listen to the lyrics of the song "Me and Bobby McGee" and discuss the line "Freedom's just another word for nothin' left to lose" in terms of this story. Do some research to find other songs or poems that portray the idea of hopelessness, hitting bottom, or similar sentiments. Write a poem, song, or rap on the same theme.
- Imagine that Tiffany's mother has called the police and that you are the social worker assigned to their case. Alone or with others, decide what Tiffany, her mother, and Kyle need. Do some research on the resources available in your

community. What services would be available to them and how much would they cost? How easy or difficult would it be for them to qualify for or use those services? In both a short and longer-term sense, how much impact would a specific service or resource have in meeting the needs you've assessed? How do you imagine Tiffany, her mother, and Kyle responding to your suggestions? How would you persuade the three of them?

• Use any one of these four lines taken from the story as the opening line of your own story, poem, or journal entry:

> ~ That white little belly breaks my heart.
> ~ It's sick and yet it's also like hope.
> ~ He hovers over her like he has trapped her with his secret powers and she will never be free.
> ~ [His smile] has got the sticky warmth of not being able to live right.

Synopsis

Dean Durber writes that "Bleeding Toy Boys" "explores different possibilities for understanding same-sex sexual(ized) contact across class borders. While 'gay' seems concerned with conformity and assimilation, 'queer' suggests a more radical restructuring of social norms that could potentially undermine the 'normal gay' model." True to that philosophical underpinning, Dan and Joe's relationship in this story may be seen as a love affair between a "queer" working-class man and a "gay" middle-class one, though the story also attempts to complicate sexual and "romantic" categories. Themes of violence, masculinity, and thwarted intimacy as well as descriptions of the characters' home lives and family backgrounds are especially revealing.

Discussion Questions

- Consider the concept of "disease" in "Bleeding Toy Boys" ("It's her smell on my fingers, in my clothes, in the disease of my blackening lungs"). What "disease" does Dan share with his mother? What do you learn—about his feelings toward her, his family, his background, and the possibilities he sees for his life—from what he says about smoking?
- When Dan reflects that "This place was never built for the likes of me," what "place" is he talking about? And who are "the likes of me"? Do you agree or disagree with his assessment of himself and his surroundings? Similarly, what does Dan mean when he tells Joe, "I don't want to be like you"? What does "like you" mean, for him?
- When he goes to Joe's house for Christmas, Dan doesn't tell Joe's mom the name of the town he really comes from. What does he fear would be revealed if he told the truth? Would you consider Dan's concern to be justified, given what you know about Joe and his family?
- Describe Dan's and Joe's family and social backgrounds, particularly as they are revealed in the characters of the boys'

The Guide for "Bleeding Toy Boys" was prepared with the kind contributions of the author, Dean Durber.

mothers. Note how stilted and difficult conversations are between Dan and his mother, with much (apparently) left unsaid. How is Dan's mode of communication reflected in what he does or does not say (in words and silences) to Joe?

- Describe the relationship between Dan and Joe in a way that does not make use of the terms "gay," "homosexual," or any similar words that refer to their sexuality. Why do we so often rely on the heterosexual/homosexual binary as the main, if not the only way we describe and understand human romantic/ sexual/ intimate/partnered relationships? What other options exist? What keeps us from using them? How is it that we so rarely use the term "heterosexual" to describe opposite-gender relationships?
- The very first time Dan meets Joe, he deliberately injures him by slamming a door into his face. He seems thereafter to feel the desire to physically hurt Joe about as much as he feels the desire to be tender toward him. What accounts for this ambivalence? How is the Dan/Joe relationship similar to or different from the Rat/Crow relationship in "Skins"?

Writing and Other Directions

- Journal or free write about a social situation in which you've lied to avoid presenting yourself as you truly are. Use that writing to begin a fiction or non-fiction piece in which you include such a scene.
- Assume the identity of Joe or of Dan's mother. Describe your relationship with Dan. Tell what you fear about him, what you hope for him, what you would like him to do or say to you. Use the format of a letter, a screenplay, a poem, or whatever strikes you as most evocative.
- Choose an experience from a past relationship—with a partner, friend, or relative—in which you felt you were unable to be "yourself." List a few specific incidents that were emblematic of the ways in which your reality was challenged or your sense of personal integrity seemed to be "overridden" by the other person. Weave those incidents into writing that discusses either the expression or the frustration of the desire to be fully "visible" in relationship to others.
- Write the scene that would naturally seem to follow the story's last paragraph. Describe where Joe goes when he gets into his car finally and leaves the university. Can you imagine him returning home? Where does he go?

"Red vs. Blue"
by Tara Hardy

Synopsis

"Red vs. Blue" is a performance piece originally intended to be delivered before a live audience. Even on the printed page, however, Hardy's language is direct, raw, and passionate. Overall, Hardy focuses on the experience of being torn between apparently warring home places—she is, as she puts it, "straddling two boats hell bent on rowing in opposite directions." Hardy hints that she, too, might have lived an existence of "oversimplified, deep-fried versions of the truth" had she not left her family and, in the process, had the opportunity to be both formally educated and exposed to other social and political perspectives. Still, as she makes clear, some basic truths are not "complex," and her journey from "there" to "here" has left her in a "state" of profound ambivalence.

Discussion Questions

- How does the second line of "Red vs. Blue" work against the reader's expectations? When the word "Stupid" follows "For the Red States," what does Hardy presume the audience will understand her to be saying? How does she dismantle the audience's assumption?
- The red state/blue state divide—terminology that emerged during the contested election of President George W. Bush in 2000—can be seen both as a literal description and as a kind of metaphor. Aside from the actual borders between physical states, what other kinds of figurative or metaphorical "colonies" and borders does Hardy touch on in the piece? Is Hardy suggesting that being a lesbian is a political position? That being working-class is?
- How satisfied are you with Hardy's analysis that her Uncle's situation is the result of brainwashing, low pay, and contending with negative situations he has no means to remedy (his wife's pain, the rabbits in the flowerbed)? If she is correct that Melvin "votes his pocketbook," what are the consequences for him of doing so? If people like Melvin truly do vote for "the guy who promises to put more power in

[their] pocket"—and yet over time continue to remain poor—what explains their reluctance to vote differently?

- In the last paragraphs of the piece, Hardy refers several times to "we." Who is included in this "we"? Who is excluded? How do you know? Contrast these instances with her use of the word "we" at other points in the poem.

- Discuss Hardy's concept that "an hour is an hour is an hour." What specifically is she suggesting? How would you argue for or against such a standard? What would shift in the world if wages were attuned to a standard of "everyone's time is equally precious" vs. the current one in which some people's time is treated as more valuable? How do we justify paying for people's time at such widely divergent rates?

- How is your work valued? Who decides what it is worth? Whose work is "worth" more than yours in dollars and cents? Whose is worth less? Are these fair distinctions? Is salary or pay rate the only way to determine the value of work? Consider, for example, that pay is actually often inversely related to the usefulness of particular work. Social work, teaching, nursing, and elder and child care are among the lowest-paid of all professions, but the benefits to society are considerable. Investment banking, corporate law, and hedge-fund management, conversely, are among the highest-paid professions, yet one could argue that the benefit of this work to society in general is negligible. (See, e.g., www.alternet.org/labor/robert-reich-just-imagine-if-people-were-paid-what-their-work-really-worth-society.)

- Is the amount of pay someone receives a moral question? Is access to affordable healthcare an ethical question? What about having the economic means to attend a decent university or own one's own home? How many of the inequalities we see around us (homelessness, disparities in access to education and healthcare, mass incarceration) indicate genuine moral dilemmas and to what extent are they "natural," "inevitable," or simply unsolvable conditions? Is Melvin and Juanita's economic situation "natural" or "inevitable"? What place do ethical and moral considerations even have in a discussion of socio-economic and class issues? Support your position.

Writing and Other Directions

- Perform "Red vs. Blue" out loud or have different people perform sections of it. What emotions do you experience in speaking these words and why? What parts are most difficult to say out loud? How does the piece change when a live performer assumes the voice of the "I" in the poem?

- Research the concepts of "equal pay for equal work," "pay equity" (equal pay for work of equal value), "living wage," and "comparable worth"—all of which are approaches to compensating people fairly for their labor. How do some of these philosophies "preserve the class order," as Hardy puts it? Report on the differences among these approaches and, alone or with others, come up with a proposal to create fairness in pay and ensure that workers can count on basics like safe housing, medical care, and enough to eat.

- Find out what you can about gentrification and about its impact on affordable housing in American urban, working-class neighborhoods. (You might start with the *"Gay Market," Affluence/Income, Consumerism & Gentrification* section of the Annotated Bibliography.) Peter Cohen, the executive director of the San Francisco Council of Community Housing Organizations says, "There are a lot of annoying opinions out there on both sides of the debate [about gentrification].... It's a kind of [a] softball [issue]; anyone can hit it ... but there are real people who actually get hurt while [others are pretending to be experts]." Do your best to avoid "softball" responses and annoying opinions. Instead, once you've done your research on the points listed below, create a three-part visual presentation (no PowerPoints, please) that addresses these issues: (1) How do neighborhoods become eligible for "gentrification" in the first place? In other words, what is the process by which an area becomes "run down" or "blighted" (and, thus, in need of "redevelopment")? (2) If changes in a neighborhood attract younger, college-educated, professional people who are sophisticated, liberal, and artsy, is that an unequivocal good (and, if so, for whom)? (3) Robert J. Sampson, an urban sociologist at Harvard University, says, "The affluent moving [into middle-class neighborhoods]—that's an urban battle, but not gentrification." Find out who *is* displaced in actual gentrification—the "real people" that Cohen refers to. How are poor and working people directly affected when they must leave cities for the periphery (consider issues like transportation, access to medical care or services for the elderly, the availability of child care, etc.)? Bring some of their stories back to the group.

"advancedELVIScourse"
by CAConrad

Synopsis

The sections of "advancedELVIScourse" that appear in *Blue, Too* are taken from CAConrad's book-length work of the same name. Conrad employs an episodic, non-linear, and non-narrative structure to create an impressionistic and stylized reflection on Presley, on Presley's social class, and on Presley's status as a cultural (and sexual) icon. By juxtaposing vignettes, literary quotations, personal reflections, and fantasies that border on the surreal, Conrad seems to come at the topic of Elvis from every angle at once, looking, in particular, for points of contact between the "fantasy" of Elvis and the author's realities as a queer man from a working-class background.

Discussion Questions

- Discuss Elvis Presley as a gay icon, as a celebrity who could (and, no doubt, did) serve as romantic and sexual fantasy material for (some) men as well as for (some) women. How does Conrad suggest a "queer" reading of Elvis? What purpose is there in undertaking such an attempt to "recontextualize" or "re-imagine" Elvis?
- If we assume that writers often both "respond to" and "react against" in their work, what would prompt a writer to favor the style, structure, and language that is found in "advancedELVIScourse" over a more "traditional," linear approach to his or her subject? Are there drawbacks to either approach?
- Do you believe that people can ever really completely erase a poverty-class or working-class background? Did Elvis succeed in becoming "middle class" or "upper class"? Support your position with evidence.
- In a 2005 documentary on the life of Presley, a reporter was quoted as saying that "Elvis and Priscilla were the perfect couple. Any red-blooded American woman would have been in love with Elvis, and any red-blooded American man would have been in love with Priscilla." What problems do you see in linking the concepts of "red blooded" and "American" with

the concept of heterosexuality? Whose realities might be excluded from a statement such as the one the reporter made? Does it matter that they are excluded? What exactly is meant by the phrase "red-blooded American"?

Writing and Other Directions

- For a week, keep a journal of the times you encounter the words "we," "us," "they," and "them"—in books, magazines, and newspapers; on the news or talk shows; or in popular music or movies; or when you say, write, or hear them in your own interactions with others. Pay special attention to comments that purport to describe what large groups of people (Americans, women, the working class, African-Americans, Republicans) feel, do, or believe. Can you identify instances in which the realities or experiences of specific groups are assumed to be universally true of everyone (we/us) or of a particular group (they/them)? Based on your observations, what do you think lies behind such blanket statements? Why might a writer or speaker want to use (or avoid) them?

- Research Elvis Presley's life. Present what you learn about his class background and upbringing. Although Presley became wealthy by anyone's standards, are there ways in which his life and music continued to be marked by his poor and/or working-class roots? In what ways? Find the lyrics of three or four of his songs and use them to illustrate your points.

- Identify a singer, living or dead, whose work speaks to you. Write something inspired by the singer: a letter to him or her, a song, a poem, a reflection. Imagine that he or she will actually read what you wrote. Now write his or her response back to you in any form you like.

- Conduct biographical research to identify living celebrities or sports stars who grew up in poor or working-class settings. In what ways do they appear to continue to feel connected to where they came from, even after becoming wealthy? Alternately, in what ways have they distanced themselves from their roots? What makes it so unlikely that we will see or learn about stars with poor or working-class backgrounds unless we look specifically for them? Why, in the context of rap and country-western music (to name two genres where it is common), do performers often instead seem to be flaunting childhood hardship, violence, poverty, or deprivation?

```
┌─────────────────────────────────────┐
│  ┌───────────────────────────────┐  │
│  │                               │  │
│  │          "Walls"              │  │
│  │       by L. A. Fields         │  │
│  │                               │  │
│  └───────────────────────────────┘  │
└─────────────────────────────────────┘
```

Synopsis

The action in "Walls" is circumscribed in time and space, and the action is very limited. Essentially all that happens is that the main character, Tulsa, calls an employee into his office on a construction site, has a brief conversation with him, and then goes home at the end of the day with his spouse. Yet a great deal of emotional drama and even the threat of danger lurk in the background. The story's power lies in what remains unspoken—and in the ominous suggestion that trouble is waiting just ahead.

Discussion Questions

- In what ways are Terrence and Tulsa "in the closet?" In not making the nature of their relationship clear to those they work with, are they pragmatic or cowardly? How would your view change if they were a heterosexual married couple? What differences exist between "hiding what you are" and "letting people make their own assumptions"?

- What historical fact is Tulsa referring to when he mentions the "don't ask, don't tell policy"? Think about some of the things you "don't tell" or the people you "don't tell" them to (but don't feel pressured to say anything out loud). Reflect on how you negotiate the boundaries between environments in which you can "tell" and those in which you cannot. How do Tulsa and Terrence negotiate those boundaries?

- What actual event is the author alluding to when she has Tulsa reflect that he "isn't looking to get chained to one of his own company trucks and dragged around behind it"? (Hint: check materials on the site of the Southern Poverty Law Center: www.splcenter.org.)

- One of the realities of LGBTQ lives is that it is sometimes necessary to manage other people's homophobia, including the possibility of violence. What are some of the Tulsa and Terrence's strategies for maintaining equilibrium at the work site and safeguarding their personal safety?

- Review what Tulsa says about his "hateful little office" and how it reminds him of things he "doesn't like to be reminded of." When he notices that the "office doesn't seem to like Jaspers either," he seems relieved. Why would that be? If not for Jaspers' homophobia, on what basis might he and Tulsa experience solidarity despite their different sexual orientations?
- When Tulsa calls Jaspers in to talk, neither one of them specifically names Jaspers' objectionable behavior. Why do you suppose that is? What would have been different about the conversation if Tulsa had explicitly told Jaspers to stop making anti-gay comments?
- Tulsa attempts to draw a comparison between racism and homophobia when he asks Jaspers whether he'd call their boss a "nigger." Jaspers defensively responds that "he's no racist." How would Jaspers explain a mindset in which being known as a homophobe is acceptable but being known as a racist is not?

Writing and Other Directions

- Research violence against gay men, lesbians, and transgendered people in the U.S. (or anywhere else that interests you). A couple of places to start are the website of the Leadership Conference on Civil and Human Rights or materials about hate crimes and anti-gay bullying on the sites of the Safe Schools Coalition (safeschoolscoalition.org), Campus Pride's "Stop the Hate" campaign (campuspride.org/stop-the-hate), or the Matthew Shepard Foundation (matthewshepard.org). If you don't know anything about the murder of Matthew Shepard in 1998, you might start there and with the 2012 film about his life and death, *Matt Shepard is a Friend of Mine*. Report on what you find. Organize a debate on hate-crime laws and their effectiveness.
- Should there be limits on what people say at school or in the workplace? Design a "hate speech and verbal harassment" policy for your school or the place where you work. Do your best to balance the right to free speech and expression against the right of people to be free of verbal harassment in the places where they work or go to school. To get some ideas, research existing policies or codes.
- Research and report on the U.S. military's "Don't Ask, Don't Tell" policy, in effect from 1994 to 2011. As a project, create a sexual-orientation-related "Don't Ask, Don't Tell" policy for

your group, and leave it in place for at reasonable number of meetings. No one may indicate anything about romantic relationships, dating behavior, marital status, etc., or anything else that might allow someone to conclude that the person in question was heterosexual, homosexual, or bisexual. Assign monitors to keep track of "violations" and, at the end of the experiment, report on your findings.

- If creating such a policy is impractical for your group to carry out, take your policy out into the world and use it as the basis for observations you make of those around you. Take notes on the ways in which people "out" themselves as heterosexual—both explicit and subtle. Be sure to include things like wedding rings, photographs, mentions of children, jokes, social media, the use of pronouns, etc. How difficult does it appear to be to "not tell"?

"Saving"
by Carter Sickels

Synopsis

The sadness that runs deeply through "Saving" is the sadness of those for whom the concept of "home" has become a complicated proposition. After his aged grandmother is moved to a nursing home, Dean returns to his birthplace in Perry, Kentucky, to close up her house. He brings his girlfriend, Jillian, along for company. From the moment they arrive in Dean's "native" land, however, the differences between them seem to loom larger. For Jillian, Dean's homecoming provides rich material for the documentary film she intends to make. For Dean, the return to Perry is more profoundly troubling, more closely connected to the question of his true place in the world, and more private than Jillian is able to comprehend.

Discussion Questions

- What is the significance of the story's title? What or who is being saved? Who is doing the saving? What is Dean saving (or throwing out) in specific? Talk about the multiple meanings of "saving" in the context of the story.
- What are some of the markers of the class differences between Jillian and Dean? What is Sickels' purpose in including such details of Jillian's life as tickets to the opera, the Whitney Biennial, being in therapy, talking about feelings? Certainly, anyone from any background could go to the opera, talk about art, or go into therapy, but do they? Are they likely to in Perry, Kentucky? Why or why not? What is it that makes such behaviors or interests "classed"?
- What does Jillian mean when she says that Dean's growing up was "more real" than hers? For Dean, is that a compliment? What does the "realness" of his youth represent for Dean?
- Dean is probably not wrong when he says that he and Jillian need to be careful in Perry, that they "can't be raging queers out here." It also seems likely that living openly in Perry as a transman would be nearly impossible. At the same time, Dean's attachment to the physical place, to his grandmother,

and to the memories and history that are rooted in Perry is obvious. Discuss how this complicates Dean's life.

- Both Jillian and the nursing home director suggest that Dean's grandmother's stories about being raped or attacked come from her "mixing up" something that happened to her in the past. Dean doesn't accept this explanation easily. What do you make of his reluctance to dismiss his grandmother's version of events?

- Discuss the character of Paul. To the extent that he identifies Dean as a heterosexual man, Paul speaks to him in what Paul apparently considers the language of solidarity among straight men. When Paul complains about his divorce and says, "*Women,*" what makes him confident of a sympathetic response (or, at least, not a negative one)? What makes his comment ironic under the circumstances? Dean is officially neutral in his responses to Paul, but he does allow Paul to state his opinions without challenge. What are Dean's reasons for doing so (note that Dean calls himself a "coward")? Who else identifies Dean as a straight man? Should Dean correct these assumptions?

- Throughout most of the story, Jillian is intent on filming Dean for her documentary. Dean is acquiescent, if not always enthusiastic. Taken as a metaphor, what does the detail of the documentary suggest about the way Dean experiences his return to Perry and the way Jillian sees him? What does Dean mean when he says that, when Jillian's film is done, "I will not recognize myself"? How else is Dean not "recognized"?

- Writes Sickels, "Jillian spends the days behind her camera, filming me, filming the house. I spend the days organizing and cleaning...." They would both probably say they were "working," but what different meanings do Jillian's work and Dean's work have? What keeps Jillian from helping Dean with the physical labor of cleaning, sorting, and moving?

- Talk about the concept of "transitioning" as it is used in "Saving." Carter is "transitioning" in terms of his gender, but he is also, in a way, "transitioning" from his youth in Kentucky to an adult life elsewhere. Jillian and Dean are transitioning out of their relationship. Dean's grandmother is transitioning in more than one sense. In all of these transitions, arguably, something is lost and something is retained. What does Dean lose and what does he keep? What does he keep despite himself?

- Leaving a small town for a new home—usually a city—is a common theme in LGBTQ literature. The process is often described as liberating and celebratory, but what makes it more complicated for Dean? What might make it more complicated for any queer person who grew up poor or working class? Dean says that his grandmother's broken-down house, the place where he was raised, represents something that "will always be a separate part of my life, the part that is the deepest and oldest." Is this "separation" between his present and the "deepest and oldest" part of his life inevitable? What dimension does being a transman add to the rupture between past and present?

Writing and Other Directions

- For the next week, pay attention to "small talk"—the kind of conversation that goes on between people who have just met or don't know each other well. Consider: elevator chat, barista/waitperson banter, standing-in-line and waiting-room talk, and party or workplace conversation. Take notes or keep a log. What do strangers or near-strangers consider "safe" topics to broach with you? What do you assume are safe topics to raise with someone you don't know well (or at all)? What assumptions do people make about you (or you about them) in these conversations—about personal interests, politics, or social or religious views? Which of those topics seem gender-specific? Is there such a thing as "guy talk" or "gal talk"? If so, what is it? Write about a time when someone spoke to you in a way that seemed based upon an inaccurate assumption about who you are. Alternately, write an invented dialogue in which two people of the same gender meet in a casual circumstance you invent; have them engage in "guy talk" or "gal talk." Compare what you and others in your group come up with.
- Create a map, a diagram, a flow chart, a timeline—or in some other way visually represent the major transitions that you have experienced in your life and that lie ahead of you. From this design, choose a moment that seems particularly fruitful and write down what was (or will be) gained, lost, or transformed in that transition. From these materials, create a poem, song, or prose piece whose purpose is to communicate the emotion associated with that moment or transition. Include any details you want, but your main goal is to transmit the sensations behind the facts.

"My Special Friend"
by Christopher Lord

Synopsis

"My Special Friend" is both a love story and the story of a homecoming, and one of its notable features is a happy ending on both counts. Rudy and Harley have been together as a couple for something less than eight months when Rudy's parents invite them to spend Christmas with them at the rural home where Rudy grew up. Though Harley is also a working-class man, Rudy at times seems embarrassed by him. For most of the story, in fact, he behaves badly, ignoring the love that literally surrounds him. Lord focuses on possibilities of harmony and reconciliation, suggesting that unresolvable conflict need not be the only result of interaction with our families of origin and that the urban world need not be the only locus of acceptance and respect for working-class queer men.

Discussion Questions

- Consider how easily Rudy's family accepts Harley. Would you describe this acceptance as a typical family reaction? A typical working-class family reaction? Discuss the belief that working-class families are more homophobic and have a harder time accepting a gay or lesbian child. What can you find out about the sources of this belief? What elements of truth does it contain, if any? What experiences do you have that shed light on the issue?

- Discuss the moments in the story when Harley and Rudy describe their respective jobs. What do you learn about them from the way they talk about their work? What do you learn from the other characters' reactions? Note that Rudy's father plans to work part of Christmas Eve and that Rudy must return to work at the restaurant on Christmas Day. Make a list of the people who must work on holidays. What kind of impact does such a work schedule have on their families?

- Two-year colleges that grant associate ("AA") degrees are arguably America's most democratic and staunchly working-class educational institutions. Compare the attitudes toward education in "My Special Friend" with those in Dean Durber's

"Bleeding Toy Boys," Renny Christopher's "Middle-Class Drag" and other pieces. Is there a "working-class attitude" toward education?

- What kinds of ambivalences toward his social class is Rudy struggling with? Note, for example, that Rudy tells his mother that Harley "wants to learn stuff" and "doesn't want to be a grease monkey forever"—though she is not actually concerned about Harley's job and though Harley himself describes Midas as "a good employer." Note, too, Rudy's comment about the "bad taste" of the aluminum Christmas tree his parents once had. Rudy seems, in some ways, to be unable to take part in a kind of comfort that the other characters experience with each other. How would you explain that?

- Ootie understands Rudy's "problem" to be shame, a lack of "gay pride," while Rudy himself comes to recognize that the source of his "meanness" is fear—of falling in love, of accepting Harley's importance in his life. What's your analysis of Rudy and of his participation in his relationship with Harley?

- Ootie also says that Harley is the real Megillah" and she tells Rudy that Harley is "the real thing." What is she talking about? What does she see in Harley?

Writing and Other Directions

- There's no shortage of articles, stories, and films that include "back home for the holidays" scenes, often played for their comic potential (see, e.g., the film *Home for the Holidays* [1995], *Pieces of April* [2003], the "Homo for the Holidays" episode of *Will & Grace* [1999] or, on a darker note, read or see Harold Pinter's *The Homecoming*; Jim Grimsley's novel, *Comfort & Joy* also explores this theme). Write a scene for a screenplay or the theatre that exploits the comedy or tragedy of holiday homecoming for a character who is no longer comfortable in his or her family of origin or who, like Tara Hardy in "Red vs. Blue," is torn between "homes." You invent the reason why.

┌───┐
│   │
│   **"Boys at the Rodeo"**   │
│   **by Judy Grahn**   │
│   │
└───┘

Synopsis

Set in 1972, "Boys at the Rodeo" is the story of six women who attend a rodeo near the women's farm (apparently in Texas) where they are spending the summer. As soon as they arrive at the rodeo gate, and for the rest of the story, they are mistaken for and treated like teenaged boys. As "boys," then, but also as grown women, the narrator and her friends observe the rodeo. Grahn's narrator offers rich and insightful commentary regarding how men interact with women (and each other) in the microcosm of the rodeo grounds and what the women around them appear to accept as their "place." Her observant eye takes in the differences between boys and men, women and girls, "dykes" and rodeo queens, and people whose "family name is all over the county" vs. those who compete with dignity in contests they know they cannot win.

Discussion Questions

- The women's physical appearance (short hair, Levis and shirts, bodies muscled from outdoor work) certainly contributes to their being mistaken for boys, but it is not the only reason. What other aspects of their behavior cause the men at the rodeo to place them "outside" the category of women (or, as Grahn says, "girls," which is what "all the other women at the rodeo are called")? Can you imagine a scenario in which a thirty-year-old man could pass—without intentionally meaning to—as a "girl at the rodeo"? What do you make of that?
- For the men in the story, gender-based categories seem relatively few: there are girls, boys, and men. The narrator and her friends clearly aren't men, but they don't seem to be girls. And yet the possibility of butch women, of lesbians, of women who dress differently, "who are not the rancher's wife, mother earth, Virgin Mary or the rodeo queen" don't occur spontaneously to the men at the rodeo. How does this both create freedom and produce constraint for the women in the story?

- Is what Grahn describes an artifact of time and setting or could it still happen? Is there more space today for us to make choices in which we are not hemmed in by our gender—or by people's expectations based on their perceptions of our gender? Consider such issues as men who wear skirts, male nurses, women in combat, women sportscasters in men's locker rooms, or the controversy that has erupted in many places over transpeople in the "wrong" public restrooms.
- What clues are there to the class setting of the story? What makes "Boys at the Rodeo" a story in which social class figures? What are some examples of how Grahn places a consideration of class alongside commentary regarding other social inequalities?
- Are rodeos "working-class entertainment"? What other public events or pastimes would you associate more closely with the working class? Specific sports? Do particular performers appeal to working-class audiences? (If so, how do they do that?) Are certain styles of music "working class" (rap, punk, heavy metal, or country, for example)? Is the association positive or negative? Compare your lists with those of other group members and see if you can tease out any common threads in your definitions.
- Grahn's narrator expresses both admiration for some aspects of maleness and rejection of other aspects. What does she like about men? What does she find troubling? Why does she consider it "depressing" to be "easily accepted" among the young men watching the bull riders? What does Grahn mean when she writes, "I have never decided if it is worse to be thirty-one years old and called a boy or to be thirty-one years old and called a girl"?
- People from so-called devalued groups tend to be astute observers of those who belong to more highly valued or "majority" groups. When Grahn says "fourteen year old boys—what a disguise for travelling through the world," what does that disguise allow her to do or to see? In what ways does the narrator's position as a woman and as a lesbian allow her to "see" gender, class, and racial inequalities that others in the story might perhaps accept as natural or not notice at all?
- The narrator—admitting it is "speculation without clues" decides that several of the young women she sees are "dykes." In the context of what happens in the story, what

does "dyke" mean for the narrator? What is Grahn saying when her narrator labels some women "dykes" because they appear to be resisting roles constructed for them?

- Some years after Grahn's story appeared, queer theoretician and cultural philosopher Judith Butler revolutionized feminist and literary criticism by writing about gender as performance. In very broad terms, Butler's concept was that gender is always "performed" and that it is in no way the natural or inevitable expression of an innate or biological condition. Butler argues that we cannot choose to perform gender, only the form our performance will take. (See, for example, Butler's 1990 *Gender Trouble: Feminism and the Subversion of Identity*.) "Boys at the Rodeo" seems to anticipate these ideas by describing instance after instance in which characters in the story "perform" gender or demand or expect particular "gender performances" from others. Find examples and discuss them.

Writing and Other Directions

- Write about a time when you did your best in a competition even though you knew you would not succeed or "win"— that is, about a time you deserved a reward for "believing there ever was a contest, for not being the daughter [or son] of anyone who owns thousands of acres of anything." Don't be too literal; interpret the prompt in a way that fits your experience.
- Use creative writing as an opportunity to "perform" an identity that is not yours. Write in first person "as" the character you choose, of whatever class, race, gender, sexual orientation, profession, ability, age, etc., you decide, but do your best to be specific and true to your character's authentic experience (as you imagine it). The goal here isn't just the finished piece of writing, but the opportunity to be conscious about your process. To that end, keep careful notes and be ready to talk about the difficulties you encountered, the decisions you made, the points at which you felt you didn't have sufficient information, and the moments when you felt most confident. As a second step, show what you've written to the group and get their feedback on the authenticity of the character you created.

Reading Blue:
An Annotated Bibliography
by Wendell Ricketts

This bibliography, which accompanies the study guide for *Blue, Too: More Writing By (For or About) Working-Class Queers*, is intended both as an ending and as a beginning: an ending, once and for all, to the argument that materials for the study of working-class queers—and, in particular, for the study of a tradition of cultural production by, for, or about working-class queers—do not exist. And a beginning because the materials collected here are only the tip of an iceberg.

For one thing, they represent, with only a few exceptions, materials published in English and in the United States. It scarcely needs to be said how vast a world lies outside that framework, and none of us can be unmindful that most of the working-class texts on the planet, however defined, are not in English. This is a difficulty that similarly plagues working-class studies programs, working-class anthologies, and so on.

The bibliography evinces a temporal bias as well. The farther back in time we move from the present day, the more the question of what constitutes LGBTQ "studies" (including literature) bogs down in issues of definition and category. Original materials (as opposed to scholarly or retrospective studies) become harder to find and harder to place in meaningful context.

No less tricky, of course, is grasping how same-sex relationships "mean" in all the places where they exist and, in turn, understanding what and how people write about those relationships (if they write about them at all). What is gathered here speaks very much to the explosion of interest in the rather odd (historically and geographically speaking) phenomenon of "sexual identity" in the West over the last half century or so.

The enormous shifts in labor, education, and mobility in the United States and around the world during the last hundred years, moreover, together with the difficulty of creating any meaningful index of social class across the disparate cultures and economies of our planet, means that anyone who tries to conceptualize "working class" in global or historical perspective aims at an eternally moving target. And if pinning down the concepts of "social class" or "working class" presents a knotty problem, then identifying working-class writers and writing is complex in consequence.

There is, of course, an additional complicating factor: the fact that working-class writing (and working-class lives) must often be re-recognized and reclaimed in the first place, over time and geography, for what they are—a legitimate cultural product, a literature, a worthy subject of inquiry, a vehicle for valid perspectives. In that regard, and solely in passing, I'll note that I'm fascinated by the way the memoir trend of the last couple of decades has led to the publication of so much LGBTQ writing and, in turn, to the publication of writing by LGBTQ people who grew up poor or working-class.

Rigoberto González's 2006 *Butterfly Boy: Memories of a Chicano Mariposa* and Renny Christopher's *A Carpenter's Daughter* (2009) are two fine examples, but I am also thinking of the so-called "celebrity" biographies that are so easy to dismiss. Life stories from military men and women, artists, media stars and celebrities (Lance Bass's 2007 *Out of Sync: A Memoir*, Boy George's 1995 *Take It Like a Man*, Bill T. Jones' 1995 *Last Night on Earth*, and Janet Mock's 2014 *Redefining Realness* come to mind), and from athletes (such as the 2009 autobiography of Irish hurling champion, Dónal Óg Cusack, *Come What May*; Rudy Galindo's 1997 *Icebreaker*; Brittney Griner's 2014 *In My Skin: My Life On and Off the Basketball Court*; or Esera Tuaolo's account of growing up as an impoverished immigrant in his 2006 *Alone in the Trenches: My Life As a Gay Man in the NFL*), often contain important clues about how poor and working-class kids grow up to be more-or-less queer adults and about the strategies they find for coping with conflicts in what we might call their "communities of belonging."

If commentary on the intersections of class and sexual identity is not generally the primary objective of such authors, and if their books are virtually never categorized as "working-class literature," such writing is nevertheless intriguing for what it reveals (sometimes inadvertently) about the way "gay identity" is forced to come to terms with working-class allegiances and cultural knowledge (and vice versa). On a related note, it's no less essential to recognize that much of what is written about working-class queers of color tends to be shelved (literally and figuratively) according to race and ethnicity, obscuring the writers' experiences with class, and that much of the writing about "rural" or "southern" queers in the United States also happens to be about poor or working-class people.

Meanwhile, if "class" very broadly refers to systems created for the accumulation of power and influence and for the allocation of goods and resources, then it seems clear that who can write, who does write, and whose writing is rewarded with publication and distribution (and, thus, tends to survive) is not random. We have Walt Whitman's moving accounts of the working-class soldiers he loved and cared for in Civil War hospitals, for example, but nothing in which they tell us, in their own words, how he fit into the way they saw their lives.

Paradoxically, much of today's true cutting-edge in working-class queer cultural production can also be difficult to find or is in danger of being lost, particularly in the area of performance. Increasingly, such work tends to be advertised and disseminated via Twitter and Facebook posts, through blogs and Kickstarter campaigns, or in YouTube videos, and much of it fails to stand out in the online sea. I think specifically of gay country-western singers and of gay hip-hop artists (Tori Fixx and Juba Kalamka's Deep Dickollective, e.g.; see also the perhaps-defunct-perhaps-not Butchlalis de Panochtitlan, a Los Angeles-based queer performance ensemble; the work of so-called performance poets or "spoken word" performers; and the very limited-release documentary, *Pick Up the Mic* [pickupthemic.com/Pick_Up_The_Mic]).

Finally, a couple of caveats. Not all of the materials listed here deal exclusively with the specific category of working-class queers; rather, many shed light on intersections of and among race, class, gender, and sexuality more generally or provide insights that require a between-the-lines reading or a broader perspective.

Paul Monette and Mark Doty, for instance (who are not included in this bibliography), both wrote important books about losing a loved one to AIDS. I would argue, however, that their work *also* reveals something about gay male "identity" and class—that it is, in fact, highly "classed" as literature, deeply marked *also* by the privileges, assumptions, and rewards that come with middle- and upper-class upbringing and education (including, but not limited to, the publication and diffusion of their work). That's not a criticism; it's simply an observation.*

To take another example of a writer whose work has always struck me as significantly "classed" (though class is not primarily his subject), I would point to Quentin Crisp. Crisp, whose work I have included, described himself as solidly "middle-class" but consciously chose to lead a louche existence in London's Soho and later in New York (you have to come from class, Crisp seemed to say, before you can elect to become déclassé). In any case, his arch commentaries about "gay life" and mass culture have more than a little to say about social class and queerness (and are also most entertaining).

My final warning is that the materials I've included here reflect, above all, my own interests and idiosyncrasies. As will quickly become clear, I've made no attempt to be all-inclusive or "representative." Indeed, how could I be? Rather, the bibliography is meant to make you, the reader, say to yourself, "Now why didn't he include...?" and then to see you off on your own voyage of discovery. Send me a postcard, if you will, from wherever you land.

Abbreviations Used in This Bibliography

Abs. = Journal- or author-provided article abstract.
Desc. = Author's or publisher's description of the item.
KR = *Kirkus Reviews*
LJ = *Library Journal*
PW = *Publisher's Weekly*

---

*See, e.g., Bertram Cohler's work on the biographical nature of writing by Monette, Doty, Edmund White, and others—*Writing Desire: Sixty Years of Gay Autobiography*. Madison: University of Wisconsin Press, 2007; and Life-Stories and Storied Lives: Genre and Reports of Lived Experience in Gay Personal Literature. *Journal of Homosexuality*, 2008, *54*(4): 362-380.

Fiction, Poetry & Theatre

Ackerley, J. R. (1960/2000). *We Think the World of You.* New York: NYRB Classics. [In this powerful short novel, Frank, the narrator, is a middle-aged civil servant, intelligent, acerbic, self-righteous, angry. He is in love with Johnny, a young, married, working-class man with a sweetly easy-going nature. When Johnny is sent to prison for committing a petty theft, Frank gets caught up in a struggle with Johnny's wife and parents for access to him. (*Desc.*)]

Alfaro, Luis. (1992). Pico Union. In George Stambolian, Ed., *Men on Men 4: Best New Gay Fiction.* New York: Plume, 268-283.

Alfaro, Luis. (1998). *Downtown.* In Holly Hughes and David Roman, Eds., *O Solo Homo: The New Queer Performance.* New York: Grove Press, 313-348.

Alfaro, Luis. (1999). *Straight As a Line.* In Caridad Svich and Maria Teresa Marrero, Eds., *Out of the Fringe: Contemporary Latina/Latino Theatre and Performance.* New York: Theatre Communications Group, 1-42.

Alfaro, Luis. *Bitter Homes and Gardens.* In José Cruz González and Juliette Carrillo, Eds., *Latino Plays from South Coast Repertory: Hispanic Playwrights Project Anthology.* New York: Broadway Play Publishing, 2-40.

Allison, Dorothy (1991). *Trash: Stories.* Ithaca, NY: Firebrand Books. [In fourteen gritty, intimate stories, Allison's fictional persona exposes with poetic frankness the complexities of being "a cross-eyed working-class lesbian, addicted to violence, language, and hope," rebelling against the Southern "poor white trash" roots that inevitably define her. (*PW*)]

Arobateau, Red Jordan (1996). *Boys Night Out.* [Arobateau is the prolific FTM author of some forty-five, mostly self-published "street dyke" books, including *The Bars Across Heaven* (1975) and *Rough Trade* (1996). His novels and short stories focus on the "queer community (gay men, lesbians, bisexuals and transsexuals) including underclass whites, African Americans, and queers of mixed race heritage." See www.redjordanarobateau.com. ~WR]

Arroyo, Rane (2005). *How to Name a Hurricane.* Tucson: University of Arizona Press. [*How to Name a Hurricane* collects short stories and other fictions depicting Latino drag queens and leather men, religious sinners and happy atheists, working-class heroes and cyberspace vaqueros—a parade of characters that invites readers to consider whether one is more authentic a gay Latino than another. (*Desc.*)]

Banner, Keith (2004). *The Smallest People Alive.* Pittsburgh, PA: Carnegie Mellon University Press. [Banner's ... stories, mainly set in Ohio and Tennessee, read like small revelations, perhaps because they focus on people usually ignored in gay fiction—rural, low-income, overweight, largely uneducated folks with dead-end or thankless jobs; they might call themselves "white trash," but Banner gives them a dark and fragile dignity. (*PW*)]

Banner, Keith (2014). *Next to Nothing: Stories*. Maple Shade, NJ: Lethe Press. [Keith Banner's new collection stands next to nothing, but all by itself, distinguished by a hard-won realism of the modern working class, amid the abandoned malls and the barely surviving towns of the rustbelt. This is Raymond Carver reinvented, filtered through a dark and richly queer perspective. (Christopher Barzak.)]

Barr, James (1950/1991). *Quatrefoil*. New York: Greenberg. Reissued by Alyson. [James Barr was born in an oilfield boomtown in either Texas or Oklahoma.... Early in 1942 he enlisted in the U.S. Navy and sailed from San Francisco for Guadalcanal.... Looking back from 1990, he recalled: 'Somewhere along the way, I finally tumbled to the fact that I was gay as pink ink, as we said in those days.... From then on the Navy became a demi-paradise: fifteen-cent Martinis in the Officers Club bars and half-naked sailors wherever one looked.'" (From "A Touch of Royalty" by Hubert Kennedy.) A "gay classic," this semi-autobiographical work marked a milestone in gay writing by including two of the very first non-stereotyped gay men to appear in American fiction. ~WR]]

Barr, James (1951). *Derricks*. New York: Greenburg. [Several stories in this collection explore working-class/homosexual characters. See also Barr's 1966 novel, *The Occasional Man*, which draws on his later experience of New York gay life. ~WR]

Bartlett, Neil (1991). *Ready to Catch Him Should He Fall*. London: Serpent's Tail. [An erotic fable, chockablock with literary allusion, about a homosexual subculture obsessed with a young man and his older lover. Bartlett's fable ... traces the growth of the community from narcissism to tragedy. The narrator—the voice of the subculture—writes from a nameless city about the affair and eventual 'marriage' of Boy and O, his older lover. (*KR*)]

Bechdel, Alison (2008). *The Essential Dykes to Watch Out For*. Boston: Houghton Mifflin Harcourt. [Bechdel's serial comic, "Dykes to Watch Out For," ran from 1987 to 2008, and some dozen volumes of collected strips have been published; this one is as good a place to start as any. As a political cartoonist, Bechdel has always been aware of class and economic issues in DTWOF, treating them sometimes humorously but always with great respect and insight. ~WR]

Bellerose, Sally (2011). *The Girls Club*. Ann Arbor, MI: Bywater Books. [Sisterhood. The buzzword of the seventies, the key to women's liberation. But for Catholic working class girls like Marie, Renee, and Cora Rose LaBarre, sisterhood is a word that covers a multitude of attitudes.... Set in the decade of opening doors, *The Girls Club* follows the three sisters as they love, argue, and struggle their way through adolescence to womanhood. (*Desc.*)]

Billany, Dan, with David Dowie (1949). *The Cage*. London: Longmans, Green. [Billany was born into a working-class family in Hull, Britain, and went on to be a teacher, a socialist, and a soldier. *The Cage* was written while he was a POW in Italy during WWII, together with the man he met in the camps and was apparently in love with. *The Cage*, published posthumously, tells of a male soldier's romantic love for another. Billany and Dowie disappeared and are presumed to have died while trying to cross the Apennines after Mussolini's fall. ~WR]

Boyd, Blanche McCrary (1982/1995). *The Redneck Way of Knowledge: Down-Home Tales.* New York: Knopf/Vintage Books.

Brant, Beth (Degonwadonti) (1985). *Mohawk Trail*. Ithaca, NY: Firebrand Books. [Here are memorable stories of the author's Mohawk foremothers, a working-class childhood in Detroit, lesbian parenting, women making a living and surviving a mental hospital, and a lesbian Coyote story. (*Desc.*)]

Brown, Michael David (1989). *Under Heat.* New York: Penguin Books/New American Library. [This is the dark and aching story of a man who goes home to rural Kentucky for a vacation but finds his return to the family dynamic anything but restorative. (*PW*)]

Brown, Rita Mae (1988/1973). *Rubyfruit Jungle*. New York: Bantam Books. [See discussion in this volume. ~WR]

Bulkin, Elly (Ed.) (1981). *Lesbian Fiction: An Anthology*. Watertown, MA: Persephone Press. [See, in particular, Judy Grahn's "Boys at the Rodeo" (in this volume), Maureen Brady's "Grinning Underneath," Audre Lorde's "The Beginning," and Dorothy Allison's "A River of Names." ~WR]

Burford, Barbara (1987). *The Threshing Floor: Short Stories*. Ithaca, NY: Firebrand Books. [First published in England, this collection of short stories and a novella contains several stories that are written from the viewpoint of foreign, working-class women.) (*PW*)]

Burns, John Horne (1947/2004). *The Gallery*. New York and London: Harper & Brothers. [Of special interest is "Fifth Portrait: Momma," a brilliant fictional (or was it?) description of a working-class gay bar in Naples where soldiers and natives rubbed elbows during the Second World War. ~WR]

Caffey, John (1982/2002). *The Coming Out Party*. New York: Pinnacle Books. [*My Fair Lady* meets *La Cage Aux Folles* in this award-winning novel set in West Hollywood in the late 70s. Two bored queens pick up an overweight Midwest boy off Santa Monica Boulevard and train him to be the perfect homosexual. See discussion in this volume. ~WR]

Califia, Pat[rick] (2000). *Doc and Fluff: The Dystopian Tale of a Girl and Her Biker*. Boston: Alyson Publications. [*Doc and Fluff* is described as "dyke feminist futurist fiction," and Califia's many other works of fiction include the short-story collections *Melting Point* (1993), *Macho Sluts* (1994), and *No Mercy* (2000), all issued by the now-defunct Alyson Press. The word that is probably most often applied to Califia's fiction is "raunchy," and it is certainly that. At the same time, few contemporary fiction writers keep gender, class, desire, shame, and sexual politics—

and the ways they combine and overlap, not just in bed—in clearer, more consistent focus or write about them more skillfully. See also Califia's nonfiction works in the "Essays, Cultural Studies & Reportage" section. ~WR]

Carson, Michael (1988). *Brothers in Arms*. New York: Pantheon. [Fat and unhappy, besotted with guilt and furtive sexual longings, Michael Benson is growing up in a working-class neighborhood on the northwestern coast of England in the early '60s.... Benson rushes headlong into the Catholic faith, leaving ... to begin his novitiate at St. Finbar's Seminary. St. Finbar's (where) fire-and-brimstone dogma and homosexual intrigues (prove) disastrous..., and he is sent home, where he learn[s] to accept his homosexuality and reject an uncomfortable faith. (*PW*)]

Coleman, Lonnie (1981). *Mark*. New York: Simon & Schuster. [See also his earlier book of short stories, *Ship's Company* (New York: Dell Press, 1957), set among sailors and officers on the *U.S.S. Nellie Crockes* during WWII and very slightly reminiscent of Burns' earlier *The Gallery*; several of the stories are quite daring for their time. *Mark*, meanwhile, is a touching (some would say sentimental) fictional memoir set among eccentrics in the pre-WWII South; Mark's lonely wandering seems relieved when he falls in love with a fellow university student, but there is no happy ending here. ~WR]

Cullen, Nancy Jo (2013). *Canary: Stories*. Windsor, Ontario: Biblioasis. ["Gas, grass, or ass: No one rides for free." So begins this cheeky and chirpy short story debut. Working-class, a little queer, and hysterically funny, Cullen's characters—from the hymn-singing Catholic merchandise salesman to a young lez, hitching cross-country beside a born-again pile of ashes—all encounter the killer decisions that invisibly, quietly, and quirkily shape their lives. (*Desc.*)]

Davies, Terence (1993/1984). *Hallelujah Now*. New York/London: Penguin Books. [Documents, in a fragmentary and elliptical way, the life of a working-class gay man from childhood to death. [Jim Ellis, glbtq.com)]

DeCaro, Frank (1996). *A Boy Named Phyllis: A Suburban Memoir*. Viking/Penguin. [DeCaro, a contributing editor to *Martha Stewart Living* and author of the only gay humor column in *New York Newsday*, traces the development of his gay identity in the aluminum-sided wilds of New Jersey among working-class Italian folk. Kitschy but low on substance. ~WR]

deVries, Rachel Guido (1986). *Tender Warriors*. Ithaca, NY: Firebrand Books. [An Italian-American working-class family comes alive in this engaging book as Rose—daughter, sister, nurse, photographer, lesbian—narrates their story. This is a novel about outsiders ... down and out or on the way up. (*Desc.*)]

Dixon, Melvin (2001). *Vanishing Rooms: A Novel*. Berkeley, CA: Cleis Press. [Set in New York City in the fall of 1975, the story shifts fluidly among the voices of Jesse (a young black dancer whose drugged-out white boyfriend Metro has just been brutally murdered by Village gaybashers), Ruella (a sassy, lonely black female dancer who falls in love with grief-stricken Jesse after taking him in), and Lonny (a fifteen-year-old, sexually confused Italian street tough so freaked out by his gang's murder of Metro that police find him curled up inside the white chalk outlines of Metro's body on the street the next day). [Timothy Murphy, Amazon.com)]

Doenges, Judy (1999). *What She Left Me: Stories and a Novella*. Lebanon, NH: University Press of New England. [These stories of marginal, blue-collar people, many of them lesbian or gay, living difficult lives far removed from urban glamor or the fast lane of pop or gay culture, are unsentimentally yet sensitively told. (*Desc.*) The novella, "God of Gods," is a moving meditation featuring a six-foot-six butcher in a Chicago supermarket, Odin Tollefson, and his fraught coming-out as a gay man in the midst of the racial upheavals of the early 1970s. Elegantly contextualizing Odin's sensitive, tentative coming to terms with his sexuality within a gritty, working-class urban setting, the narrative offers a respectful, finely tuned perspective on blue-collar gay life. (*PW*)]

Duffy, Stella (2008). *The Room of Lost Things.* London: Virago Press. [Duffy, the youngest of seven children in a working-class family, grew up in a small mill town in New Zealand. Today based in London, she has published fourteen novels, including mysteries, historical fiction, and this work, a paean to a multicultural working-class neighborhood of Loughborough Junction in south London. The protagonist of *The Room of Lost Things*, Robert, is on the verge of retiring after a lifetime in his shop, and the novel follows his developing friendship with Akeel, a Pakistani Muslim, who proposes to take over Robert's business. The book touches on the lives of a large and varied cast of neighbors, customers, and passersby. ~WR]

Eighner, Lars (1997). *Pawn to Queen Four: A Novel.* New York: St. Martin's Press.

Feinberg, Leslie (1993/2004). *Stone Butch Blues.* Ithaca, NY: Firebrand Books. [Reissued by Alyson.] [Woman or man? That's the question that rages like a storm around Jess Goldberg, clouding her life and her identity. Growing up differently gendered in a blue-collar town in the 1950s. Coming out as a butch in the bars and factories of the prefeminist '60s. Deciding to pass as a man in order to survive when she is left without work or a community in the early '70s. This powerful, provocative, and deeply moving novel sees Jess coming full circle, learning to accept the complexities of being a transgendered person in a world demanding simple explanations. (*Desc.*)]

Feinberg, Leslie (2006). *Drag King Dreams.* New York: Carroll & Graf. [A veteran of the women's and gay movement of the past thirty years, Max Rabinowitz, a butch lesbian bartender at an East Village club where drag kings ... perform, is experiencing a mid-life crisis in the midst of the post-9/11 world. Max is lonely and uncertain about her future [but] is shaken from her crisis ... by the news that her friend Vickie, a transvestite, has been found murdered.... (A) community of cross-dressers, drag queens, lesbians and gay men, and "genderqueers" of all kinds (stands) up together in the face of this tragedy. (*Desc.*)]

Ferrell, Anderson (2004). *Have You Heard.* New York: Bloomsbury. [Jerry Chiffon, protagonist of this funny, poignant tragicomedy, is something of a gay prodigy. Born to poor tobacco farmers, Jerry is blessed from the cradle with a penchant for child care and housewifery and a preternatural decorating sense. The attempted murder of a right-wing North Carolina senator throws a sudden media spotlight onto the alleged would-be assassin—Jerry Chiffon, who just happened to be sporting a red ladies' suit, a wig, and a fake Chanel purse at the time. (*Desc.*)]

Flagg, Fannie (1987). *Fried Green Tomatoes at the Whistle Stop Café.* [Set in a small Alabama train stop town in the 1930s, this gem of a book almost could have been shelved as just another light romantic comedy. The storytellers never find use for the label "lesbian," but this is nevertheless the irresistible story of a fierce and true love between two women.... Flagg mixes direct and empowering confrontations with racism, sexism, and ageism with the colorful and endearing language of the depression-era South. (Colleen McQueen, 500 Great Books by Women)]

Forster, E. M. (1971/2005). *Maurice.* New York: W. W. Norton & Company. [Various editions exist. See discussion in this volume. ~WR]]

Forster, E. M. (1987). *The Life to Come and Other Short Stories.* New York: W. W. Norton & Company. [Various editions exist.]

Frank, Judith (2004). *Crybaby Butch.* Ithaca, NY: Firebrand Books. [Drawing on Frank's experience as an adult literacy tutor, this first novel traces the difficult and sometimes hilarious connection between two butches of different generations—a middle-class, thirty-something adult literacy teacher and her older, working-class student. With a disparate group of adult learners as the backdrop, Frank examines ... the relationship between education and gender, class, and racial identity. (*Desc.*)]

Freeman, Gillian (writing as Eliot George) (1961). *The Leather Boys.* London: Anthony Blond. [Originally published under a pseudonym, presumably because its theme of gay love among working-class youth was considered controversial, *The Leather Boys* is essentially a boy-meets-boy romance set among the "mods" and "motorcycle cowboys" of England in the 1950s. It was published as a "pulp" but is a cut above the genre. ~WR]

Gilgun, John (1989). *Music I Never Dreamed Of.* New York: Amethyst Press.

Gilgun, John (1994). *Your Buddy Misses You.* Mulvane, KS: Three Phase Publishing.

Gill, Peter (2001). *The York Realist.* London: Faber and Faber. [When farm laborer George is cast in an amateur revival of the York Mystery Plays, he meets Assistant Director John. Their relationship develops and soon John wants him to move to London with him. This finely drawn love story explores class allegiances, the family, and the origins and ownership of art. (*Desc.*)]

González, Rigoberto (2008). *Men without Bliss.* Norman, OK: University of Oklahoma Press. [Complex portraits of Latinos leading ordinary, practically invisible lives while navigating the dark waters of suppressed emotion—true-to-life characters who face emotional hurt, socioeconomic injustice, indignities in the workplace, or sexual repression. (*Desc.*)]

Gorham, Charles (1961). *McCaffery.* New York: Dial Press. [Another pot-boiler from the 1960s, *McCaffery* is the portrait of a working-class Irish boy who becomes a bisexual hustler—and the kept boy of a gay millionaire. If the novel goes a bit over the top toward the climax, Gorham still does some interesting things (especially for the era) with issues of sexuality, masculinity, and class, including a complex turn on inter-class punishment and revenge. ~WR]

Graczyk, Ed (1982). *Come Back to the Five and Dime, Jimmy Dean, Jimmy Dean: A Comedy-Drama.* New York: Samuel French.

Grahn, Judy (Ed.) (1978). *True to Life Adventure Stories: Volume One.* Oakland, CA: Diana Press. [See also *True to Life Adventure Stories: Volume Two.* Trumansburg, NY: The Crossing Press, 1983.]

Greenwell, J. R. (2013). *Who the Hell is Rachel Wells?* New York: Chelsea Station Editions.[Full of snappy and sharp Southern characters, [this] is a debut collection of clever, big-hearted tales of spunky souls and damaged hearts. (*Desc.*) Includes such characters as a gay teen living on the streets, coworkers at a community center who are held hostage by a gunman, and a pair of drag queens who take on a protégé and teach him the unfathomable ways of beauty. ~WR]

Greig, Noel (1979). *The Dear Love of Comrades.* In *Two Gay Sweatshop Plays.* London: Gay Men's Press. [A dramatization of the thirty-year relationship between socialist writer and reformer Edward Carpenter and George Merrill, a working-class laborer. Greig was an important voice in early gay theater. In the 1970s, he joined the socialist theatre collective General Will, later staging a gentle "coup" in order to bring gay liberation into the group's artistic consciousness, and joined the London theatre company, Gay Sweatshop, in 1977. Greig died in 2009. ~WR]

Greig, Noel (1983). *Poppies* (A Gay Sweatshop Play). London: Gay Men's Press.

Grimsley, Jim. 1999. *Comfort & Joy.* Algonquin Books. [It's Christmas, and Danny and Ford are going to visit Danny's mother for the holidays. In successfully handled flashbacks, we learn the circumstances of their meeting and of their quite dissimilar family backgrounds: Danny from dysfunction and lack of privilege, Ford from nothing but privilege.... (O)ver the course of this particular Christmas, the two of them take some major steps in giving a secure future to their partnership. (Brad Hooper, Booklist)]

Gurganus, Allan (1991). *White People: Stories and Novellas.* New York: Knopf.

Hardy, James Earl (1994). *B-Boy Blues: A Seriously Sexy, Fiercely Funny, Black-on-Black Love Story*. Los Angeles: Alyson Publications. [See also the other novels in this series. ~WR]

Harvey, Jonathan (1999). *Jonathan Harvey Plays: Beautiful Thing/Babies/Boom Bang-A-Bang/Rupert Street Lonely Hearts Club*. London: Methuen. [See, in particular, *Beautiful Thing*, the story of a teenaged boy in London's lower class suburbs who discovers his love for the boy who lives next door; it has been made into a movie, listed here under "Film, TV & Video." ~WR]

Hayes, Joseph G. (2002). *This Thing Called Courage: South Boston Stories*. New York: Haworth Press, Inc. [Set in the rough neighborhoods of South Boston, this collection of seven moving stories deals with sexual desire among young, working-class Irish Catholic men. Hayes does an excellent job of capturing the conflicting emotions of his characters as they wrestle with "some bastard child of ... shame and desire." (*PW*) See discussion in this volume. Hayes' second volume of short stories, *Now Batting for Boston*, was published by Southern Tier Editions in 2005. ~WR]

Haylock, John (2007). *Sex Gets in the Way*. Arcadia Books. [This slight comic novel follows its two heroes from the 1950s through the 1970s—one of them comfortable and middle class, the other a working-class orphan. Set in England, Australia, and the high seas (the working-class character joins the Merchant Navy and becomes a steward on the *Queen Elizabeth*), this is broad farce, but the skewering of middle-class snobbery is fun. ~WR]

Hazeldine, Peter (1983). *Raptures of the Deep*. London: Brilliance Books. [Astonishing journey into the life of a young, working-class homosexual man in Northern England. (*Desc.*)]

Highsmith, Patricia (1955). *The Talented Mr. Ripley*. New York: Coward-McCann. [The themes of class-envy and class revenge are palpable as the polymorphous and definitely perverse Tom Ripley employs his criminal skills to leave behind his life as a concert-hall bathroom attendant and enter high society. Highsmith's 1955 Ripley is a good deal less gay than he is in the 1999 film version, but his anxiety with class "passing" and his skillful observation and mimicry of the wealthy are telling. ~WR]

Hucklenbroich, Frankie (1997). *A Crystal Diary: A Novel*. Ithaca, NY: Firebrand Books. [Hucklenbroich's autobiographical first novel combines fine writing and a gritty, cinematic story that hauls us through rarely charted lesbian locales. Her captivating first-person narration depicts the violent, drunken meat-packing district of '50s St. Louis; a sex-sodden '60s Hollywood; and the loopy drugged-out ambience of '70s San Francisco.... There have been other white-trash-lesbian-makes-good novels, but Hucklenbroich wails these stone-butch blues with a resounding cry all her own. (Robert L. Pela, *The Advocate*.)]

Hyatt, Martin (2006). *A Scarecrow's Bible*. San Francisco: Suspect Thoughts Press. [In a house trailer in rural Mississippi, Gary, a married Vietnam veteran, addicted to drugs, haunted by memories of the past, is on the brink of collapse. Just when he thinks the dream of another life is over, the unspeakable happens. He falls in love with a frail, ghostly younger man who reminds him of youth, beauty, and the possibility of a life beyond the prison he has created for himself. [This]is the story of how working-class men and women in a small town adapt to changes that somehow seem impossible. (*Desc.*)]

Jones, Sam John (2003). *Fishboys of Vernazza*. Aberteifi, Wales: Parthian. [Jones is the Welsh author of a number of other short-story collections (including the three volumes in his *Welsh Boys* series) and a novel, *With Angels and Furies*. His focus is largely, but not exclusively, on young gay men in rural families in the north of Wales including the vexations of religious intolerance, "dour Calvinism" (as Booklist's review put it), race, language, and class. The quality of the stories varies, but Jones provides an unusual and important cultural and social perspective on the small-town coming-out/coming-of-age story. ~WR]

Kenna, Peter (1974). *A Hard God: A Play*. Sydney, Australia: Currency Press. [Set in Sydney during the early post-war years and with a working-class theme, the play explores the trials and tribulations suffered by three brothers who, during a drought, are forced off the land and into the city. (*Desc.*)]

Kureishi, Hanif (1986). *My Beautiful Laundrette*. In *My Beautiful Laundrette and The Rainbow Sign*. London: Faber and Faber.

Lemebel, Pedro (1996). *Loco Afán: Crónicas de Sidario*. Santiago, Chile: Lom]. [Loco Afán is a collection of thirty-one chronicles which relate with poignancy and acerbic wit the experiences of a group of impoverished, HIV-positive, transvestite, gay men. The title ... could be translated as "Mad Desire: Chronicles from the Sidarium," where "sidarium" is a neologism, as is "sidario," based on the Spanish acronym for AIDS, "SIDA." (Kate Averis, "Queering the Margins: Pedro Lemebel's Loco Afán.")]

LeRoy, JT (2000). *Sarah*. New York: Bloomsbury. [Cherry Vanilla, twelve years old and with a penchant for short leather skirts and make-up, has one dream: to become the most famous "lot lizard" ... in the business. With his blond curls and his naked ambition, he is determined to be more woman than most. (*Desc.*) Leroy was unmasked in 2005 as the literary persona of Laura Albert, who was neither transgendered nor a victim of child abuse and had never been either a prostitute or homeless. LeRoy's work, however, including the 1999 story collection, *The Heart Is Deceitful Above All Things*, continue to resonate with readers despite disappointment that LeRoy, the heroic survivor of these supposedly autobiographical tales, does not actually exist. ~WR]

Luscombe, Jeffrey (2012). *Shirts and Skins*. New York: Chelsea Station Editions. [Josh Moore lives with his family on the "wrong side" of Hamilton, a gritty industrial city in southwestern Ontario. As a young boy, Josh plots an escape for a better life far from the steel mills that lined the bay. But fate has other plans, and Josh discovers his adult life in Toronto is just as fraught with insecurities and missteps.... (N)o matter how far away he might run, he will never be able to leave his hometown behind. (*Desc.*)]

Mallon, Thomas (2007). *Fellow Travelers*. New York: Pantheon Books. [Hawkins Fuller is a handsome, Park Avenue WASP, and Tim Laughlin is a skittishly devout working-class Irish Catholic. They both work for the federal government in Washington [during] the heyday of Sen. Joe McCarthy and the moment when the ... initiative to purge its workforce of homosexual men and women was at its zenith... [W]hen ... Tim finds himself being groped by a drunk Joe McCarthy, *Fellow Travelers* reaches an apotheosis of its own. [David Leavitt, *The Washington Post.*)]

Malloy, Brian (2007). *Brendan Wolf*. New York: St. Martin's Press. [Brendan Wolf, a gay 35-year-old perennial menial employee, can't cover rent and food on $7 an hour. His brother, Ian—in prison for fraud— directs him to Marv, a wealthy, withering elderly gay man. Though Brendan's plan is to trade housework for room and board, Marv has other transactions in mind.... Malloy's stripped-down prose makes for quick and immersive reading; an interesting spin on classic noir. (*PW*)]

Manley, Joey (1991). *The Death of Donna-May Dean*. New York: St. Martin's Press/Stonewall Inn Editions. [Similar in ways to Caffey's *The Coming Out Party*. A teenager unsure about his sexuality is taken off the streets by a "wise old queen" who instructs him in the ways of gay. *Donna-May Dean* is fairly self-conscious and reaches harder for significance in ways that the superficial treatment of its subject matter and over-the-top characters can't entirely justify. ~WR]

McNicholl, Damian (2004). *A Son Called Gabriel*. New York: CDS Books. [Gabriel Harkin, the eldest of four children in a working-class family in the hills of Northern Ireland in the 1960s and 70s, struggles through a loving yet often brutal childhood. As Gabriel begins to suspect that he's not like other boys, he tries desperately to lock away his feelings and his fears. (*Desc.*)]

Merlis, Mark (1994). *American Studies*. Houghton Mifflin. [The (narrator of this ambitious and intelligent first novel) is a middle-level federal bureaucrat in the bad old pre-Stonewall days of the dual McCarthyisms, red-hunting and gay-baiting, lying in a hospital bed after "an especially unrewarding encounter with rough trade" has left him battered and nearly blinded in one eye. Given so much time to reflect on his wasted life, the sixty-two-year-old thinks back to his friend and mentor, a prominent literary critic who committed suicide after being hounded by a '50s witch-hunt that threatened to expose his homosexuality and a former dalliance with the Communist Party (based loosely on F.O. Matthiessen). (*KR*)]

Miner, Valerie (1997). *Winter's Edge*. New York: Feminist Press. [Set in one block of the San Francisco's tenderloin district in the late 1970s, *Winter's Edge* centers on the lives of two older, working-class women: Chrissie MacInnes, a tough, outspoken, Scottish-born waitress, and the more subdued Margaret Sawyer, a clerk in a news shop. When a local political election threatens their neighborhood with gentrification, it also threatens their friendship. (*Desc.*)] See also Miner's many important novels (*All Good Women*, e.g.), short-story collections (*Trespassing and Other Stories*, e.g.), and books of essays, memoir, and reportage. ~WR]

Moraga, Cherrie (2002). *Watsonville/Circle in the Dirt: Some Place Not Here/El Pueblo De East Palo Alto*. Albuquerque, NM: West End Press. [These three plays document the incursion of the white world of power and authority into poor, racially mixed communities. In vividly realized drama, Moraga shows the communities mounting their own bold resistance to cultural domination and the threat of economic enslavement. The indigenous and feminist consciousness of the two communities brings them together to struggle against their oppressors, from within and without. (*Desc.*)]

Mordden, Ethan (1996). "Interview with the Drag Queen," from *I've A Feeling We're Not In Kansas Anymore: Tales from Gay Manhattan*. New York: St. Martin's/Griffin. Originally published 1985. [Mordden is about as far from being a working-class writer as it is humanly possible to be, but this story nonetheless captures an important working-class-queer reality, and Mordden pulls it off with sensibility, insight, and even compassion—perhaps in large part because the narrator of the story is exactly what Mordden is: a sophisticate full of social prejudices who observes a world he neither fully understands nor entirely respects, but whose details he nonetheless faithfully records. ~WR]

Murphy, Timothy (1997). *Getting Off Clean*. New York: St. Martin's Press. [The one thing that Eric Fitzpatrick wants is to escape--both from his family and the racially tense town in which he lives. The only son of an Italian-Irish family in a working class suburb of Boston, he intends to go away to college and leave his old life far behind. But all his plans are set askew when he meets Brooks, a mysterious, wealthy, black student at a local prep school. As their relationship grows ever deeper and more complicated, Eric must come to terms not only with his family and community, but with his warring ambitions and desires. (*Desc.*)]

Myles, Eileen (2008). *Cool for You: A Novel*. Berkeley, CA: Soft Skull Press. [Myles's working-class lesbian perspective links her to Dorothy Allison, Pat Califia, and Leslie Feinberg.... (She) has an exquisite sense of the borderline, where people hide or are transformed according to luck and will. [Ann Powers, *New York Times Book Review*.)]

Nevaquaya, Joe Dale Tate (2011). *Leaving Holes and Selected New Writings*. Norman, OK: Mongrel Empire Press. [Nevaquaya ...spent his childhood years in Bristow (Oklahoma) and on skid row in Oklahoma City.... He writes about poverty, pain and his decision to make a life for himself despite the obstacles he encountered.... (As a child, Nevaquaya says), "I saw the tragic beauty that was our lives. It was horrible and beautiful at the same time." (Tami Althoff, *NewsOK*). Poems and writings by a gay working-class Native American and co-winner of the 1992 Native Writer's Circle Award for Poetry. ~WR]

O'Carroll, Brendan (1995). *The Chisellers*. Dublin, Ireland: O'Brien Press, 1995.

Obejas, Achy (1994). *We Came All the Way from Cuba So You Could Dress Like This?* Berkeley, CA: Cleis Press. [Whether she chronicles the obsessions of a broken-hearted, jilted lover trying unsuccessfully not to circle the block of her ex-girlfriend's apartment, or the humiliation of being offered donated, unwashed clothing as part of the alternately boring and anxious 'processing' into the U.S. as a political refugee from Castro's Cuba, Obejas' prose moves us. (Booklist)]

Obejas, Achy (1996). *Memory Mambo*. Berkeley, CA: Cleis Press. [Juani Casas, a Cuban-born American lesbian in her early 20s ... manages her family's laundromat in a Cuban neighborhood of Chicago. Juani walks a fine line between being out about her sexuality and being discrete enough not to alienate her family. (*PW*)]

Ong, Han (2001). *Fixer Chao*. New York: Farrar, Straus and Giroux. [Ong puts feng shui to good use in this superb and scathingly satirical first novel that paints a fiercely condemning portrait of a shallow and overprivileged upper class. Set in the always class-stratified Manhattan, this novel tells of William Narcisco Paulinha, a Filipino male prostitute who is offered the opportunity to escape his wretched existence.... William assumes the role of Master Chao, a feng shui expert, and begins to rob New York's superwealthy of both their money and their well-being by "fixing" their homes. As William moves through the class spectrum of Manhattan, he offers sardonic and keen observations about social, racial, and cultural distinctions and privileges.[*LJ*)]

Parker, Pat (1990). *Movement in Black: The Collected Poetry of Pat Parker, 1961-1978*. Ithaca, NY: Firebrand Books. [See also Parker's writing in *This Bridge Called My Back*, *Home Girls*, and her 1985 collection, *Jonestown and Other Madness: Poetry* (Firebrand). ~WR]

Phillips, Thomas Hal (1950/1996). *The Bitterweed Path*. University of North Carolina Press.

Plante, David (1986). *The Catholic*. New York: Atheneum. [See also "The Francoeur Trilogy" (*The Family*, 1978; *The Country*, 1981; and *The Woods*, 1982). Plante's Francoeur novels explore the saga of a large working-class French Canadian family in Providence, Rhode Island. Several of his later novels, including *The Catholic*, are more-or-less directly connected to the Francoeur books. Plante's spare, very personal style and his treatment of sexuality (which reviewers tend to call "low-key," "unacknowledged," or "ambiguous") may present certain challenges, but they also reward careful attention. During decades in which writers and critics frequently called for a more "integrated" literary approach to homosexuality, Plante was accomplishing exactly that in his novels. ~WR]

Poet On Watch and Williams, Amber N. (Eds.) (2013). *G.R.I.T.S.—Girls Raised In the South: An Anthology of Southern Queer Womyns' Voices and Their Allies*. Austin, TX: Freeverse Publishing. [Claiming a lesbian identity is radical if it is layered with a radical politics of race, gender, sexuality, and class.... Lesbians aren't radical unless we are transgressing some hidebound institution, turning it over on its ass, and making way for some new flesh. (Cheryl Clark, from the Introduction.)]

Pratt, Minnie Bruce (2011). *Inside the Money Machine*. Durham, NC: Carolina Wren Press. [(P)oetry for the immense majority for those who work for a living, out of the house or at home, from the laundromat to the classroom, from blue-collar construction sites to white-collar desk jobs. These fresh, gritty and passionate poems are about the people who survive and resist inside the money machine of 21st-century capitalism. (*Desc.*)]

Proulx, Annie (1997, October 13). "Brokeback Mountain." *The New Yorker*: 74-85. ["Brokeback Mountain" appeared in Proulx's 1998 collection, *Close Range: Wyoming Stories* and has been republished in a number of editions. ~WR]

Quinn, Jay (Ed.) (2001). *Rebel Yell: Stories of Contemporary Gay Authors*. New York: Haworth Press. [Quinn presents a superb collection of stories relating the Southern gay experience.... (V)oices from the South and from rural areas are absent in most gay literature collections..., (and) these authors have something important to say. (*LJ*) See also *Rebel Yell 2: More Stories of Contemporary Gay Southern Men* (2002).]

Rechy, John. (1963) *City of Night* and *Numbers* (1967). Both published by Grove Press.

Repetto, Vittoria (1994). *Head for the Van Wyck*. New York: Monkey Cat Press. [Repetto offers staccato, in-your-face poetry depicting a New York world filled with surreal cab rides, angry lesbian lovers, and a bizarre world where someone who might be Camille Paglia stiffs Repetto for a cab fare. Repetto deconstructs her identities as working-class, Italian-American, lesbian, poet, women without apology and without the mask of esoteric language and theory. (Carmela Delia Lanza, *Voices in Italian Americana*)]

Rice-González, Charles (2011). *Chulito: A Novel*. New York: Magnus Books. [Set against a vibrant South Bronx neighborhood and the queer youth culture of Manhattan's piers, *Chulito* is a coming-of-age, coming out love story of a sexy, tough, hip hop-loving, young Latino man and the colorful characters who populate his block. (E)veryone in his neighborhood has seen (Chulito) grow up—the owner of the local bodega, the Lees from the Chinese restaurant, his buddies from the corner, and all of his neighbors and friends, including Carlos, who was Chulito's best friend until they hit puberty and people started calling Carlos a *pato* ... a faggot. (*Desc.*)]

Ricketts, Wendell (Ed.) (2005). *Everything I Have Is Blue: Short Fiction by Working-Class Men about More-or-Less Gay Life*. San Francisco: Suspect Thoughts Press.

Rule, Jane (1964/1991). *Desert of the Heart*. Vancouver, BC: Talonbooks. [Rule's rather open-ended question [in *Desert of the*

Heart] is whether or not [the Ann/Evelyn relationship] can survive the toxic atmosphere, not simply of an unruly gambling town, but of the past sorrows and hardships each of the characters is attempting to put behind [her]. (*Desc.*) The basis for Donna Deitch's popular 1985 film, *Desert Hearts*. ~WR]

Ryan, Patrick (2006). *Send Me*. New York: Dial Press.[As an adolescent, Frankie happily embraces his belief that he is gay, dreaming wistfully of Luke Skywalker. Next oldest Joe ... has a more painful time sorting through his own messy sexuality.... Ryan gets the dreariness and tumult of the Kerrigan lives right, presenting Teresa as flawed but sympathetic, and her brood as reactive in familiar but nicely specified ways. (*PW*)]

Saba, Umberto (1975/1987). *Ernesto*. Tr. Mark Thompson. Manchester & New York: Carcanet. [Saba wrote *Ernesto* in 1953, but left it unfinished at his death in 1957; it was not published in Italian until 1975. Set at the end of the nineteenth century, *Ernesto* is an odd, disjointed story that follows seventeen-year-old Ernesto as he engages in sexual encounters with a male laborer ten years his senior (whom he rejects, in part, because of their class difference); ultimately, Ernesto meets a slightly younger boy, a music lover like himself, and Saba suggests a real relationship may develop between them. *Ernesto* is often called a story of "homosexual education," and there is much speculation about the extent to which the troubled, complex Saba intended his novel to be autobiographical. Thompson's notes are especially helpful. ~WR]

Sáenz, Benjamin Alire (2012). *Everything Begins & Ends at the Kentucky Club*. El Paso, TX: Cinco Puntos Press. [(A)ll borders—real, imagined, sexual, human, the line between dark and light, addict and straight— entangle those who live on either side. Take, for instance, the Kentucky Club on Avenida Juárez two blocks south of the Rio Grande. It's a touchstone for each of Sáenz's stories. His characters walk by, they might go in for a drink or to score, or they might just stay there for a while and let their story be told.... The Kentucky Club ... welcomes Spanish and English, Mexicans and gringos, poor and rich, gay and straight, drug addicts and drunks, laughter and sadness, and even despair. (*Desc.*)]

Saint, Assotto (1996). *Spells of a Voodoo Doll: The Poems, Fiction, Essays and Plays of Assotto Saint*. New York: Masquerade Books. [A] Haitian- born American poet, performance artist, musician, and editor and publisher, Saint increased the visibility of black queer authors and themes during the 1980s and early 1990s.... His theatrical and multimedia productions made him one of the central figures in the black gay cultural arts movement of his time; as the editor and publisher of several important literary anthologies, he helped to make queerness an important element within the black literary community. (Luca Prono, glbtq.com)]

Selby, Hubert (1964/1988). *Last Exit to Brooklyn*. New York: Grove Press (reissue). [The first novel to articulate the rage and pain of life in "the other America," (this book) is a classic of postwar American writing.

Selby's searing portrait of the powerless, the homeless, the dispossessed, is as fiercely and frighteningly apposite today as it was when it was first published. (*Desc.*)]

Shockley, Ann Allen (1982). *Say Jesus and Come to Me.* New York: Avon. [Much-reprinted. Shockley was one of the first modern writers to write about interracial lesbian relationships and, in her earlier *Loving Her*, about a mixed-class one as well. At times there's more ideology than realism in Shockley's couples and the prose is not infrequently purple, but these are extremely significant works in the history of the literature of queers/class/race. ~ WR]

Sickles, Carter (2012). *The Evening Hour.* New York: The Bloomsbury Group. [Most of the wealth in Dove Creek, West Virginia, is in the ... coal seams that have provided generations with a way of life, but little prosperity. (T)wenty-seven-year-old Cole Freeman sidestepped work as a miner to become an aide in a nursing home... He's also a drug dealer, reselling the prescription pills of the older population to a younger crowd. Cole's work leads him down back roads and hollows, and into the homes of the town's uncommon characters: an openly gay ex-con, an octogenarian environmentalist, and a myriad of old-timers, war veterans, shut-ins, and church-goers. As Heritage Coal razes the mountains, some choose to leave, a few fight, and most, like Cole, try to ignore the devastation. (*Desc.*)]

Silvera, Makeda (1994). *Her Head A Village.* Vancouver: Press Gang Publishers. [A Canadian Afro-Caribbean writer's short stories of working-class immigrant and lesbian life. (Bolerium Books.)]

Smith, Barbara (Ed.) (1983). *Home Girls: A Black Feminist Anthology.* New York: Kitchen Table/Women of Color Press. [Reissued in 2000 by Rutgers University Press. Includes contributions by Pat Parker, June Jordan, Audre Lorde, Michelle T. Clinton, and many others. ~WR]

Spanbauer, Tom (1991/2000). *The Man Who Fell in Love with the Moon.* New York: Atlantic Monthly Press. [(T)his deeply felt tale of love and loss is told by Shed, a half-breed bisexual Indian. In the 1880s, Shed ... is raped at gunpoint by the man who then murders his mother (and) raised by Ida Richilieu—prostitute, mayor of Excellent, Idaho, proprietress of a hotel/whorehouse painted pink. Under Ida's tutelage, Shed becomes a berdache.... Leaving home to seek the meaning of his Indian name, he becomes friend and lover of Montana rancher Dellwood Barker, who converses with the moon and may well be his father. Returning to Idaho, the two men join ... an odd extended family involving various sexual liaisons. (*PW*)]

Taïa, Abdellah (2012). *An Arab Melancholia.* (Frank Stock, trans.) Los Angeles: Semiotext(e). [Salé, near Rabat. The mid 1980s. A lower-class teenager is running until he's out of breath. He's running after his dream ... to become a movie director. He's running after the Egyptian movie star, Souad Hosni, who's out there somewhere, miles away from this neighborhood ... the home at which he is not at home, an environment that will only allow him his identity through the cultural lens of shame and silence.... (T)his autobiographical novel traces the emergence of Taïa's identity as an openly gay Arab man living between cultures. (*Desc.*)]

Tea, Michelle (2006). *Rose of No Man's Land.* San Francisco: MacAdam/Cage. [Trisha is a doughy, alcoholic 10th-grade denizen of Mogsfield, Mass., a fictional white trash nowhere. Her father is long gone; her mother ... does not leave the couch; her mother's boyfriend, Donnie, enters the kitchen only to make ramen; her younger sister, Kristy ... constantly films the family dysfunctioning around her.... Add in minor characters like the never-seen but oft-discussed Kim Porciatti and various dumb guys in cars, and you have a postmillennial, class-adjusted *My So-Called Life.* (*PW*)]

Tester, Royston (2004). *Summat Else: Stories.* Erin, Ontario: The Porcupine's Quill. [A most remarkable series of linked stories, encompassing a young working-class Englishman's coming of age, written with great humor and pathos. (*Desc.*)]

Thorogood, Stuart (1999). *Outcast.* London: Gay Men's Press. [Thorogood's first novel tells the coming-out story of Mark Holly, a twenty-year-old working-class boy from a small English town. It's a novella more than a novel (150 pages) and a certain callowness betrays its author's age (19). Still, among the plethora of gay romances and coming-out stories, it's better written than most and does a decent job of foregrounding working-class London. ~WR]

Tremblay, Michel (2004). *Some Night My Prince Will Come.* Sheila Fischman, Tr. Vancouver, BC: Talonbooks. [This is just one of several novels and other works by this important, prolific, gay, working-class Quebecois writer. He's celebrated in Canada, but not nearly well enough known in the U.S. Check out the novels, *The Fat Woman Next Door Is Pregnant* (Sheila Fischman, Tr., 1981) and *The Heart Laid Bare* (Sheila Fischman, Tr., 2002); the play, *The Driving Force* (Linda Gaboriau, Tr., 2005); and Tremblay's memoir, *Twelve Opening Acts* (Sheila Fischman, Tr., 2002), all published by Talonbooks. ~WR]

Trujillo, Carla (2003). *What Night Brings.* Willimantic, CT: Curbstone Press. [Focuses on a Chicano working-class family living in California during the 1960s. Marci—smart, feisty and funny—tells the story with the wisdom of someone twice her age as she determines to defy her family and God in order to find her identity, sexuality, and freedom. (*Desc.*)]

Truong, Monique (2003). *The Book of Salt.* Boston: Houghton Mifflin. [In this imaginary look inside the famed literary household of Gertrude Stein and Alice B. Toklas, Truong imagines a Vietnamese cook, Binh, hired to delight and to serve at 27 rue de Fleurus. After his cruel father discovers Binh in a relationship with another man, Binh is banished from his homeland and ends up in Paris. Binh is a cogent and rascally witness as he searches for love and human contact in the demiworld of Paris. The prose is rich and sensual and, even if the plot doesn't amount to all that much, Binh is a fine example of that most fascinating of narrators: the servant who sees all, the exile whose reflections on his condition and on his adopted land are pungent and vivid. ~WR]

Valentine, John (1979). *Puppies*. Glen Ellen, CA: Entwhistle Books.

Warren, Patricia Nell (2001). *The Wild Man*. Beverly Hills, CA: Wildcat Press. [With his overweening machismo, Warren's complex hero, a closeted matador at the end of Franco's rule in Spain, is never entirely sympathetic but is always fascinating. He is aware of the political and social changes of the 1960s but must face the conflict between the demands of his aristocratic family and the traditions of his sport, on the one hand, and his growing love for an idealistic young peasant on the other. [Daniel Starr.)]

Wood, Roy F. (1985). *Restless Rednecks: Gay Tales of the Changing South*. San Francisco: Grey Fox Press.

Woodrell, Daniel (1998). *Tomato Red*. New York: Henry Holt & Company. [The novel begins with a heady methedrine rush, as Sammy celebrates payday by letting himself be talked into robbing a nearby mansion.... The break-in leads Sammy into an unlikely alliance with the Merridew family, including Jamalee ... (who) plans on using (her brother) Jason's extraordinary beauty as her ticket out of West Table, Missouri. Jason, however, seems to be shaping up as what Sammy calls "country queer"—which, as Sammy observes, "ain't the easiest walk to take amongst your throng of fellow humankind." (Amazon.com)]

Wright, Bil (2000). *Sunday You Learn How to Box*. New York: Scribner Paperback Fiction/Touchstone Books. [Growing up in urban Connecticut's impoverished Stratfield Projects in the late '60s is hard enough for Louis Bowman, the fourteen-year-old narrator of this excellent, plainspoken debut novel.... To make matters more difficult, Louis is gay, a realization he comes to slowly as he becomes enthralled with Ray Anthony Robinson, an older boy his neighbors consider an "out-and-out-hoodlum." Enigmatic Ray becomes Louis's unofficial protector, though the two teens never speak of their bond.... Wright's prose is both straightforward and subtle, and his ear for dialogue is first-rate. (*PW*)]

Xavier, Emanuel (2013). *Nefarious*. Hulls Cove, ME: QueerMojo/Rebel Satori Press. [Xavier's latest [poetry] collection is a testament whose utterance often feels less printed than voiced by a cool gust pushing newspapers along the city's now-gentrified streets and renovated piers, where hustlers and other outcasts of society once made defiant gestures of survival. (Jerome Murphy, lambdaliterary.org)]

Memoirs, Biography & Autobiography

Alexander, Jonathan (2000). Telling the Stories of Our Lives: An Interview with John Gilgun. *International Journal of Sexuality and Gender Studies* 5(4): 341-351.

Allison, Dorothy (1995). *Two or Three Things I Know for Sure.* New York: Penguin Putnam, Inc. [Resounding with a familiarity of the intimate turned universal, this brief memoir recounts the episodes and people of Allison's life who created her and her own re-creation of herself. "Two or three things I know for sure, and one is that I would rather go naked than wear the coat the world has made for me." [Eric Bryant, *LJ*)]

Anderson, Timothy J. *Graced By Amazing: One Man's Journey Across the Blacktop of North America.* [The first installment of the "road trilogy," detailing rural gay America, the trucking industry, and life among the working class. See Anderson's High Mountain Ranch site (highmountainranch.com) for this and other writing. ~WR]

Bailey, Paul (1990). *An Immaculate Mistake: Scenes from Childhood and Beyond.* London: Penguin Books UK Ltd. [Born in 1937 suburban London to a professional maid and a road-sweeper, Bailey was their late-in-life "mistake" … and was both saddled and blessed in his mother, a woman of remarkable prejudices who'd nonetheless remain a touchstone.... Bailey figured out quickly that he couldn't ever be "natural" ... but he didn't anguish over it much.... (A) fine evocation of time and place offered by a man who knows precisely where he came from. [*KR*)]

Barr, Damian (2013). *Maggie and Me.* London: Bloomsbury Publishing. [(This) is a touching and darkly witty memoir about surviving Thatcher's Britain; a story of growing up gay in a straight world and coming out the other side in spite of, and maybe because of, the iron lady. (*Desc.*) (Barr's father worked in just the sort of heavy industry that was on the way out in the Thatcher years, while Damian and his mother ended up living as part of a ramshackle extended family dependent on benefits, petty crime and drink. They seem to personify respectively the respectable and unrespectable poor, at a time when the government was making poverty itself unrespectable. (Adam Mars-Jones, *The Guardian*).]

Bérubé, Allan with Florence Bérubé (2011). Sunset Trailer Park. In *My Desire for History: Essays in Gay, Community, and Labor History.* Chapel Hill: University of North Carolina Press, 182-201. [An outstanding working-class historian and archivist, Bérubé here writes (with his mother) about growing up "gay trailer trash" in Bayonne, NJ. ~WR]

Boy George (1995). *Take It Like a Man: The Autobiography of Boy George.* New York: Harper Collins. [In this highly entertaining autobiography, the singer details with wit and pathos his working-class childhood as the self-dubbed "pink sheep" of a large suburban family, his teenage fascination with and emulation of glam-rock icons like David Bowie and Marc Bolan; his years as a London punk scenester; his jet-setting life as a pop celebrity; and his painful descent into and recovery from heroin addiction. *(PW)]*

Chin, Staceyann (2009). *The Other Side of Paradise: A Memoir.* New York: Scribner. [The Paradise of the title is the slum of Montego Bay, Jamaica, where Chin spent her hardscrabble adolescence.... Early on, the spirited, defiant youngster learned to lie about her parentage, while the poverty and neediness of the siblings rendered them charity cases for relatives in Bethel Town and Kingston. Nonetheless, Chin excelled at school ... and became an emigrant success story later in New York. *(PW)]*

Christopher, Renny (2009). *A Carpenter's Daughter: A Working-Class Woman In Higher Education.* Rotterdam, The Netherlands: SensePublishers. [The story of the difficulties and rewards of the educational system for one who was not meant to go through it.... Both a memoir of the author's experiences growing up, going to school, and becoming an academic and a thoughtful commentary on the meaning of class in American culture. *(Desc.)]*

Cogswell, Kelly J. (2014). *Eating Fire: My Life as a Lesbian Avenger. Minneapolis:* University of Minnesota Press. [The first in-depth account of the influential Lesbian Avengers" *(Desc.)* "I'm trying to remember what those days were like ..., when the East Village really did seem like a small town, and my dyke friends lived just around the corner, dragging their politics and art into the street..... There were ... the ambulatory skeletons of people dying from AIDS ... [and the] Women's Action Coalition ... stuffed with those good-smelling SoHo types who had never applied for Medicaid. (From the book.)]

Crisp, Quentin (1968). *The Naked Civil Servant.* London: Jonathan Cape. (Several editions exist.) Crisp, the author of *How to Have a Life Style, How to Become a Virgin,* and *Resident Alien: The New York Diaries,* among several other books, deserves to be read not solely for its considerable humor, but for what his sarcastic iconoclasm and social criticisms reveal about the gay "lifestyle" and myriad other topics. ~WR]

Cusack, Dónal Óg (2009). *Come What May: The Autobiography.* Dublin: Penguin Ireland.

Ditto, Beth with Michelle Tea (2013). *Coal to Diamonds: A Memoir.* New York: Spiegel & Grau. [Born and raised in Judsonia, Arkansas—a place where indoor plumbing was a luxury, squirrel was a meal, and sex ed was taught ... long after many girls had gotten pregnant and dropped out—Beth Ditto stood out [as a] fat, pro-choice, sexually confused choir nerd with a great voice, an eighties perm, and a Kool Aid dye job.... Her punk education began in high school under the tutelage of a group of teens ... who embraced their outsider status and introduced her to safety-pinned clothing, mail-order tapes, queer and fat-positive zines, and any shred of counterculture they could smuggle into Arkansas. *(Desc.)]*

Eighner, Lars (1993). *Travels With Lizbeth: Three Years on the Road and on the Streets.* New York: St. Martin's Press. [Eighner's theme is homelessness and, since [he] is knowledgeable, clear-eyed, and sharply articulate about the social welfare system, his book is also about waste, self-righteousness, and generosity in an affluent society. It's a story of poverty, physical stress, and ever-present anxiety, yet his dog Lizbeth, who can't be trusted to guard anything or keep quiet when necessary, brings with her a warm and amusing story of man and pet. (Booklist)]

Eribon, Didier (2013). *Returning to Reims.* Tr. Michael Lucey. Cambridge, MA: The MIT Press. [(P)resents fresh insight into examining social class as an integral part of gay identity. Part personal memoir, part philosophical treatise on the relationship between sexual identity and social class, Eribon's book is both a delicately told tale of a young Frenchman crafting a gay self in the working-class world and a stunning analysis of how acculturation into a social class identity affects sexual identity and vice versa. (Charles Dimock, lambdaliterary.org)]

Faderman, Lillian (2003). *Naked in the Promised Land: A Memoir.* Madison: University of Wisconsin Press. [This is a sense, a story of rags to riches—rags, almost literally, and, if not strictly material riches, then at least enviable achievement as a feminist scholar and historian, teacher, writer, and university administrator. It is, at the same time, the story of the familiar guilt of the successful offspring of immigrant parents; of the resourceful child who identifies education as a means of escape, jumps at the first chance she gets, and then, far from the mythology of the working-class social climber who "never looks back," looks back obsessively. ~WR]

Flame (1984). *Flame: A Life on the Game.* London: Gay Men's Press. [In 1971, working-class life in Liverpool holds little promise for fourteen-year-old Stephen.... Two years before, he'd had a love affair with a construction worker. Then during the school holidays he'd tried out a new role, dressing and living as a woman in a midlands town. Now it had to be London and the bright lights. (*Desc.*)]

Galindo, Rudy, with Eric Marcus (1997). *Icebreaker: The Autobiography of Rudy Galindo.* New York: Simon & Schuster/Pocket Books. [Autobiography of U.S. men's figure skating champion, a gay Mexican-American from a working-class family, who achieved his dream of winning the U.S. figure skating championship in 1996. (*Quill Quire*)]

González, Rigoberto (2006). *Butterfly Boy: Memories of a Chicano Mariposa.* Madison: University of Wisconsin Press. [This stirring memoir of a first-generation Mexican American's coming-of-age and coming out is wrenching, angry, passionate, ironic, and always eloquent about conflicts of family, class, and sexuality.... The first in his family to graduate from high school, he may be the innocent immigrant when his mostly white college class talks about weekends at the beach and other mysterious pastimes, but he has lived through traumatic separation they know nothing about. [Hazel Rochman, Booklist)]

González, Rigoberto (2013). *Autobiography of My Hungers.* Madison: University of Wisconsin Press. [González ... takes a second piercing look at his past through a startling new lens: hunger. The need for sustenance originating in childhood poverty, the adolescent emotional need for solace and comfort, the adult desire for a larger world, another lover, a different body—all are explored in a series of heartbreaking and poetic vignettes. (*Desc.*)]

Grahn, Judy (2012). *A Simple Revolution: The Making of an Activist Poet.* San Francisco: Aunt Lute Book. [A unique memoir and a dramatic narrative of Judy Grahn's working-class roots, her army career and discharge for being lesbian, her education as one of the first whites to attend Howard University, and her life as a celebrated poet in the Bay Area during the tumultuous beginnings of the lesbian movement in the late '60s. (*Desc.*)]

Hall-Carpenter Archives, Gay Men's Oral History Group (Eds.) (1989). *Walking After Midnight: Gay Men's Life Stories.* London: Routledge.

Hall-Carpenter Archives, Lesbian Oral History Group (Eds.) (1990). *Inventing Ourselves: Lesbian Life Stories.* London: Routledge.

Hay, Harry and Will Roscoe (Ed.) (1996). *Radically Gay: Gay Liberation in the Words of its Founder.* Boston: Beacon Press.

Hollibaugh, Amber (2000). *My Dangerous Desires: A Queer Girl Dreaming Her Way Home.* Durham, NC: Duke University Press. [A lesbian sex radical, ex-hooker, incest survivor, gypsy child, poor-white-trash, high femme dyke, Hollibaugh is also an award-winning filmmaker, feminist, Left political organizer, public speaker, and journalist. This book presents over twenty years of Hollibaugh's writing (and examines) themes such as the relationship between activism and desire or how sexuality can be intimately tied to one's class identity. (*Desc.*)]

Jennings, Kevin (2007). *Mama's Boy, Preacher's Son: A Memoir of Growing Up, Coming Out, and Changing America's Schools.* Boston: Beacon Press. [The youngest son of a born-again Southern Baptist preacher ... and a mother from Appalachian Tennessee, Jennings led an itinerant youth among trailer parks.... With his father's abrupt death ... Jennings ... became a "mama's boy,"' introverted, brainy and overweight, and ridden by guilt at his incipient homosexuality. Supported by his scarcely educated mother, who became the first woman manager at McDonald's, Jennings excelled in school ... and was accepted to Harvard by 1981. Jennings became a high-school teacher (and later created) GLSEN (Gay, Lesbian and Straight Education Network) to protect students from the kind of harassment he experienced firsthand. (*PW*)]

Johnson, E. Patrick (2011). Queer Epistemologies: Theorizing The Self from a Writerly Place Called Home. *Biography 34*(3): 429-446. [As a queer teen trying to come to terms with my sexuality, overweight body, and working-class social status, keeping a journal and writing poetry were my life buoys in what was otherwise a sea of despair.... It was in the projects where I absorbed the knowledge that my family, extended family, and community folk shared over meals at the dinner table, at the local barbershop, on the front porch, and at church. (They) taught me about politics ... social etiquette, the "man," (black) history, and about queerness. (From the essay.)]

Jones, Bill T. (1995). *Last Night on Earth.* New York: Pantheon. [The son of migrant field-workers who left rural Florida in 1955 to settle in a nearly all-white upstate New York town when he was three, Jones writes affectingly of his boyhood, his bohemian years in Amsterdam and San Francisco, his struggle for artistic identity and his creative work in New York City as director of the Bill T. Jones/Arnie Zane Dance Company. (*PW*)]

Jones, William E. (2011). *Halsted Plays Himself.* Los Angeles: Semiotext(e). [Fred Halsted's *L.A. Plays Itself* (1972) was gay porn's first masterpiece.... Halsted, a self-taught filmmaker, shot the film over a period of three years in a now-vanished Los Angeles, a city at once rural and sleazy.... (A)cclaimed artist and filmmaker Jones documents his quest to capture the elusive public and private personas of Halsted ... (and) assembles a narrative of a long-gone gay lifestyle and an extinct Hollywood underground. (*Desc.*)]

Kennedy, Hubert (2002). *A Touch of Royalty: Gay Author James Barr.* San Francisco: Peremptory Publications. Web: hubertkennedy. angelfire.com/Barr.pdf.

King, Florence (1985). *Confessions of a Failed Southern Lady.* New York: St. Martin's Press. [King's classic memoir of her upbringing in an eccentric Southern family [is] told with ... uproarious wit and gusto.... King may have been a disappointment to her Granny, whose dream of rearing a Perfect Southern Lady would never be quite fulfilled. But after all, as Florence reminds us, "no matter which sex I went to bed with, I never smoked on the street." (*Desc.*)]

Mann, Jeff (2005). *Loving Mountains, Loving Men.* Athens: Ohio University Press. [(T)he first book-length treatment of a topic rarely discussed or examined: gay life in Appalachia.... Mann describes his life as an openly gay man who has remained true to his mountain roots ... reconcil(ing) his homosexuality with both traditional definitions of Appalachian manhood and his own attachment to home and kin. (*Desc.*)]

Minero, Emelina (2014, 17 February). *Curve.* Web: curvemag.com/ Curve-Magazine/Web-Articles-2014/I-Am-Queer-Working-Class-Fat-and-Mixed-Race.

Mirosevich, Toni (1996). *The Rooms We Make Our Own.* Ithaca, NY: Firebrand Books. [(Mirosevich writes) about what it is like to grow up in a working-class commercial fishing family, work as a nontraditional laborer in the physical trades, labor in a marriage and then come out, emerge from the assumption of excellent health into the reality of chronic illness, return to school, and become a writer and a teacher of writing. (*Desc.*)]

Mock, Janet (2014). *Redefining Realness: My Path to Womanhood, Identity, Love & So Much More.* New York: Atria Books. [What underpins and sustains this memoir is Mock's unflinching honesty about her childhood in poverty, her drug-addict father, her years as a prostitute on the tough backstreets of downtown Honolulu, and of, as Susan Stryker put it, "the life-sustaining bonds of family, friendships, and a powerful trans sisterhood." To be sure, this is no superficial "it gets better" story, but Mock makes clear that she learned survival, solidarity, and grace from some of the culture's most devalued people. At the end of the book, what you wish most is that you had a friend like Janet Mock. ~WR]

Nestle, Joan (1987/2003). *A Restricted Country.* Ithaca, NY: Firebrand Books. [A proud working class woman, and an "out" lesbian long before the Rainbow revolution, Nestle has stood at the forefront of American freedom struggles from the McCarthy era to the present day. Available for the first time in years, this revised classic collection of personal essays offers an intimate account of the lesbian, feminist, and civil rights movements. (*Desc.*)]

Orton, Joe (1986). *The Orton Diaries.* J. Lahr, Ed. London: Methuen.

Pratt, Minnie Bruce (1995). *S/He.* Ithaca, NY: Firebrand Books. [In a long series of vignettes, Pratt chronicles her Southern youth, during which she was "trained into the cult of pure white womanhood" and raised to be subjugated by a man; her lengthy marriage, the birth of two sons, and her eventual leave-taking from that traditional role; her coming out, living as a lesbian, and the fear it brought of "a sisterhood based on biological definitions." (A)t the book's pulsing, erotic core (is) her passionate love for a woman born female but male in gender expression, who often lives as a man and whom Pratt calls "my husband." [Whitney Scott, Booklist)]

Read, Kirk (2001). *How I Learned to Snap: A Small-Town Coming-Out and Coming-of-Age Story.* Athens, GA: Hill Street Press. [Read's youth in Virginia's Shenandoah Valley had the outward signs of a comfortable adolescence in the Reagan-era South. Dad: career military. Mom: a homemaker. Son: Little League/soccer player, Baptist youth group member, a straight-jawed boy from a long line of VMI men. (*Desc.*) See discussion in this volume. ~WR]

Rodriguez, Richard (1992). *Days of Obligation: An Argument with My Mexican Father.* New York: Viking.

Rouse, Wade (2006). *America's Boy: A Memoir.* New York: Dutton. [The tacky environs of the Missouri Ozarks in the 1970s set in relief a budding gay sensibility in this funny, affecting, overripe memoir.... The plight of a queer soul fighting for life in rural America is familiar literary terrain, and Rouse renders it as a duel between flamboyant camp and white-trash kitsch. (*PW*)]

Stewart, Jim (2011). *Folsom Street Blues: A Memoir of 1970s SoMa and Leatherfolk in Gay San Francisco.* San Francisco: Palm Drive Publishing. [In 1976, San Francisco's South of Market neighborhood was a hub for gay men into leather, public sex, and BDSM. It was a time when a raw, industrial, working-class spirit fused with a deep appreciation for beauty and passion. *Folsom Street Blues* takes its title from the street known for its gay bars (particularly serving the leather community) [and is] a valuable record of the freedoms that were so much more attainable in the years before the outbreak of AIDS. (Patty Comeau, *Clarion Reviews*)]

Symonds, John Addington (1984). *The Memoirs of John Addington Symonds*. Phyllis Grosskurth, Ed. London: Hutchinson and Company. [Symonds was by no means a member of the working-classes, but his reflections, in the final chapter of his *Memoirs*, on his twelve-year relationship with a nearly destitute Italian gondolier is a classic of the genre—the genre being cross-class relationships between middle- and upper-class Brits and poor or working-class men in the nineteenth and early twentieth centuries. ~WR]

White, Dave (2006). *Exile in Guyville: How a Punk-Rock Redneck Faggot Texan Moved to West Hollywood and Refused to Be Shiny and Happy*. New York: Alyson Books.

Wojnarowicz, David (1992). *Close to the Knives: A Memoir of Disintegration*. London: Serpent's Tail. [The alternation of poetic observations of a desolate, at times dissolute life on the road and in squalid urban settings with indictments of a homophobic "establishment" might at first appear ill-advised; soon, however, it becomes clear that Wojnarowicz's visual and verbal gifts are inextricably bound to his experience as a homosexual in an American underclass.... In the course of this memoir, the author coolly sketches the outlines of a troubled adolescence—parental kidnapping, drug use, prostitution—making survival alone seem miraculous. (*PW*)]

Wojnarowicz, David (1997). *The Waterfront Journals*. New York: Grove Press. [With a raw, empathic ventriloquism, Wojnarowicz fashions monologues from his encounters with hobos, truckers, hustlers and junkies he met during his years of cross-country travel. (*PW*)]

Wojnarowicz, David (2000). *In the Shadow of the American Dream: The Diaries of David Wojnarowicz*. New York: Grove Press.

Wright, Chely (2010). *Like Me: Confessions of a Heartland Country Singer*. New York: Pantheon Books. [Chely Wright, singer, songwriter, and country music star, writes in this moving, telling memoir about her life and her career, about growing up in America's heartland, and about barely remembering a time when she didn't know she was different... Wright's journey was dictated by keeping the truth of who she was closeted in a world in which country music stars had never been—and could not be—openly gay. (*Desc.*)]

Yeskel, Felice (1989). You Didn't Talk About These Things: Growing Up Jewish, Lesbian, and Working-Class. In Christie Balka and Andy Rose, Eds., *Twice Blessed: On Being Lesbian, Gay, and Jewish*. Boston: Beacon Press, 40-47.

Essays, Cultural Studies & Reportage

Allison, Dorothy (1994). *Skin: Talking About Sex, Class, and Literature.* Ithaca, NY: Firebrand Books. [*Skin* is, so to say, the germinal document for modern queer/class studies, and Allison provides a great place to start. ~WR]

Amory, Deborah P. (1996). Club Q: Dancing with (a) Difference. In Ellen Lewin, Ed., *Inventing Lesbian Cultures in America.* Boston: Beacon Press, 145-160.

Anzaldúa, Gloria (1987). *Borderlands/La Frontera: The New Mestiza.* San Francisco: Aunt Lute. [The ... physical borderland that I'm dealing with in this book is the U.S. Southwest/Mexican border. The psychological borderlands, the sexual borderlands, and spiritual borderlands are ... physically present wherever two or more cultures edge each other, where people of different races occupy the same territory, where under, lower, middle and upper classes touch. (From the book.)]

Anzaldúa, Gloria (1990). *Making Face, Making Soul/Haciendo Caras: Creative and Critical Perspectives by Women of Color.* San Francisco: Aunt Lute. [(R)eading this book is a cathartic and, potentially, individuating experience; one can gloss over the jargon-laden, anachronistic essays by academically entrenched feminists and take great pleasure reading the writings of students, activists, and artists who speak from an experiential viewpoint on such disarming subjects as "oppressed hair." (*PW*)]

Beemyn, Brett (Ed.) (1997). *Creating a Place for Ourselves: Lesbian, Gay, and Bisexual Community Histories.* London and New York: Routledge. [See especially Allen Drexel's "Before Paris Burned: Race, Class, and Male Homosexuality on the Chicago South Side"; Roey Thorpe's "The Changing Face of Lesbian Bars in Detroit"; Brett Beemyn's "A Queer Capital Race, Class, Gender, and the Changing Social Landscape of Washington's Gay Communities"; and Tim Retzloff's "Cars and Bars Assembling Gay Men in Postwar Flint, Michigan." ~WR]

Bell, D.J. & Valentine, G. (1995). Queer Country: Rural Lesbian and Gay Lives. *Journal of Rural Studies 11*(2): 113-122.

Benderson, Bruce (2007). *Sex and Isolation: And Other Essays.* Madison: University of Wisconsin Press. [See, in particular, Benderson's famous 1997 essay, "Toward the New Degeneracy," reprinted here. "How could I have guessed that my sexual freedom would become shrouded by condom-consciousness?" Benderson asks. "How would I have known that my hippie friends' nostalgia for rural space would mutate into the activism of the block association and its sullen war against street people? ... Or that violent campus uprisings would give birth to grievance committees that haggled over the crimes of politically incorrect speech? I didn't; but perhaps it was because I had never considered the class context in which the supposedly seismic changes of the sixties occurred." ~WR]

Brown, Rita Mae (1972). The Last Straw. *Motive 32*(1): 56-59. [Focuses on the class differences between working-class and middle-class lesbians in the U.S., beliefs of middle class women regarding working women, and the effects of downward mobility in reduction of class differences on the working class. (*Abs.*)]

Browne, K. (2008). Imagining Cities: Living the Other: Between the Gay Urban Idyll and Rural Lesbian Lives. *The Open Geography Journal 1*: 25-32.

Bunch, Charlotte & Myron, Nancy (Eds.) (1974). *Class and Feminism: A Collection of Essays from the Furies.* Baltimore: Diana Press. [These articles were written out of the experiences of the Furies, a lesbian/feminist collective composed of white lower, working, and middle class women. (From the Introduction.)]

Califia, Pat[rick] (2000). *Public Sex: The Culture of Radical Sex* and *Speaking Sex to Power: The Politics of Queer Sex* (2012). Both from Berkeley, CA: Cleis Press.

Champagne, John (1993). Seven Speculations on Queers and Class. *Journal of Homosexuality 26*(1): 159-174.

Christopher, Renny (2004) Shame and the Search for Home. *Feminist Studies 30*(1): 178-192.

Conrad, Ryan (Ed.) (2014) *Against Equality: Queer Revolution, Not Mere Inclusion.* Oakland, CA: AK Press.[This collection reinvigorates the queer political imagination with contemporary radical voices critical of the gay community's uncritical investment in single-issue 'equality' politics. Centered on the holy trinity of gay marriage, gays in the military, and hate crime legislation, *Against Equality* is a nuanced and honest appraisal of the effects of three decades of neoliberalism on a once-liberatory social movement. (*Desc.*)]

Dews, Carlos L. & Law, Carolyn Leste (Eds.) (2001). *Out in the South.* [(F)ifteen essays ... that powerfully convey the complexity of homosexual lives in the South at the turn of the millennium. While homophobia, racism, xenophobia, and fundamentalism remain potent forces, even affecting relationships within the community, it is clear why many have chosen to stay to forge their own unique queer identities in such unlikely places as the Appalachian Mountains, small towns, and the military. (Richard J. Violette, *LJ*)]

Duggan, Lisa (1995/2006). Crossing the Line: The Brandon Teena Case and the Social Psychology of Working-Class Resentment. In Lisa Duggan and Nan D. Hunter, Eds., *Sex Wars: Sexual Dissent and Political Culture.* New York: Routledge, 213-220.

Estes, Steve (2010). The Long Gay Line: Gender and Sexual Orientation at The Citadel. *Southern Cultures 16*(1): 46-64. [Joe Johnson was born in Palatka, Florida.... His father was a logger, and his mother worked various jobs.... Coming from a working-class family, college was only an option if admission came with a generous scholarship. The Citadel's acceptance letter did, and Johnson decided to go.... The Citadel's mission was to fashion whole men, men who would become leaders in the military and in civil society. Most of these men were southern. A few, like Joe Johnson, were gay. (From the article.)]

Fellows, Will (Ed.) (1996). *Farm Boys: Lives of Gay Men from the Rural Midwest.* University of Wisconsin Press. [A fascinating collection of materials from thirty-seven gay male oral histories of growing up on farms in the Midwest. Fellows provides succinct analysis of the changing economics of agriculture in the region ... changes which few of his interviewees seem to be aware, though some of their natal families have been squeezed out of business and off the land.... The accounts he elicited are often moving and are invariably informative about the life experiences and life worlds of heretofore invisible gay men. [Stephen O. Murray, *Committee for Lesbian and Gay History.*)]

Gay Left Collective (Eds.) (1980). *Homosexuality: Power and Politics.* London & New York: Allison & Busby.

Gill, John (1998). *Hard Times: Working-Class Queer Culture.* London: Continuum International Publishing.

Gilmartin, Katie (1996). 'We Weren't Bar People': Middle-Class Lesbian Identities and Cultural Spaces. *GLQ 3*(1): 1-51.

Gozemba, P. (1984, July 28). Scenes From A Working Class Bar. *Gay Community News 12*(3): 8.

Grahn, Judy (2009). *The Judy Grahn Reader.* Lisa Maria Hogeland, Ed. San Francisco: Aunt Lute Books. [Contains work from every phase of Grahn's career, including poems from all of her major poetry collections, such as "The Common Woman," "A Woman is Talking to Death," and the previously unpublished "Mental"; a number of her groundbreaking essays; as well as selected fiction and the full-length play, *The Queen of Swords. (Desc.)*]

Healey, Murray (1996). *Gay Skins: Class, Masculinity and Queer Appropriation.* Herndon, VA: Cassell Academic. [Through accounts from straight skinhead subculture, contemporary news coverage, subcultural theorists and the memories of gay skins in the 1960s, 1970s, and 1980s, Healy puts the boot into those myths of masculinity which constitute and which are seemingly evidenced by the skinhead, and challenges assumptions about class, queerness, and real men. *(International Gay & Lesbian Review.)*]

Herring, Scott (2007). Out of the Closets, Into the Woods: RFD, Country Women, and the Post-Stonewall Emergence of Queer Anti-Urbanism. *American Quarterly 59*(2): 341-372. [This essay revisits post-Stonewall lesbian and gay U.S. cultures of the 1970s to analyze the anti-urban politics of two rural-based journals—*RFD* (*Radical Fairy Digest*) and *Country Women*—as they countered the metronormativity of slick leisure magazines such as *The Advocate....* [B]oth working-class rural-based journals extended the radical critiques of the Gay Liberation Front

[and] presented alternative aesthetic opportunities to dominant U.S. gay and lesbian lifestyles. (*Abs.*)]

Hollibaugh, Amber (1980). Right to Rebel. In Gay Left Collective, Ed., *Homosexuality: Power and Politics.* London: Allison and Busby, 205-215.

Howard, John (Ed.) (1997). *Carryin' On in the Lesbian and Gay South.* New York University Press. [Southerners wrestle with their past, lesbians and gays wrestle for visibility, historians wrestle over the South—yet rarely have the three crossed paths. Howard's ground-breaking anthology casts its net broadly [and] does not shy away from thorny, self-critical questions: What allows us to label a historical figure with the relatively recent category of "lesbian" or "gay"? Further, exactly who is a Southerner? (*Desc.*)]

Hubbs, Nadine (2014). *Rednecks, Queers, and Country Music.* Berkeley: University of California Press. [Skillfully weaving historical inquiry with an examination of classed cultural repertoires and close listening to country songs, Hubbs confronts the shifting and deeply entangled workings of taste, sexuality, and class politics.... With a powerful combination of music criticism, cultural critique, and sociological analysis of contemporary class formation, Hubbs ... shows how dismissive, politically loaded middle-class discourses devalue country's manifestations of working-class culture, politics, and values, and render working-class acceptance of queerness invisible. (*Desc.*)]

Kadi, Joanna (1996). *Thinking Class: Sketches from a Cultural Worker.* Boston: South End Press.

Larson, D. (1990). When You Read between the Lines: Class and Complicity. *Gay Community News 17*(29): 17.

Lorde, Audre (1984). *Sister Outsider: Essays and Speeches.* Trumansburg, NY: Crossing Press.

Manalansan IV, M.F. (2007). Of Closets and Other Rural Voids. *GLQ: A Journal of Lesbian and Gay Studies 13*(1): 100-102.

Martin, J. (1990, January 21). I Came from a Blue Collar World. *Gay Community News 17*(27): 5.

McBride, Dwight A. (2005). *Why I Hate Abercrombie & Fitch: Essays on Race and Sexuality.* New York: New York University Press.

Minkowitz, Donna (1991, November 5). The Conference Made Me Feel Like a Working-Class Spy Among Elites. (Human Rights Campaign Fund "Corporate Agenda" Seminar). *The Advocate*: 37.

Minkowitz, Donna (1999, 12 July). Love and Hate in Laramie. *The Nation*: 18+. [A remarkable and genuinely unsettling parsing of the dynamics of class and sexuality in the 1998 Matthew Shepard murder. ~WR]

Moraga, Cherrie & Anzaldúa, Gloria (Eds.) (1981/2002). *This Bridge Called My Back: Writings By Radical Women of Color.* Watertown, MA: Persephone Press.

Moraga, Cherrie (1983/2002). *Loving in the War Years: Lo que Nunca Pasó por Sus Labios.* Boston: South End Press.

Moran, Leslie J. (2000). Homophobic Violence: The Hidden Injuries of Class. In Sally Munt, Ed., *Cultural Studies and the Working Class: Subject to Change.* London: Cassell, 206-218.

Morgan, Peter (1998, March). Class Divisions in the Gay Community. *International Socialism,* Issue 78 (Socialist Workers Party, Britain). Web: pubs.socialistreviewindex.org.uk/isj78/morgan.htm.

Myron, Nancy (1972). Class Beginnings. *Furies 1*(3): 2-3. [Discusses several issues concerning the barriers posed by social class to feminist movements: the reinforcement of sexism and classism in the U.S., the importance of putting racism in a political context for women, and the consequences of refusing to deal with class behavior in a lesbian or feminist movement. (*Abs.*)]

Nestle, Joan (1998). *A Fragile Union: New & Selected Writings.* Berkeley, CA: Cleis Press.

Norton, Rictor (1999). Class-Based Erotics. Web: rictornorton.co.uk/class.htm.

Oldfield, Kenneth and Johnson, Richard (Eds.) (2008). *Resilience: Queer Professors from the Working Class.* Albany, NY: State University of New York Press. [Academia can be overwhelmingly foreign and hostile to those who have poor or working-class backgrounds.... Resilience offers inspiring personal stories of those who made it: thirteen professors and administrators provide their moving accounts of struggle, marginalization, and triumph in the accomplishments that their parents, guidance counselors, and sometimes even they themselves would have thought out of reach. (*Desc.*)]

Penelope, Julia (Ed.) (1994). *Out of the Class Closet: Lesbians Speak.* Freedom, CA: The Crossing Press.

Penelope, Julia and Wolfe, Susan (Eds.) (1993). *Lesbian Culture: An Anthology—The Lives, Work, Ideas, Art and Visions of Lesbians Past And Present.* Freedom, CA: The Crossing Press. [Includes essays on class distinctions, prostitution, consumerism, and politically correct food. The contributors' list is long and impressive. ~WR]

Preston, John (Ed.) (1991). *Hometowns: Gay Men Write about Where They Belong.* New York: Dutton. [See discussion in this volume. Some of the contributors in Preston's 1992 edited anthology, *A Member of the Family: Gay Men Write about Their Lives*, also touch on working-class themes. ~WR]

Raffo, Susan (Ed.) (1997). *Queerly Classed: Gay Men and Lesbians Write About Class.* Boston: South End Press. [Gay and lesbian cultures have learned how to talk—and talk and talk and talk—about sex; no aspect of erotic life is too taboo for discussion. Issues of class and economics, however, have been so closeted that they are rarely discussed. *Queerly Classed* breaks through this door with almost two dozen personal and critical essays that explore the intersections between class and alternative sexual identity. (Amazon.com)]

Rist, Darrell Yates (1992). *Heartlands: A Gay Man's Odyssey Across America.* New York: Dutton. [For three years, activist and journalist

Rist sought to observe the lives of gay people outside ... big-city communities.... Rist not only captures the texture of gay life in places such as Reno, Nevada and Tupelo, Mississippi..., his trip forces him to reconsider his previous, perhaps naïve belief in gay brotherhood: most men he met had more in common with their neighbors than with all the other homosexual men he had ever known. (*PW*) See discussion in this volume. ~WR]

Rodríguez, Richard T. (2006). Queering the Homeboy Aesthetic. *Aztlan: A Journal of Chicano Studies 31*(2): 127-137. [The homeboy aesthetic is an assemblage of signifiers: clothing, hair, a bold stance, and a distinct language, all combining to form a distinguishable cultural affectation hard to miss on Los Angeles city streets. The homeboy aesthetic is ... embraced and resisted as a mode of working-class sensibility and a marker of cultural difference.... This essay ... foregrounds the historical and social settings in which the queer homeboy aesthetic materializes ... and presents ... the work of the Chicano artist, Hector Silva, whose work establishes fantasy spaces within which to queer the homeboy aesthetic. (*Abs.*)]

Samson, JD (2011, 5 October). I Love My Job, But It Made Me Poorer. *Huffpost Gay Voices.* Web: huffingtonpost.com/jd-samson/i-love-my-job-but-it-made_b_987680.html. [I have to ask myself: where did I go wrong? And I can only guess that the answer lies in a combination of three things: 1) my family is not rich, 2) I am a queer woman, and 3) I am trying so desperately to keep up with my peers that I am living beyond my means. (From the essay.)]

Sellars, Nick (1995). A Rough Trade. Originally published in *XY: Men, Sex, Politics.* Web: www.xyonline.net/content/rough-trade. [Class differences within the gay community keep gay men separated through fear, historically grounded but unreliable feelings of disgust for other classes, and pressure to conform and participate in a community where we (can) all be "out" together. Class differences are a major barrier to gay liberation. (From the essay.)]

Simpson, Mark (2007, June 18). Trading in the Past. Web: marksimpson.com/blog/2007/06/18/trading-in-the-past. [Once upon a time the streets of the capital heaved with jolly sailors and guardsmen just looking for gentlemen to have fun with. Then gay liberation came along and ruined it for everyone, complains Mark Simpson.]

Simpson, Mark (Ed.). *Anti-Gay.* London: Freedom Editions. [Simpson savages what he calls "gay fundamentalists" in *Anti-Gay*, one of the first entries in what has become a significant genre of sacred-cow murdering, orthodoxy-challenging, and assimilation-bashing. As the *London Tribune* wrote, Anti-Gay is "an intellectual enema for today's mentally constipated gay generation." ~WR]

Smith, Barbara (1998). *The Truth That Never Hurts: Writings on Race, Gender, and Freedom.* New Brunswick, NJ: Rutgers University Press. [A feminist writer and theorist, Smith founded Kitchen Table/Women of

Color Press with the late Audre Lorde.... [T]his collection [contains] newer and older, still vibrant works, most previously published in often hard-to-find journals or anthologies.... Smith's writing frequently reaches strident polemicist peaks, but, just as frequently, stretches of sublime prose translate her crystalline intellect to the page, exciting both mind and senses. (*PW*)]

Sonnie, Amy (2000). *Revolutionary Voices: A Multicultural Queer Youth Anthology.* Los Angeles: Alyson Books. [Described as a "multicultural, multigender, multigenre" anthology, *Revolutionary Voices* contains work of very mixed quality, but a number of the contributors focus on their experiences as poverty-class/working-class students, activists, and artists. ~WR]

Sycamore, Matt Bernstein (Ed.) (2008). *That's Revolting! Queer Strategies for Resisting Assimilation.* Rev. Ed. Brooklyn: Soft Skull Press. [This updated edition (of the 2004 original) contains seven new selections that cover everything from rural, working-class youth in Massachusetts to gay life in New Orleans to the infamous Drop the Debt/Stop AIDS action in New York. This lively composite portrait of cutting-edge queer activism is a clarion call for anyone who questions the value of becoming the Stepford Homosexual. (*Desc.*)]

Sycamore, Mattilda Bernstein (2013). *The End of San Francisco.* San Francisco: City Lights Publishers. [Sycamore gets all the issues right and deserves respect as much for staying power as for sheer gall, but the occasionally unbalanced ranting and relentless us/them thinking becomes a distraction. Asserting, even with great conviction, that horrifying inequalities and deeply troubling inconsistencies exist isn't the same as having insight into their cause or resolution. ~WR]

Tea, Michelle (2005, September). Dykes and the Dollar: A History (interview with Lillian Faderman). *Girlfriends*: 36-38.

Tea, Michelle (Ed.) (2004). *Without a Net: The Female Experience of Growing Up Working Class.* Emeryville, CA: Seal Press. [A number of important queer voices appear in this highly recommended anthology, including Eileen Myles, Dorothy Allison, and Meliza Bañales. ~WR]

Tongson, Karen (2011). *Relocations: Queer Suburban Imaginaries.* New York: NYU Press. [Moving beyond the imbedded urban/rural binary, *Relocations* offers the first major queer cultural study of sexuality, race and representation in the suburbs. (*Desc.*) See, in particular, the chapter entitled "The Light That Never Goes Out: Butchlalis de Panochtitlan Reclaim 'Lesser Los Angeles.'" ~WR]

Tucker, Scott (1995). *Fighting Words: An Open Letter to Queers and Radicals.* London: Cassell.

Tucker, Scott (1996, April). Class Struggle: It's Here. It's Queer. Get Used to It. *The Humanist 56*(2): 44-46.

Tucker, Scott (1997). *The Queer Question: Essays on Desire and Democracy.* Boston: South End Press. [The real achievement ... is Tucker's linkage of queer consciousness with class: "For many people in this country, including queers, the social climate is only tolerable at best, and sometimes murderous at worst." His idealism consists in connecting the oppression queers feel to sexism, classism and the horrors of the corporate state. (Lawrence Richette, *International Gay & Lesbian Review*)]

Vaid, Urvashi (2002, 29 October). Separate and Unequal. The *Advocate* 875: 72.

Venable, Malcolm (2001, July). A Question of Identity. *VIBE*: 98-106. [Here, we meet young, black, same-sex loving males who say they despise gay people and seem to loathe their own existence. Fascinating discussions of the multiple meanings of "gay," frequently rejected not solely for its feminizing force but for its racial and class connotations. ~WR]

Weston, K. (1995). Get Thee to a Big City: Sexual Imaginary and the Great Gay Migration. *GLQ: A Journal of Lesbian and Gay Studies 2*(3): 253-277.

Weston, Kath (Ed.) (1996). *Render Me, Gender Me: Lesbians Talk Sex, Class, Color, Nation, Studmuffins.* Columbia University Press.

Whitlock, Ugena (2013). *Queer South Rising: Voices of a Contested Place.* Charlotte, NC: Information Age Publishing. [The rising Whitlock envisions is akin to breaking and turning over meanings of Southern place ... [calling] into question notions of a universal, homogenous LGBT, queer, identity.... Essays explore multiple intersections of Southern place—religion, politics, sexuality, race, education—that transcend regional boundaries. (*Desc.*)]

Young, K. (1978, Summer). Working-Class Lesbians. *Gay Left 6*: 21.

Zeeland, Steven (1993). *Barrack Buddies and Soldier Lovers: Dialogues with Gay Young Men in the U.S. Military.* New York: Harrington Park Press. [This is one of Zeeland's several books on gay and gay-behaving men in the various branches of the U.S. military. Though Zeeland is frequently more focused on the titillating details of his subjects' sex lives than on other issues, his interviewees are, almost by definition, working-class men, and what they have to say about the management of their sexuality in the context of other "allegiances" is often instructive. ~WR]

Academic Considerations
of Queers & Class

Appleby, George A. (Ed.) (2001). *Working-Class Gay and Bisexual Men.* Special issue of *Journal of Gay & Lesbian Social Service 12*(3/4). [See, in particular, Appleby's "Ethnographic Study of Gay and Bisexual Working-Class Men in the United States" and Gerald Mallon's "Oh, Canada: The Experience of Working-Class Gay Men in Toronto." ~WR]

Barrett, Donald C. & Pollack, Lance M. (2005). Whose Gay Community? Social Class, Sexual Self-Expression, and Gay Community Involvement. *The Sociological Quarterly 46*(3): 437-456.

Barrett, Donald C. (2000). Masculinity Among Working-Class Gay Males. In Peter M. Nardi, Ed., *Gay Masculinities.* Thousand Oaks, CA: Sage Publications, 176-205.

Boag, Peter (2003). Same-Sex Affairs: Constructing and Controlling Homosexuality in the Pacific Northwest. Berkeley: University of California Press. [At the turn of the twentieth century, two distinct, yet at times overlapping, male same-sex sexual subcultures had emerged in the Pacific Northwest: one among the men and boys who toiled in the region's logging, fishing, mining, farming, and railroad-building industries; the other among the young urban white-collar workers of the emerging corporate order. Boag draws on police logs, court records, and newspaper accounts to create a vivid picture of the lives of these men and youths. (*Desc.*) (Note, in particular, "Part I: Working-Class Affairs." ~WR)]

Brewis, Joanna & Jack, Gavin (2010, April). Consuming Chavs: The Ambiguous Politics of Gay Chavinism. *Sociology 44*: 251-268. [The article speculates on the ambiguous implications of the commodification of the male chav for consumption by middle-class homosexual men, further developing the concept of "hegemonic masculinity" to discuss what gay chavinism might mean for "hegemonic homosexuality." (*Abs.*)]

Castells, Manuel (Ed.) (1983). Cultural Identity, Sexual Liberation and Urban Structure: The Gay Community in San Francisco. In *The City and the Grassroots: A Cross-Cultural Theory of Urban Social Movements.* Berkeley & Los Angeles: University of California Press, 138-172.

Chapple, M. J., Kippax, S. & Smith, G. (1998). 'Semi-Straight Sort of Sex': Class and Gay Community Attachment Explored Within a Framework of Older Homosexually Active Men. *Journal of Homosexuality 35*(2): 65-83.

Clarkson, Jay (2006). "Everyday Joe" versus "Pissy, Bitchy, Queens": Gay Masculinity on StraightActing.com. *The Journal of Men's Studies 14*(2): 191-207. [Analyzes discourse on Straight-Acting.com; the author argues that straight-acting gay men model their version of masculinity on working-class aesthetics.... While their rejection of the link between effeminacy and homosexuality has the potential to undermine dominant gender ideology, ultimately they reinscribe hegemonic masculinity through their marginalization of women and other gay men. (*Abs.*)]

Connell, R. W., Davis, M. D. & Dowsett, G. W. (1993, March). A Bastard of a Life: Homosexual Desire and Practice Among Men in Working-Class Milieux. *Australian and New Zealand Journal of Sociology 29*(1): 112-135.

Connell, Raewyn, Dowsett, Gary, Rodden, Pam, Davis, Mark, Watson, Lex & Don Baxter (1991) Social Class, Gay Men, and AIDS Prevention. *Australian Journal of Public Health 15*(3): 178-189.

Coston, Bethany M. and Michael Kimmel (2012). Seeing Privilege Where It Isn't: Marginalized Masculinities and the Intersectionality of Privilege. *Journal of Social Issues* 68: 97-111. [Because privilege is distributed along a range of axes, we consider three sites in which male privilege is compromised ... by other statuses: disability, sexuality, and class. Employing a Symbolic Interactionist approach, we observe strategies employed by disabled men, gay men and working-class men to reduce, neutralize, or resist the problematization of masculinity. (*Abs.*)]

Crawley, Sara L. (2001). Are Butch And Fem Working-Class and Antifeminist? *Gender & Society 15*(2): 175-196. [(This study) suggests that middle-class lesbians were less likely to present themselves as butch or fem than working-class lesbians but no less likely to be seeking a butch or fem partner. Also, butch and fem were found to be much more prevalent in the 1990s than in the 1970s or 1980s. (*Abs.*)]

Dews, Carlos L. & Law, Carolyn Leste (1998, Fall). Anti-Intellectualism, Homophobia, and the Working-Class Gay/Lesbian Academic. *Radical Teacher 53*(8): 8-12.

Donaldson, Stephen (1990). Eroticization of the Working Class. In Wayne R. Dynes, Ed., *Encyclopedia of Homosexuality.* New York: Garland, 1405-1406.

Dowsett, G. W., Davis, M. D. & Connell, R. W. (1992). Working Class Homosexuality and HIV/AIDS Prevention: Some Recent Research from Sydney, Australia. *Psychology and Health 6*(4): 313-324.

Dowsett, Gary W. (1994 Autumn). Working-Class Homosexuality, Gay Community, and the Masculine Sexual (Dis)Order. *Revue Sexologique 2*(2): 75-105.

Embrick, David, Walther, Carol & Wickens, Corrine (2007, June). Working Class Masculinity: Keeping Gay Men and Lesbians Out of the Workplace. *Sex Roles 56*(11-12): 757-766.

Foley, Douglas E. (1989). Does the Working Class Have a Culture in the Anthropological Sense? *Cultural Anthropology 4*(2): 137-162. [This article starts with Paul Willis's concept of a class culture and further develops his ideas with critical theory, symbolic interactionist, and anthropological perspectives. This reading of class and cultural theory suggests a more political concept of culture and cultural assimilation (and) suggests ... questions ... about everyday cultural life and communicative practices in capitalist societies. (*Abs.*)]

Fraser, Mariam (1999). Classing Queer: Politics in Competition. In Vikki Bell, Ed., *Performativity and Belonging.* London: Sage Publications, 107-131.

Garber, Linda (2001). *Identity Poetics: Race, Class and the Lesbian-Feminist Roots of Queer Theory.* New York: Columbia University Press. [Makes a case for the significant role of lesbian poets as theorists of lesbian identity and activism. (*Desc.*)]

Gibson, Alexandra and Macleod, Catriona (2012). (Dis)allowances of Lesbians' Sexual Identities: Lesbian Identity Construction in Racialised, Classed, Familial, and Institutional Spaces. *Feminism and Psychology* 22(4): 462-481. [Explores how lesbian identity construction is facilitated and constrained by the raced, classed, gendered, familial, and geographical spaces that women occupy. We present a narrative-discursive analysis of eight lesbians' stories of sexuality, told within a historically white university in South Africa. (*Abs.*)]

Hall, Ruth L. & Greene, Beverly (2002). Not Any One Thing: The Complex Legacy of Social Class on African American Lesbian Relationships. *Journal of Lesbian Studies* 6(1): 65-74.

Heaphy, Brian (2013). Situating Lesbian and Gay Cultures of Class Identification. *Cultural Sociology* 7(3): 303-319. [In the 1990s some theorists implied that lesbian and gay identities were classless or post-class ones. This paper challenges this idea by considering personal narratives of class (dis)identification that were generated via interviews with lesbians and gay men in the 1990s.... [T]heir narratives troubled the idea that lesbian and gay identities override or transcend class ones[,] undermine arguments about the insignificance of class to identities more generally, and complicate arguments about the individualization of class. (*Abs.*)]

Henderson, Lisa (2007). Queer Visibility and Social Class. In Kevin G. Barnhurst, Ed., *Media Q, Media/Queered: Visibility and Its Discontents.* New York: Peter Lang Publishing, Inc., 197-216.

Henderson, Lisa (2013). *Love and Money: Queers, Class, and Cultural Production.* New York: New York University Press. [Argues that we can't understand contemporary queer cultures without looking through the lens of social class. Resisting old divisions between culture and economy, identity and privilege, left and queer, recognition and redistribution, *Love and Money* offers supple approaches to capturing class experience and class ... in and around queerness. (*Desc.*)]

Hidalgo, Hilda A. & Christensen, Elia (1976-1977). The Puerto Rican Lesbian and the Puerto Rican Community. *Journal of Homosexuality* 2(2): 109-121.

Hodge, G. Derrick (2000). Retrenchment from a Queer ideal: Class Privilege and the Failure of Identity Politics in AIDS Activism. *Environment and Planning D: Society and Space,* 18(3): 355-376. [The AIDS activism movement which emerged in the form of ACT UP/New

York was born from within the gay identity, but embraced a more expansive coalitional politic [that called for a critique] of the larger political-economic and social structures that had translated a medical emergency into a social catastrophe. This more expansive politics gave rise to the Queer movement ... but this political evolution was not internally uncontested: the more privileged white middle-class men within ACT UP resisted any movement away from a narrowly medical approach to AIDS for those with access. The resulting conflict eventually crippled ACT UP. (*Abs.*)]

Hostetler, Andrew J. & Herdt, Gilbert H. (1998, Summer). Culture, Sexual Lifeways, and Developmental Subjectivities: Rethinking Sexual Taxonomies. *Social Research* 65(2): 249-290.

Johnson, Colin R. (2013). *Just Queer Folks: Gender and Sexuality in Rural America.* Philadelphia, PA: Temple University Press. [Via carefully prepared case (studies), Johnson shows us how largely poor and working-class men and women lived out their queer diversity in situ, and he argues that small towns and rural communities accommodated eccentricity and often protected "their own." Throughout, he ... challenges the preconception that to be queer is to be urban, white, and middle class. (Sally R. Munt, *Times Higher Education.*]

Johnson, Paul (2008). "Rude Boys": The Homosexual Eroticization of Class. *Sociology* 42(1): 65-82. [Since 2002, the 'chav' has become a ubiquitous symbol of class difference in Britain. Simultaneously, a heterogeneous industry has appropriated 'chav culture' in order to market a range of products and services orientated to gay men. In this article ... I argue that a form of symbolic violence is created by such representation. (*Abs.*)]

Kaye, Kerwin (2003). Male Prostitution in the Twentieth Century: Pseudohomosexuals, Hoodlum Homosexuals, and Exploited Teens. *Journal of Homosexuality* 46(1/2): 1-77. [Male prostitution altered its form dramatically over the course of the twentieth century. While some of these changes relate to economics and general cultural shifts..., some of the most important changes have arisen in response to transformations in the idea of "homosexuality," and the growing influence this idea had within middle-class and then working-class culture. (*Abs.*)]

Keogh, Peter, Dodds, Catherine & Henderson, Laurie (2004). *Working Class Gay Men: Redefining Community, Restoring Identity.* London: Sigma Research Reports. Web: www.sigmaresearch.org.uk/downloads/report04a.pdf.

Lauria, M. and Knopp, L. (1985). Toward an Analysis of the Role of Gay Communities in the Urban Renaissance. *Urban Geography* 6: 152-169.

Lemke, Jurgen & Borneman, John (Eds.) (1991). Tr. Steven Stoltenberg, et al. *Gay Voices from East Germany.* Bloomington, IN: Indiana University Press. [Lemke's interviews with fourteen gay men, mainly working class, not only encompass a range of gay lifestyles—from married men leading double lives to men proud of passing as "straight" in military service—but reflect almost a century of German history. (*PW*)]

Libretti, Tim (2004, November). Sexual Outlaws and Class Struggle: Rethinking History and Class Consciousness from a Queer Perspective. *College English 67*(2): 154-171.

Maynard, Steven (1997, June). 'Horrible Temptations': Sex, Men, and Working-Class Male Youth in Urban Ontario, 1890-1935. *Canadian Historical Review 78*(2): 191-236. [Explores the sexual relations between boys and men during the period 1890-1935 in urban Ontario with emphasis on subculture of homosexual exchange. (*Abs.*)]

Maynard, Steven (1998). Rough Work and Rugged Men: The Social Construction of Masculinity in Working-Class History. *Labour 23*: 159-169.

Morton, Donald (1996). The Class Politics of Queer Theory. *College English 58*(4): 471-583. [Reviews the books *Homos* by Leo Bersani, *Gay and Lesbian Politics: Sexuality and the Emergence of a New Ethic* by Mark Blasius, and *Over the Rainbow: Money, Class and Homophobia* by Nicola Field.]

Prieur, Annick (2008). *Mema's House, Mexico City: On Transvestites, Queens, and Machos.* University Of Chicago Press. [Prieur analyzes the complicated relations between the effeminate homosexuals, most of them transvestites, and their partners, masculine-looking bisexual men, ultimately asking why these particular gender constructions exist in the Mexican working classes and how they can be so widespread in a male-dominated society. (*Desc.*)]

Rayside, David M. (1992). Homophobia, Class and Party in England. *Canadian Journal of Political Science 25*(1): 121-149. (Looks at institutionalized homophobia in England and how it has intensified over the last ten years; anti-gay norms that have long been embedded in working-class and middle-class cultures; and the New Right politics of the Conservative party under Margaret Thatcher and John Major. (*Abs.*)]

Ridge, Damien & Minichiello, Victor (1997). Queer Connections: Community, "The Scene," and an Epidemic. *Journal of Contemporary Ethnography 26*(2): 146-181.

Shepard, Alan (1998). Teaching 'The Renaissance': Queer Consciousness and Class Dysphoria. In Alan Shepard, John McMillan and Gary Tate, Eds., *Coming to Class: Pedagogy and the Social Class of Teachers.* Portsmouth, NH: Boynton/Cook (Heinemann), 209-230.

Taylor, Yvette (2005). Real Politik or Real Politics? Working-Class Lesbians' Political "Awareness" and Activism." *Women's Studies International Forum 28*(6): 484-494.

Taylor, Yvette (2005). The Gap and How To Mind It: Intersections of Class and Sexuality (Research Note). *Sociological Research Online 10*(3). Web: socresonline.org.uk/10/3/taylor.html.

Taylor, Yvette (2007). *Working Class Lesbian Life: Classed Outsiders.* New York: Palgrave Macmillan. [Exploring the relationship between class, sexuality and social exclusion, this is an original study of women who identify themselves as working-class and lesbian, highlighting the significance of class and sexuality in their biographies, everyday lives, and identities. (*Desc.*)]

Taylor, Yvette (2007, April). 'If Your Face Doesn't Fit...': The Misrecognition of Working-Class Lesbians in Scene Space. *Leisure Studies 26*(2): 161-178. [This article examines the significance of class and sexuality in the lives of women who self-identify themselves as working-class and lesbian. (*Abs.*)]

Taylor, Yvette (2008, October). 'That's Not Really My Scene': Working-Class Lesbians In (and Out of) Place. *Sexualities 11*(5): 523-546.

Weber, Janis C. (1996, September). Social Class as a Correlate of Gender Identity among Lesbian Women. *Sex Roles 35*(5-6): 271-281.

Wight, Daniel (1994, November). Boys' Thoughts and Talk About Sex in a Working-Class Locality of Glasgow. *Sociological Review 42*(4): 703-737.

Woollacott, Angela (1994, April). "Khaki Fever" and its Control: Gender, Class, Age and Sexual Morality on the British Homefront in the First World War. *Journal of Contemporary History 29*(2): 325-347.

Perspectives on History, Literature, Art & Media

Anzaldúa, Gloria (1991). To(o) Queer the Writer: *Loca, Escritora y Chicana*. In Betsy Warland, Ed., *InVersions: Writings by Dykes, Queers, and Lesbians*. Vancouver: Press Gang, 249-263.

Arriola, Elvia R. (1995). Faeries, Marimachas, Queens, and Lezzies: The Construction of Homosexuality Before the 1969 Stonewall Riots, *Columbia Journal of Gender & Law 5*(1): 33-77. [Shows contrast between political activism of pre-Stonewall largely closeted white middle-class gay world and that of highly visible black, Latino/a, transgendered, and working class gays and lesbians. Argues that the radically diverse origins of the lesbian/gay/bi civil rights movement, often ignored by white middle-class organizers, deserve. (Jean Stefancic)]

Becker, Ron (2006). The Affordable, Multicultural Politics of Gay Chic in *Gay TV and Straight America*. New Brunswick, NJ: Rutgers University Press, 108-135.

Bérubé, Allan (1990). *Coming Out Under Fire: The History of Gay Men and Women in World War Two*. New York: The Free Press. [As the title suggests, Bérubé's award-winning book is primarily focused on the gay men and lesbians who served their country during WWII, but he brings a class-analysis to his work and to his understanding of the way that ex-soldiers fit—or failed to fit—their newfound sexualities into their lives when they returned home. ~WR]

Bérubé, Allan, edited and with an introduction by J. D'Emilio and E. B. Freedman (2011). *My Desire for History: Essays in Gay, Community, and Labor History.* Chapel Hill: University of North Carolina Press. [A self-taught historian and MacArthur Fellow, Bérubé, who died in 2007, was a pioneer in the study of lesbian and gay history in the United States. and wrote extensively on the relationship between sexuality, class, and race. [This volume contains] sixteen of his most important essays, including hard-to-access articles and unpublished writing. (*Desc.*)]

Brock, Deborah (n.d.). "Workers of the World Caress": An interview with Gary Kinsman on Gay and Lesbian Organizing in the 1970s Toronto Left. Web: yorku.ca/lefthist/online/brock_kinsman.html. [Special online feature to accompany *Left History*'s Spring/Summer 2004 special LGBTQ studies issue. ~WR]

Brown, Ricardo J. (William Reichard, Ed.) (2001). *The Evening Crowd at Kirmser's: A Gay Life in the 1940s.* Minneapolis, MN: University of Minnesota Press. [This remarkable little book touches on the lives of a small group of gay men and lesbians in St. Paul, MN, during World War II..., a small, close-knit community centered around Kirmser's, an inner-city dive run by two German immigrants. This book is as much about class and race prejudice as it is about homophobia, and the men and women portrayed are as much products of their lower- and working-class backgrounds as of their sexual orientation. (*LJ*)]

Chamberland, Line (1993). Remembering Lesbian Bars: Montreal, 1955-1975. *Journal of Homosexuality* 25(3): 231-270. [Retraces the development of lesbian bars in Montreal, Canada between 1955 and 1975 and the key role played by working-class lesbians; explains class-related differences in bar-going habits and ways of expressing lesbian identity. (*Abs.*)]

Chauncey, George (1994). *Gay New York: Gender, Urban Culture, and the Making of the Gay Male World, 1890-1940.* New York: Basic Books.

Chenier, Elise. (2004, Spring/Summer). Rethinking Class in a Lesbian Bar Culture: Living "The Gay Life" in Toronto, 1955-1965. *Left History* 9(2): 85-118.

Colson, Nicole (2003, August 15). Same Old Stereotypes. *Socialist Worker*: 9. [Reviews "the new, gay-themed television," including *Queer Eye for the Straight Guy* and *Boy Meets Boy*. Web: socialistworker.org/2003-2/464/464_09_GayTV.shtml. ~WR]

D'Emilio, John (1983). *Sexual Politics, Sexual Communities: The Making of a Homosexual Minority in the United States, 1940-1970.* Chicago: University of Chicago Press.

Faderman, Lillian (1991). *Odd Girls and Twilight Lovers: A History of Lesbian Life in Twentieth-Century America.* New York: Columbia University Press.

Faderman, Lillian (1992, April). The Return of Butch and Femme: A Phenomenon in Lesbian Sexuality of the 1980s and 1990s. *Journal of the History of Sexuality* 2(4): 578-596.

Forrest, Katherine V. (Ed.) (2005). *Lesbian Pulp Fiction: The Sexually Intrepid World of Lesbian Paperback Novels 1950-1965.* Berkeley, CA: Cleis Press. [Forrest's excellent study is a good introduction to the literally hundreds of novels published in the "twilight" years of McCarthy-era oppression and beyond. Though not all of them were written by lesbians or even intended for lesbians, many lesbian-identified women (as Forrest says of herself in her terrific introduction) found such novels and believed they "saved their lives." The treatment of class varies hugely in this immense genre, but there is no small number of fully-fleshed, realistic portraits of working-class lesbians to be found among the "pulps." ~WR]

Freedman, Estelle B. (1995). The Historical Construction of Homosexuality in the US. *Socialist Review* 25(1): 31-46.

Gardiner, James (1993). *A Class Apart: The Private Pictures of Montague Glover.* New York: Serpent's Tail. [A selection of photographs and letters culled from the archive of Montague Glover (1898-1983), documenting the intimate, rarely recorded lives of gay men in Britain from the First World War to the 1950s. The book features Glover's three obsessions: the Armed Forces, working-class men, and his lifelong lover, Ralph Hall. A seamless blend of the personal and the historical make this a unique portrait of a secret relationship and of an undiscovered period in British gay history. (*Desc.*)]

Garman, Bryan K. (2000). *A Race of Singers: Whitman's Working-Class Hero from Guthrie to Springsteen.* Chapel Hill: University of North Carolina Press. [While Whitman's verse propounded notions of sexual freedom and renounced the competitiveness of capitalism, it also safeguarded the interests of the white workingman, often at the expense of women and people of color. Garman describes how each of Whitman's successors adopted the mantle of the working-class hero while adapting the role to his own generation's concerns. (*Desc.*)]

Hackett, Robin (2004). *Sapphic Primitivism: Productions of Race, Class, and Sexuality in Key Works of Modern Fiction.* New Brunswick, NJ: Rutgers University Press. [Examines portrayals of race, class, and sexuality in modernist texts by white women to argue for the existence of a literary device that Hackett calls "Sapphic primitivism" in the works of Olive Schreine, Virginia Woolf, Sylvia Townsend Warner, and Willa Cather. In each, blackness and working-class culture are seen as representing sexual autonomy, including lesbianism, for white women. (*Desc.*)]

Heep, Hartmut (1995). May I Offer You a Drink? Sex and Sexual Subtexts in Frank O'Hara's Poetry. *Journal of Homosexuality 30*(1): 75-86.

hooks, bell (1992). Is Paris Burning? In *Black Looks: Race and Representation.* Boston: South End Press, 145-156.

Houlbrook, Matt (2005). *Queer London: Perils and Pleasures in the Sexual Metropolis, 1918-1957.* Chicago: University of Chicago Press. [In particular, the chapter "London's Bad Boys": Homosex, Manliness, and Money in Working-Class Culture." ~WR]

Katz, Jonathan Ned (1990, January 30). John Addington Symonds Pops the Question: And Why Walt Whitman Said No. *The Advocate* 543: 43. [John Addington Symonds conducted a nineteen-year-long letter-writing campaign to convince Walt Whitman to publicly endorse male homosexuality as an acceptable social activity. The correspondence between these men is discussed. (*Abs.*)]

Kennedy, Elizabeth Lapovsky & Davis, Madeline D. (1993). *Boots of Leather, Slippers of Gold: The History of a Lesbian Community.* New York: Routledge. [This very first community study of working-class lesbians in Buffalo, New York, researched over thirteen years, includes such topics as sex, relationships, coming out, motherhood, work, oppression and pride. "[It] opens up the heart and mind, break[ing] new ground in women's history, lesbian history, and the history of desire as a lived force in a community under siege. (Joan Nestle.)]

Kleiner, C.B. (2003). *Doin' It for Themselves: Lesbian Land Communities in Southern Oregon, 1970-1995.* PhD diss., University of New Mexico.

Lalonde, Jeremy (2005). A "Revolutionary Outrage": The Importance of Being Earnest as Social Criticism. *Modern Drama 48*(4): 659-676. [Discusses the representations of gay masculinity in theater based on the play *The Importance of Being Earnest* and its role as social criticism. (*Abs.*)]

Loughery, John (1998). *The Other Side of Silence: Men's Lives and Gay Identities: A Twentieth-Century History.* New York: Henry Holt. [Loughery uses a variety of sources, including interviews, archival materials, and secondary sources, as he vividly conveys the evolution of a gay male identity in America. Largely focused on white urban men, it is nevertheless more analytical and inclusive of class and race than Charles Kaiser's anecdotal *The Gay Metropolis* and extends the geographical parameters to include the "self-conscious, self-directed social world" of gay life throughout the United States. (*LJ*)]

McCormack, Jerusha Hull (2000). *The Man Who Was Dorian Gray.* New York: St. Martin's Press. [Tells the story of John Gray, a working-class boy whose passionate friendship with Oscar Wilde made his name as the reputed model for Wilde's scandalous novel. McCormack traces Gray's life, from decadent poet to dedicated priest, and looks at Gray's shifting relationships with Wilde, and later, with his lifelong companion Andre Raffalovich, to reveal insights into literary society and the emerging gay culture of the period. (Book News, Inc.)]

Moses, Cat (1999). Queering Class: Leslie Feinberg's *Stone Butch Blues. Studies in the Novel 31*(1): 74-97. [Discusses the interrelationship between socioeconomic structures, gendered identity development, and resistance to oppression in the novel. (*Abs.*)]

Packard, Chris (2005). *Queer Cowboys: And Other Erotic Male Friendships in Nineteenth-Century American Literature.* London/New York: Palgrave Macmillan. [*Queer Cowboys* exposes, through books by legendary Western writers such as Mark Twain, James Fenimore Cooper, and Owen Wister, how same-sex intimacy and homoerotic admiration were key aspects of Westerns ... well before the word "homosexual" was even invented. Packard introduces readers to the males-only clubs of journalists, cowboys, miners, Indians, and vaqueros who defined themselves by excluding women and the cloying ills of domesticity and recovers a forgotten culture of exclusively masculine, sometimes erotic, and often intimate camaraderie in the fiction, photographs, and theatrical performances of America's "wild" west in the 1800s. (*Desc.*)]

Palaversich, Diana (2002). The Wounded Body of Proletarian Homosexuality in Pedro Lemebel's *Loco Afán.* Tr. Paul Allatson. *Latin American Perspectives, 29*(2): 99-118. [Pedro Lemebel describes a Santiago not depicted in news bulletins and in the discourses of the Chilean economic "miracle," a Santiago populated by beings marginalized as much by their socioeconomic position as by their sexual orientation. (*Abs.*)]

Pannapacker, William A. (2000). "The Bricklayer Shall Lay Me": Edward Carpenter, Walt Whitman, and Working-Class "Comradeship." In Jay Losey and William D. Brewer, Eds., *Mapping Male Sexuality: Nineteenth-Century England.* Madison, WI: Fairleigh Dickinson University Press, 277-298. [Explores how, in the context of his encounters with Whitman, Carpenter's various "masculinities ... both resisted and complied with the dominant models" at play in late nineteenth- and early twentieth-century British culture, and how those masculinities "were an ongoing negotiation of competing and overlapping discourses. (*Walt Whitman Quarterly Review*)]

Peiss, Kathy (1983). "Charity Girls" and City Pleasures: Historical Notes on Working-Class Sexuality, 1880-1920. In Ann Snitow, Christine Stansell, and Sharon Thompson, Eds., *Powers of Desire: The Politics of Sexuality.* New York: Monthly Review Press, 74-87.

Peiss, Kathy Lee (1986). *Cheap Amusements: Working Women and Leisure in Turn-Of-The-Century New York.* Philadelphia: Temple University Press.

Ramakers, Micha and Tom of Finland (2000). *Dirty Pictures: Tom of Finland, Masculinity, and Homosexuality.* New York: St. Martin's Press.

Richardson, Niall (2005). Queering a Gay Cliché: The Rough Trade/Sugar Daddy Relationship in Derek Jarman's *Caravaggio. Paragraph 28*(3): 36-53.

Sautman, Francesca Canade (1997). Invisible Women: Retracing the Lives of French Working-Class Lesbians, 1880-1930. In Martin Duberman, Ed., *A Queer World: The Center for Lesbian and Gay Studies Reader.* New York: New York University Press, 236-247.

Sears, James. T. (1997). *Lonely Hunters: An Oral History of Lesbian and Gay Southern Life, 1948-1968.* Boulder, CO: Westview Press.

Shively, Charley (1991). *Calamus Lovers: Walt Whitman's Working-Class Camerados.* San Francisco: Gay Sunshine Press. [Slightly unbalanced and unhistorical, but an interesting attempt to recast Whitman as a modern-day "gay" hero with an active sex life. See also Shively's *Drum Beats: Walt Whitman's Civil War Boy Lovers.* ~WR]

Sinfield, Alan (1994). *The Wilde Century: Effeminacy, Oscar Wilde, and the Queer Moment.* New York: Columbia University Press. [See, in particular, the chapter "Class Relations," pp. 130-160. ~WR]

Tokarczyk, Michelle M. (2008). *Class Definitions: On the Lives and Writings of Maxine Hong Kingston, Sandra Cisneros, and Dorothy Allison.* Selinsgrove, PA: Susquehanna University Press. [How does working-class status intersect with gender, race, sexual orientation, and religion? How do working-class status and other identities play out in the lives and work of individual writers? The text ... argues that despite the differences in the authors' ethnic backgrounds, their work is characterized by traits widely recognized as markers of working-class writing. (*Desc.*)]

The "Gay Market," Affluence/Income, Consumerism & Gentrification

A Survey of LGBT Americans: Attitudes, Experiences, and Values in Changing Times (2013). Washington, DC: Pew Research Center. Web: www.pewsocialtrends.org/2013/06/13/a-survey-of-lgbt-americans.

Ahmed, Ali, Andersson, Lina, and Hammarstedt, Mats (2013). Sexual Orientation and Full-Time Monthly Earnings, By Public and Private Sector: Evidence from Swedish Register Data. *Review of Economics of the Household 11*(1): 83-108.

Alsop, Ronald (1999, 30 December). Are Gay People More Affluent Than Others? *The Wall Street Journal*: B1, B3.

Badgett, M. V. Lee (1997). A Queer Marketplace: Books on Lesbian and Gay Consumers, Workers, and Investors. *Feminist Studies 23*(3): 607-633.

Badgett, M. V. Lee (1997). Thinking Homo/Economically. In Martin Duberman, Ed., *A Queer World: The Center for Lesbian and Gay Studies Reader*. New York: New York University Press, 467-476.

Badgett, M. V. Lee (1998). *Income Inflation: The Myth of Affluence among Gay, Lesbian, and Bisexual Americans*. Joint Publication of the National Gay Task Force & the Institute for Gay and Lesbian Strategic Studies. Web: thetaskforce.org/downloads/reports/reports/IncomeInflationMyth.pdf.

Badgett, M. V. Lee (2001). *Money, Myths, and Change: The Economic Lives of Lesbians and Gay Men*. University of Chicago Press. [(Debunks) the myths of high incomes, conspicuous consumerism, double income no kids (DINK), and the protection of the closet. Badgett closes with some recommendations on how to change public policy to bring about economic equity for gays and lesbians. (Debra Moore, *LJ*)]

Baumle, Amanda K., and Poston, Dudley L. Jr. (2011) The Economic Cost of Homosexuality: Multilevel Analyses. *Social Forces 89*(3): 1005-1031.

Bell, David & Binnie, Jon (2000). The Love that Dares Not Forget its Brand Name. In David Bell & Jon Binnie, *The Sexual Citizen: Queer Politics and Beyond*. Cambridge, England: The Polity Press: 96-107.

Binnie, J. and Skeggs, B. (2004). Cosmopolitan Knowledge and the Production and Consumption of Sexualized Space: Manchester's Gay Village. *Sociological Review* 52(1): 39-61.

Black, Dan A., Makar, Hoda R., Sanders, Seth G. & Taylor, Lowell J. (2003). The Effects of Sexual Orientation on Earnings. *Industrial and Labor Relations Review 56*(3): 449-469. [This investigation of the effect of sexual orientation on earnings employs General Social Survey data from 1989–96. Depending largely on the definition of sexual orientation used, earnings are estimated as having been between 14% and 16% lower for gay men than for heterosexual men, and between 20% and 34% higher for lesbian women than for heterosexual women. (*Abs.*)]

Black, Dan A., Sanders, Seth G. & Taylor, Lowell J. (2007). The Economics of Lesbian and Gay Families. *Journal of Economic Perspectives 21*(2): 53-70.

Blandford, John M. (2000). Evidence of the Role of Sexual Orientation in the Determination of Earnings Outcomes. University of Chicago Population Research Center. Web: web.archive.org/web/20080509061936/www.src.uchicago.edu/prc/pdfs/Blandfd.pdf.

Bordo, Susan (1999). Gay Men's Revenge. *Journal of Aesthetics & Art Criticism 57*(1): 21-26. [Focuses on the spread of consumer capitalism to gay men's markets. Promotion of the advantages of having a youthful look; changes in advertising for the heterosexual markets. (*Abs.*)]

Branchik, Blaine J. (2006). Out in the Market: The History of the Gay Market Segment in the United States. In Tevfik Dalgic, Ed., *Handbook of Niche Marketing: Principles & Practice*. New York: Best Business Books, Haworth Reference Press, 211-239. [(T)races the evolution of the gay market segment from the late-nineteenth century to the beginning of the twenty-first century. (*Abs.*)]

Brass, Perry (n.d.) Yesterday I Was A Queer; Today I Am A Gay Consumer. Web: web.archive.org/web/20080605143733/www.turnleft.com/out/brass.html.

Carpenter, Christopher S. (2007). Revisiting the Income Penalty for Behaviorally Gay Men: Evidence from NHANES III. *Labour Economics 14*(1): 25-34. [In this paper I use independent data on sexual behavior from the Third National Health and Nutrition Examination Surveys and find that same-sex behaving men experience a ... significant income penalty on the order of 23–30 percent. (*Abs.*)]

Chasin, Alexandra (2000, Winter). Interpenetrations: A Cultural Study of the Relationship Between the Gay/Lesbian Niche Market and the Gay/Lesbian Political Movement. *Cultural Critique 44*: 145-168.

Chasin, Alexandra (2001). *Selling Out: The Gay and Lesbian Movement Goes to Market*. New York: Palgrave Macmillan. [Is it possible to have a meaningful revolution in the middle of a capitalist spending frenzy? Chasin asserts that the creation of a gay-oriented consumer market—in tandem with the mainstreaming of a gay politic that disavows broad-based coalitions with women and people of color—has prevented homosexuals from pursuing a more radical vision of social change. (*PW*)]

Cimino, Ken (2001, 17 January). Unraveling the Gay Influence Income Myth. Web: web.archive.org/web/20030716045035/www.gfn.com/archives/story.phtml?sid=8355.

Clark, Danae (2000).Commodity Lesbianism. In Henry Abelove, Michèle Aina Barale, and David M. Halperin, Eds., *The Lesbian and Gay Studies Reader*. New York: Routledge, 186-201.

Cloud, John (2008, 21 October). The Co$T of Being Gay. *The Advocate* 1017: 36-44.

DeLozier, M. Wayne and Rodrigue, J. (1996). Marketing to the Homosexual (Gay) Market: A Profile and Strategy Implications. *Journal of Homosexuality 31*(2): 203-12.

Fejes, Fred (2002). Advertising and the Political Economy of Lesbian/Gay Identity. In Eileen R. Meehan and Ellen Riordan, Eds., *Sex and Money: Feminism and Political Economy in the Media*. Minneapolis: University of Minnesota Press, 196-208.

Field, Nicola (1995). *Over the Rainbow: Money, Class and Homophobia*. London: Pluto Press.

Forest, Benjamin (1995). West Hollywood as Symbol: The Significance of Place in the Construction of a Gay Identity. *Environment and Planning D: Society and Space 13*(2): 133-157.

Forrest, David (1994). 'We're Here, We're Queer, and We're Not Going Shopping': Changing Gay Male Identities in Contemporary Britain. In Andrea Cornwall & Nancy Lindisfarne, Eds., *Dislocating Masculinity: Comparative Ethnographies*. London and New York: Routledge, 97-110.

Friess, Steve (1998, 28 April). Are Gays Really Rich? *The Advocate 758*: 37-40.

Fugate, D.L. (1993). Evaluating the US Male Homosexual and Lesbian Population as a Viable Target Segment: A Review with Implications. *Journal of Consumer Marketing 10*(4): 46-57.

Gardyn, Rebecca (2001, November 13). A Market Kept in the Closet. *American Demographics*: 36-43. [Looks at the status and estimated population of the gay, lesbian, bisexual, and transgender (GLBT) market in the United States and reviews factors used in analyzing population demographics and the findings of some surveys on the GLBT market. (*Abs.*)]

Gay Urban Pioneers: Going against the Grain (1995, October 13). *CQ Researcher 5*(38): 908-909. [Discusses how in many American cities, the flight of the white middle-class has been countered with gays and lesbians who move in and renovate run-down neighborhoods; reviews studies on the impact of gay gentrification. (*Abs.*)]

Ghaziani, Amin (2014). *There Goes the Gayborhood?* Princeton, NJ: Princeton University Press. [Gay neighborhoods ... have long provided sexual minorities with safe havens in an often unsafe world. But as our society increasingly accepts gays and lesbians into the mainstream, are "gayborhoods" destined to disappear? ... Ghaziani argues that ... the dawn of a new post-gay era is altering the character and composition of existing enclaves across the country. (*Desc.*)]

Grossbard, S. & Jepsen, L. K. (2008). The Economics of Gay and Lesbian Couples. *Review of Economics of the Household 6*: 311-326.

Hanhardt, Christina B. (2013). *Safe Space: Neighborhood History and the Politics of Violence*. Durham, NC: Duke University Press. [Traces the development of LGBT politics in the US from 1965-2005 and explains how LGBT activism was transformed from a multi-racial coalitional grassroots movement with strong ties to anti-poverty groups and anti-racism organizations to a mainstream, anti-violence movement with aspirations for state recognition. (Jack Halberstam)]

Haslop, C., Hill, H. and Schmidt, R. (1998). The Gay Lifestyle—Spaces for a Subculture of Consumption. *Marketing Intelligence and Planning* *16*(5): 318-26.

Hettinger, Vanessa E. (2010, 1 June). *Influence of Misperceptions about Gay Affluence on Support for Pro-Gay Legal Reform*. Master's thesis, University of South Florida. Web: scholarcommons.usf.edu/cgi/ viewcontent.cgi?article=2656&context=etd.

Hewitt, Christopher (1995). The Socioeconomic Position of Gay Men: A Review of the Evidence. *American Journal of Economics and Sociology*, *54*(4): 461-479.

Ingebretsen, E. (1999) Gone Shopping: The Commercialization of Same-Sex Desire. *International Journal of Sexuality and Gender Studies 4*(2): 125-148. [Marketplace phenomena ... reflect the extent to which the commercialization of same-sex desire permits marginalized or stigmatized forms of sexual behavior literally to sell their way into consumer culture.... Shopping queer is only another way of redeploying very old weapons ... against ourselves. (*Abs.*)]

Jacobsen, Joyce & Zeller, Adam (Eds.) (2007). *Queer Economics: A Reader.* New York: Routledge. [An examination of and response to the effects of heteronormativity on both economic outcomes and economics as a discipline. The first book to consolidate what has been published, filling a gap in the currently available literature and edited by an expert in the field. (*Desc.*)]

Kates, Steven M. (1999). Making the Ad Perfectly Queer: Marketing "Normality" to the Gay Men's Community? *Journal of Advertising 28*(1): 25-39.

Kates, Steven M. (1999). *Twenty Million New Customers: Understanding Gay Men's Consumer Behavior.* New York: Haworth Press.

Kates, Steven M. (2000). Out of the Closet and Out on the Street!: Gay Men and Their Brand Relationships. *Psychology and Marketing 17*: 493-512.

Kates, Steven M. (2002). The Protean Quality of Subcultural Consumption: An Ethnographic Account of Gay Consumers. *Journal of Consumer Research 29*: 383-399.

Keating, A. and McLoughlin, D. (2005). Understanding the Emergence of Markets: A Social Constructionist Perspective on Gay Economy. *Consumption, Markets and Culture 8*(2): 131-52.

Krahulik, Karen Christel (2007). Cape Queer? A Case Study of Provincetown, Massachusetts. *Journal of Homosexuality 52*(1-2): 185-212. [A study of the way sexuality intersects with race, gender, and class in the development of the gay and lesbian resort community.... (The study) assesses how the global mechanics of capitalism led to the local queering and eventually un-queering of a gentrified, white, gay and lesbian enclave. (*Abs.*)]

Lukenbill, Grant (1999). *Untold Millions: Secret Truths About Marketing to Gay and Lesbian Consumers.* New York: Routledge.

Moir, Susan (1997-1998, Fall/Winter). Class Danger: The Myth of Upward Mobility. *Gay Community News 23*(2/3): 30-37. [Focuses on the impact of upward mobility in the lesbian and gay community. Discussion on working classes and perception of criteria of working classes. (*Abs.*)]

Oakenfull, G.K. and Greenlee, T.B. (2005). Queer Eye for a Gay Guy: Using Market-Specific Symbols in Advertising to Attract Gay Consumers without Alienating the Mainstream. *Psychology and Marketing 22*(5): 421-39.

Peñaloza, L. (1996). We're Here, We're Queer, and We're Going Shopping! A Critical Perspective on the Accommodation of Gays and Lesbians into the U.S. Marketplace. *Journal of Homosexuality 31*(1/2): 9-41.

Pereira, Bill Nunes, Ayrosa, Eduardo A. T. & Costa, Sayuri Ojima (2006). Brazilian Gays: Understanding the Construction of the Homosexual Identity through Consumption. *Advances in Consumer Research-Latin American Conference Proceedings 1*: 133-138. [Explores the changes that occur in the way gays interact with the world of products during the coming-out process.... The results suggest that products and services are actively used by gays in order to deny, camouflage, and reinforce their homosexual identity. (*Abs.*)]

Perez, Vanessa M. (2014, June). Political Participation of LGBT Americans (2014, June). Washington, DC: Project Vote. Web: www.projectvote.org/images/publications/Research%20Memos/RES EARCH-MEMO-LGBT-PARTICIPATION-June-20-2014.pdf.

Piore, Michael (1997). Economic Identity/Sexual Identity. In Martin Duberman, Ed., *A Queer World: The Center for Lesbian and Gay Studies Reader*. New York: New York University Press, 502-507.

Rudd, Nancy A. (1996). Appearance and Self-Presentation Research in Gay Consumer Cultures: Issues and Impact. *Journal of Homosexuality 31*(1-2): 109-135. [Studies the impact of appearance and self-presentation among gay consumers in the United States; discusses marketing strategies and aspects of appearance management as they affect marketing to gay customers. (*Abs.*)]

Sender, Katherine (2001). Gay Readers, Consumers, and a Dominant Gay Habitus: 25 Years of the *Advocate Magazine*. *Journal of Communication 51*: 73-99.

Sender, Katherine (2003). Sex Sells: Sex, Taste, and Class in Commercial Gay and Lesbian Media. *GLQ: A Journal of Lesbian and Gay Studies 9*(3): 331-365.

Sender, Katherine (2004). *Business, Not Politics: The Making of the Gay Market*. New York: Columbia University Press. [In a hard-hitting book that refutes conventional wisdom, Sender explores the connection between the business of marketing to gay consumers and the politics of gay rights and identity. She disputes ... that the business of gay marketing can be considered independently of the politics of gay rights, identity, and visibility. (*Desc.*)]

Stiffler, Scott (2009, April 27). Stereotype Persists of Gay Affluence. *EDGE Boston* (edgeboston.com). Web: tinyurl.com/pohnxn2.

Swan, Rachel (2014, 25 June). Pride of Place: As the Nation's Gay Districts Grow More Affluent, Lesbians Are Migrating to the 'Burbs. *SF Weekly*. Web: www.sfweekly.com/2014-06-25/news/bernal-heights-wild-side-west-oakland.

Tipton, Nathan (1999). Martha, Martha, Martha! Housewife or Homophobe? *to the quick* #1. Web: web.archive.org/web/20090107155959/http://to-the-quick.binghamton.edu/issue%201/stewart.html. [Stewart's appeal for gay men is, in part, her propounding to the ... "great unwashed" the aspiration for a mythically-gracious, elegant way of life.... Ironically, while Stewart's socially elite "peers" have openly characterized her as a nouveau-riche outsider, and the middle-middle class ... market has criticized her for promoting an impossible fantasy life, Stewart's gay following has remained steadfast. (From the article.)]

Valocchi, Steve (1999). The Class-Inflected Nature of Gay Identity. *Social Problems 46*(2): 207-225. [I argue that the development of gay identity is a class-inflected process.... Consumer capitalism in the 1990s is changing the nature of lesbian and gay identity from a political to a lifestyle category and, in so doing, reinforcing the already existing class-bias in the nature of gay identity. (*Abs.*)]

Ward, Jane (2003, February). Producing "Pride" in West Hollywood: A Queer Cultural Capital for Queers With Cultural Capital. *Sexualities 6*(1): 65-95.

Wardlow, Daniel L. (Ed.) (1996). *Gays, Lesbians, and Consumer Behavior: Theory, Practice, and Research Issues in Marketing.* New York: Harrington Park Press.

Welfare Warriors Research Collaborative (2010). *A Fabulous Attitude: Low-Income LGBTGNC People Surviving & Thriving on Love, Shelter & Knowledge.* New York: Queers for Economic Justice. Web: tinyurl.com/km4bzgp.

Wilke, Michael (1998, 19 October). Fewer Gays are Wealthy, Data Say. *Advertising Age 69*(42): 58. [Long considered more affluent than the mainstream, the gay market has been pursued by high-end brands such as Gucci fashion, Waterford crystal, and Movado watches. New research suggests those consumers may be closer to average incomes. (*Abs.*)]

Wilke, Michael (2000, August 21). Are Gays All Rich? Gay Financial Network. Web: tinyurl.com/kxjgclc. [We've all heard it many times: the gay market is richer, more loyal and better educated than the mainstream population—a "dream market." But are we? (*Abs.*)]

Wilke, Michael (2001, November 5). New Research Brings Updates and Controversy. Web: tinyurl.com/lm8memn. [The concept of wealthy gays is now in debate and few corporations ... have conducted their own research into the niche. (*Abs.*)]

Witeck, Robert and Combs, Wesley (2006). *Business Inside Out: Capturing Millions of Brand Loyal Gay Consumers.* Chicago: Kaplan Publishing.

Capitalism & The Left, Labor Studies, Poverty/Economic Justice Issues

Adler, Margot (2011, 20 November). Young, Gay And Homeless: Fighting For Resources. National Public Radio. Web: npr.org/2011/11/20/142364493/young-gay-and-homeless-fighting-for-resources

Albelda, Randy, Badgett, M.V. Lee, Schneebaum, Alyssa & Gates, Gary J. (2009, March). *Poverty in the Lesbian, Gay, and Bisexual Community*. Los Angeles: The Williams Institute. http://williamsinstitute.law.ucla.edu/wp-content/uploads/Albelda-Badgett-Schneebaum-Gates-LGB-Poverty-Report-March-2009.pdf

Aptheker, Bettina (2008, Summer). Keeping the Communist Party Straight, 1940s-1980s. *New Politics 12*(1): 22-27. [Explores Aptheker's experience of growing up in a communist family and her struggles of coming out as a lesbian while a member of the U.S. Communist Party. (*Abs.*)]

Averill, Linda (2001, July). Blatantly Militant: The Hidden History of Queers in the U.S. Labor Movement. *Freedom Socialist Party.* Web: www.socialism.com/drupal-6.8/articles/blatantly-militant-hidden-history-queers-us-labor-movement.

Badgett, M.V. Lee, Durso, Laura E., & Schneebaum, Alyssa (2013, June). *New Patterns of Poverty in the Lesbian, Gay, and Bisexual Community*. Los Angeles: The Williams Institute. Web: williamsinstitute.law.ucla.edu/wp-content/uploads/LGB-Poverty-Update-Jun-2013.pdf.

Berry, David (2004, Spring/Summer). "Workers of the World Embrace!" Daniel Guérin, the Labour Movement and Homosexuality. *Left History* 9(2): 11-43.

Billies, Michelle, Johnson, Juliet, Murungi, Kagendo & Pugh, Rachel (2009). Naming Our Reality: Low-Income LGBTQ People Documenting Violence, Discrimination and Assertions of Justice. *Feminism & Psychology 19*(3): 375-380.

Capitalism & Homophobia: Marxism and the Struggle for Gay/Lesbian Rights. International Bolshevik Tendency, n.d. Web: bolshevik.org/1917/no15gayq.pdf.

Carter, Julie Hope (1998, Winter). Who Cares if Barbie Loves Midge, as Long as They Get the Dreamhouse?: Poor and Working Class Lesbians of the New Millennium. *Educational Studies 29*(4): 410-34.

Cohen, Derek and Dyer, Richard (1980). The Politics of Gay Culture. In Gay Left Collective, Ed., *Homosexuality: Power and Politics*. London: Allison and Busby, 172-186.

Count Me In Too. [The Count Me In Too Project conducted unique research into lesbian, gay, bisexual, and trans lives in Brighton and Hove in the United Kingdom between 2007-2010. All of their documents and data are available to the public on their site (countmeintoo.co.uk), including findings regarding socioeconomic issues, housing, marginalized populations, etc. ~WR]

Cover, Rob (1999, April). Queer with Class: Absence of Third World Sweatshop in Lesbian/Gay Discourse and a Rearticulation of Materialist Queer Theory. *Ariel 30*(2): 29-48. [Discusses functionality of queer theory in sexuality and sexuality constructionism, inadequacy of queer theory in class analysis in the lesbian/gay discourse, and consequences of the absence of sweatshop in the lesbian/gay political and conceptual discourse. (*Abs.*)]

Cruz-Malave, Arnaldo and Manalansan, Martin F. (Eds) (2002). *Queer Globalizations: Citizenship and the Afterlife of Colonialism.* New York: New York University Press. [Globalization has a taste for queer cultures. Whether in advertising, film, performance art, the internet, or in the political discourses of human rights in emerging democracies, queerness sells and the transnational circulation of peoples, identities and social movements that we call "globalization" can be liberating to the extent that it incorporates queer lives and cultures. (*Desc.*) Includes a section of four essays entitled "Queer Values in a Global Economy," which lays out a critique of the queer marketplace as a viable vehicle for queer politics. ~WR]

D'Emilio, John (1983). Capitalism and Gay Identity. In Ann Snitow, Christine Stansell, and Sharon Thompson, Eds., *Powers of Desire: The Politics of Sexuality.* New York: Monthly Review Press, 100-113.

DeFilippis, Joseph N., Duggan, Lisa, Farrow, Kenyon, and Kim, Richard (2011 Fall-2012 Spring). A New Queer Agenda, special issue of *The Scholar & Feminist Online* 10.1-10.2. Web: http://sfonline.barnard.edu/a-new-queer-agenda. [A treasure trove of articles on economic justice, political, and social policy issues from a queer perspective, including "Common Ground: The Queerness of Welfare Policy," "Outing the Invisible Poor: Why Economic Justice and Access to Health Care is an LGBT Issue," "Cripping Queer Politics, or the Dangers of Neoliberalism," "This is What Pride Looks Like: Miss Major and the Violence, Poverty, and Incarceration of Low-Income Transgender Women," "Equality with Power: Fighting for Economic Justice at Work," "What's Home Got to Do with It? Unsheltered Queer Youth," and many others. ~WR]

DeFilippis, Joseph, Ricky Blum, and Barbara Ann Perina. "Why Welfare Is a Queer Issue." Panel presentation at Queer Law 2000: Current Issues in Lesbian, Gay, Bisexual and Transgender Law. Lesbian and Gay Law Association Foundation of Greater New York, New York University, n.d. Web: tinyurl.com/kgnz65s.

Duberman, Martin (1999). *Left Out: The Politics of Exclusion—Essays 1964-1999.* New York: Basic Books. [See especially "Queer Economic Justice" and "The Divided Left: Identity Politics vs. Class." ~WR]]

Dunne, Gillian A., Prendergrast, Shirley, and Telford, David (2002). Young, Gay, Homeless and Invisible: A Growing Population? *Culture, Health & Sexuality 4*(1): 103-115. [Describes the experiences of a hitherto invisible and possibly increasing population in England, namely young homeless lesbian, gay, and bisexual people. (*Abs.*)]

Escoffier, Jeffrey (2008, Summer). Left-Wing Homosexuality: Emancipation, Sexual Liberation, and Identity Politics. *New Politics*: 38-43.

Frank, Miriam & Holcomb, Desma (1990). *Pride at Work: Organizing for Lesbian and Gay Rights in Unions*. New York: Lesbian and Gay Labor Network.

Frank, Miriam (2014). *Out in the Union: A Labor History of Queer America*. Philadelphia, PA: Temple University Press. [A shrewd chronicle of the evolution of labor politics with queer activism and identity formation, showing how unions began affirming the rights of lesbian, gay, bisexual, and transgender workers in the 1970s and 1980s.... Featuring in-depth interviews with LGBT and labor activists, Frank provides an inclusive history of the convergence of labor and LGBT interests [and] examines organizing drives at queer workplaces, campaigns for marriage equality, and other gay civil rights issues to show the enduring power of LGBT workers. (*Desc.*)]

Gates, Gary J. (2014, February). *Food Insecurity and SNAP (Food Stamps) Participation in LGBT Communities*. Los Angeles: The Williams Institute. Web: williamsinstitute.law.ucla.edu/wp-content/uploads/Food-Insecurity-in-LGBT-Communities.pdf.

Gluckman, Amy & Betsy Reed (Eds.) (1997). *Homo Economics: Capitalism, Community, and Lesbian and Gay Life*. New York & London: Routledge. [These provocative essays explain how class biases and divisions operate to frustrate queer progress. The authors argue convincingly for a movement with the vision and willingness to tackle the gender, class, racial, and economic inequalities of capitalism (Urvashi Vaid). See, in particular, the interview with Barbara Smith, "Where Has Gay Liberation Gone?" ~WR]

Grevatt, Martha (2001). Lesbian/Gay/Bisexual/Transgender Liberation: What's Labor Got to Do with It? *Social Policy 31*(3): 63-65.

Heinze, Eric (1995, Spring). Gay and Poor. *Howard Law Journal 38*(2): 433-448.

Hekma, Gert, Oosterhuis, Harry & Steakley, James (1995). Leftist Sexual Politics and Homosexuality: A Historical Overview. *Journal of Homosexuality 29*(2-3): 1-40.

Hekma, Gert, Oosterhuis, Harry & Steakley, James (Eds.) (1995). *Gay Men and the Sexual History of the Political Left*. New York: The Haworth Press.

Hennessy, Rosemary (2000). *Profit and Pleasure: Sexual Identities in Late Capitalism*. New York and London: Routledge. [A groundbreaking attempt to understand the relationship between capitalism and sexual identity (and to reorient) queer theory away from its preoccupation with psychoanalysis, language, and performance, instead insisting upon close analysis of the structures of late capitalism, labor, and commodification. Hennessy argues that sexual identity has always been linked to gender, race, and nationality, but (that) these identities themselves arise from capitalism. (*Desc.*)]

Hollibaugh, Amber (2001, June 20-26). Queers Without Money: They Are Everywhere. But We Refuse to See Them. *Village Voice*. Web: villagevoice.com/2001-06-19/news/queers-without-money.

Hunt, Gerald & Boris, Monica Bielski (2007). The Lesbian, Gay, Bisexual, and Transgender Challenge to American Labor. In Dorothy Sue Cobble, Ed., *The Sex of Class: Women Transforming American Labor*. Ithaca, NY: Cornell University Press, 81-98.

Hussain, Pat (1997). Class Action: Bringing Economic Diversity to the Gay and Lesbian Movement. In Amy Gluckman and Betsy Reed, Eds., *Homo Economics: Capitalism, Community, and Lesbian and Gay Life*. New York & London: Routledge, 241-248. [This whole volume of essays is highly recommended. ~WR]

Jomo (2010, 8 January). Queer Liberation is Class Struggle. *Unity and Struggle*. Web: http://ge.tt/9b1jLwA/v/1.

Kelley, Robin D. G. (1997, Winter). Identity Politics & Class Struggle. *New Politics 6*(2), Web: nova.wpunj.edu/newpolitics/issue22/kelley22.htm.

Klawitter, M.M. (2002). Gays and Lesbians as Workers and Consumers in the Economy. In D. Richardson and S. Seidman (Eds.), *Handbook of Lesbian and Gay Studies*. London: Sage, 329-338.

Krehely, Jeff & Hunt, Jerome (2011, 31 January). Helping All of Our Homeless: Developing a Gay- and Transgender-Inclusive Federal Plan to End Homelessness. Washington, DC: Center for American Progress. Web: www.americanprogress.org/wp-content/uploads/issues/2011/01/pdf/lgbt_homelessness.pdf.

Mallon, Gerald P. (1998). *We Don't Exactly Get the Welcome Wagon: The Experiences of Gay and Lesbian Adolescents in Child Welfare Systems*. New York: Columbia University Press. [Drawing on over twenty years of child welfare experience and extensive interviews with fifty-four gay and lesbian young people who lived in out-of-home-care child welfare settings in three North American cities ... Mallon presents narratives of marginalized young people trying to find the "right fit." (*Desc.*)]

Manifesto of the Socialist Homosexuals (1975). "Writings from the Australian Gay Left" page, maintained by Liz Ross. Web: www.anu.edu.au/polsci/marx/gayleft/manifesto.htm.

Maskovsky, Jeff (2002). Do We All "Reek of the Commodity"? Consumption and the Erasure of Poverty and Lesbian and Gay Studies. In Ellen Lewin and William L. Leap, Eds., *Out in Theory: The Emergence of Lesbian and Gay Anthropology*. Chicago: University of Illinois Press, 264-286.

Maynard, Steven (2004). "Without Working?" Capitalism, Urban Culture, and Gay History. *Journal of Urban History 30*(3): 378-398. [Within gay/lesbian historiography, there has (long been) debate over the relative roles played by capitalism and urban culture in the historical formation of gay and lesbian identities and communities. The author argues that in recent years historians have come to favor the urban, both as a framework for inquiry and as an explanatory device. (*Abs.*)]

McCreery, Patrick & Krupat, Kitty (Eds.) (2001). *Out at Work: Building a Gay-Labor Alliance*. University of Minnesota Press.

McNeill, Brian (1998, 23 May). Coming Out of the Class Closet: Socialist Gays. Transcript of address to New Union Party, St. Paul, MN. Web: tinyurl.com/lp6rd35.

Morton, Donald (2001). Global (Sexual) Politics, Class Struggle, and the Queer Left. In John C. Hawley, Ed., *Postcolonial, Queer: Theoretical Intersections*. Albany: SUNY Press, 207-238.

Morton, Donald (Ed.) (1996). *The Material Queer: A LesBiGay Cultural Studies Reader*. Boulder, CO: Westview Press. [Overwhelmed by "Queer Theory Speak" and academic jargon, this is nevertheless one of the first attempts to analyze queerness from a working-class/Marxist position. ~WR]

Queers for Economic Justice (2008). *Poverty, Public Assistance & Privatization: The Queer Case for a New Commitment to Economic Justice*. New York: Queers for Economic Justice. Web: tinyurl.com/k6tuw6p.

Queers for Economic Justice. (n.d., circa 2009). *Tidal Wave: LGBT Poverty and Hardship in a Time of Economic Crisis*. New York: Queers for Economic Justice. Web: tinyurl.com/k6e4do3.

Reck, Jen (2009). Homeless Gay and Transgender Youth of Color in San Francisco: "No One Likes Street Kids"—Even in the Castro. *Journal of LGBTQ Youth* 6(2/3): 223-242.

Robinson, Lucy (2007). *Gay Men and the Left in Post-War Britain: How the Personal Got Political*. Manchester, UK: Manchester University Press.

Robinson, Margaret (n.d.) Why Aren't More Queers Buying Marxism? An Examination of What Ignoring Marxist Analysis has Done to Queer Activism. Web: www.etuxx.com/pdf/t_haus_robinson_engl.pdf.

Sears, Alan (2000, August). Queer in a Lean World. Paper presented at the Summer School of Solidarity (Detroit, MI). Web: www.solidarity-us.org/site/node/965.

Sears, Alan (2005). Queer Anti-Capitalism: What's Left of Lesbian and Gay Liberation? *Science & Society* 69(1): 92-112. [Lesbians and gays are on the verge of winning full citizenship in Canada and a number of Western European countries.... At the same time ... capitalist restructuring has ... created spaces for commodified forms of lesbian and gay existence.... The era of lesbian/gay citizenship and commodification opens new possibilities for anti-capitalist queer Marxist-feminist politics. (*Abs.*)]

Thorstad, David. Homosexuality and the American Left: The Impact of Stonewall. *Journal of Homosexuality* 29(4): 319-350. [Following the Stonewall Riots in New York City in June 1969, the left had to reassess negative appraisals of homosexuality that prevailed among virtually all leftist currents. By the mid-1970s, three approaches had emerged: (1) radical support for sexual liberation and acceptance of same-sex love as being on a par with heterosexuality; (2) liberal support for the civil rights of homosexuals but without challenging heterosupremacy; and (3) continued adherence to the (Stalinist) view that homosexuality is form of "bourgeois decadence" alien to the working class. (*Abs.*)]

Unterrainer, Tom (2007, 24 July). For a Working-Class LGBTQ Movement. *Workers' Liberty*. Web: www.workersliberty.org/node/8899.

Valocchi, Steve (2001, Winter). Individual Identities, Collective Identities, and Organizational Structure: The Relationship of the Political Left and Gay Liberation in the United States. *Sociological Perspectives* 44(4): 445-467. [Examines ideological connections between the Left and the gay movement from the 1930s to the 1970s and argues that the organizational centralization of the Old Left in the Communist Party prevented early "gay" activists from extending the collective identity of the Left to ... issues of same-sex oppression; alternatively, the organizational fluidity of the New Left encouraged a more flexible understanding of collective identity, and same-sex oppression was incorporated into the rhetoric, albeit in a limited way and for a brief period. (*Abs.*)]

Ward, Alan (1995). American Writers on the Left. In C. Summers, Ed., *The Gay and Lesbian Literary Heritage: A Reader's Companion to the Writers and their Works, from Antiquity to the Present*. New York: Henry Holt, 53-56.

Weeks, Jeffrey (1980). Capitalism and the Organization of Sex. In Gay Left Collective, Ed., *Homosexuality: Power and Politics*. London: Allison and Busby, 11-20.

Wolf, Kathi (2014, 15 January). I'm Coming Out: As Living Near Poverty Level. *Washington Blade*. Web: washingtonblade.com/2014/01/15/im-coming-living-near-poverty-level. [See also Wolf, Kathi (2014, 20 March). "You Can't Let Adversity Get You Down." *Washington Blade*. Web: washingtonblade.com/2014/03/20/special-report-cant-let-adversity-get; Wolf, Kathi (2014, 27 March). In Their Own Words: Elders Facing Poverty, Ageism. *Washington Blade*. Web: washingtonblade.com/2014/03/27/special-report-words-elders-facing-poverty-ageism; and other articles from the *Blade*'s "yearlong focus on poverty" on its site: washingtonblade.com/tag/poverty. ~WR]

Wolf, Sherry (2004, Sept.-Oct.). "The Roots of Gay Oppression." *International Socialist Review* 37. Web: isreview.org/issues/37/gay_oppression.shtml.

Zavarzadeh, Mas'ud, Ebert, Teresa L. & Morton, Donald E. (Eds.) (2001). *Marxism, Queer Theory, Gender*. Syracuse, NY: Red Factory. [The first, and most theoretically expansive text of the seven contributed chapters in this volume..., theorizes the enduring silence around issues of class and exploitation in contemporary forms of sex-radicalism and dominant forms of queer theory.... Morton's critique argues for a "Red Queer Theory" which "refuses to give up difference as the difference of class." (Brian Ganter)]

Adventures of Priscilla, Queen of the Desert [*The*] (1994). Australian Film Finance Corporation/Polygram Video. Directed and written by Stephan Elliott. [The story of three Sydney drag queens (including Terence Stamp as an unforgettably dignified transwoman) who embark on a bus journey to Ayers Rock, scandalizing the locals along the way. (*Desc.*)]

Beautiful Thing (1996). Channel Four Films. Directed by Hettie MacDonald; written by Jonathan Harvey. [This absolute winner, based on a stage play by Jonathan Harvey and adapted by him, is a kind of enchanted, urban slice-of-life tale about a pair of gay teens in a working-class London neighborhood who fall for each other. (Tom Keogh, Amazon.com)]

Big Eden (2000). Wolfe Video. Directed and written by Thomas Bezucha. [Henry is an artist living in New York but still carrying a torch for the guy he had a crush on in high school. When his grandfather has a stroke, Henry returns to his Montana hometown, where he rediscovers friends he hasn't seen in years. (*Desc.*)]

Borstal Boy (2000). BSkyB/Bórd Scannán na hÉireann/British Screen Productions/Strand Releasing. Directed by Peter Sheridan; written by Brendan Behan and Nye Heron. [Film based on Brendan Behan's 1958 autobiographical book of the same name. At age sixteen, idealistic Irish Republican Army freedom fighter Behan is caught with explosives and spends two years in an English borstal, or juvenile reformatory. Notable is the portrayal of Charlie, a working-class gay sailor also incarcerated with Brendan. His devotion to Brendan, and Brendan's growing attachment both to Charlie and to the warden's daughter, are instrumental in taking the hate out of Brendan. Given the true story of Behan's short, angry, and alcoholic life, the movie version is more than a little prettied up, but the movie is faithful to Behan's proletarian roots and loyalties. ~WR]

Brandon Teena Story [*The*] (1998). Bless Bless Productions. Directed by Susan Muska and Gréta Olafsdóttir. [This documentary, on which the 1999 film *Boys Don't Cry* is based, won Best Documentary at the Vancouver and the Berlin International Film Festivals in 1998. ~WR]

Butterflies on the Scaffold (*Mariposa en el Andamio*) (1996). Kangaroo Productions. Directed and written by Luis Felipe Bernaza and Margaret Gilpin. [Focuses on a troupe of drag queens who perform for workers and community members in the Havana suburb of La Güinera. Most of the members of the troupe are working-class gay men, whose emotional lives very clearly revolve around the two or three hours a night they're allowed to dress up and perform on stage in a neighborhood workers' dining hall. The real drama behind this story lies in the way this group of social and political outcasts manages to secure both a place for themselves and a kind of grudging respect in their community by winning the support of female leaders of a local construction brigade. (*Desc.*)]

Class Queers. (2003). Schoolhouse Productions/Canadian Broadcasting Company. Directed by Howard Fraiberg, Melissa Levin, and Roxana Spicer; directed and produced by Howard Fraiberg. Available from the Canadian Filmmakers Distribution Centre, Toronto, and the Filmmakers Library, New York. [Focuses on three gay teenagers living in Toronto, Ontario. Adina is the daughter of a rabbi, Adam is from a supportive middle-class family, and Richard lives with an unsupportive mother and her homophobic boyfriend in a small apartment in a working-class neighborhood. The film introduces viewers to the Triangle Program, an alternative space for gay, lesbian, bisexual and transgendered youth located in a church basement, and to a city-wide high school prom for gays and lesbians only. (*Desc.*)]

Come Back to the Five and Dime, Jimmy Dean, Jimmy Dean (1982). Sandcastle 5 Productions/Viacom Enterprises. Directed by Robert Altman; written by Ed Graczyk.

Dog Day Afternoon (1975). Artists Entertainment Complex. Directed by Sidney Lumet; screenplay by Frank Pierson. [The film was inspired by P.F. Kluge's article "The Boys in the Bank," which described the robbery of a Brooklyn bank by John Wojtowicz and Salvatore Naturale in August 1972; Lumet's movie is based upon that incident. Wojtowicz, the son of Polish immigrants, attempted to rob a Chase Manhattan branch, allegedly to pay for sex-reassignment surgery for his partner, Ernest Aron (later known as Elizabeth Debbie Eden). Though he was convicted and imprisoned, Wojtowicz later did finance Eden's surgery through profits from selling the rights to his story. ~WR

Farm Family: In Search of Gay life in Rural America (2004). T. Joe Murray Videos. Written and directed by T. Joe Murray. [Award-winning documentary featuring seldom heard voices from gay rural America.... Raised on a dairy farm in the Midwest, the filmmaker reflects back on his own roots with a look at the lives of gay men living in rural/farm environments. The film contains interviews with men who have chosen to live outside the more familiar gay urban centers ... a far cry from the stereotyped urban gay culture. (*Desc.*)]

Flag Wars (2003). Zula Pearl Films. Directed by Linda Goode Bryant and Laura Poitras. [Stark look inside the conflicts that surface when black working-class families are faced with an influx of white gay homebuyers to their Columbus, Ohio, neighborhood. Filmed over four years, *Flag Wars* captures the raw emotions and blunt honesty of unguarded moments as tensions mount between neighbors. (*Desc.*)]

Fox and His Friends (1975). City Film/Tango Film. Written by Rainer Werner Fassbinder and Christian Hohoff; directed by Rainer Werner Fassbinder. [The working-class Fox, fallen on hard times, lets himself be kept by an elegant older man who tries to teach him a taste for upper-class life. When Fox wins the lottery, his new "friends" cheat him out of his money. ~WR]

Gun Hill Road (2011). SimonSays Entertainment/A Small Production Company. Written by Rashaad Ernesto Green with poetry by Zora Howard. Directed by Rashaad Ernesto Green. [Gun Hill Road is a major street in the Bronx and gives its name to this film. Enrique, an ex-con, returns from prison to find his adolescent son, Michael, exploring a new identity as a transwoman. What *Gun Hill Road* lacks in nuance and subtlety, it makes up for in strong portrayals of working-class people of color living with circumstances that, according to the stereotype, they're not supposed to able to accommodate. One notable feature: The actor who plays Michael (Harmony Santana) is a transwoman. ~WR]

Hit and Runway. (1999). Culture Q Connection/Mirador/Lot 47 Films. Directed by Christopher Livingston, written by Jaffe Cohen and Christopher Livingston. ([Alex is a straight, talent-free, working-class Italian Catholic with a great idea for a movie and all the right Hollywood connections. Elliot is a cantankerous, gay, Jewish New Yorker who has all the talent and no one to pay him for it. When the two team up to write a script together for a top grossing Hollywood action hero, their goal becomes less about beating the deadline and more about wanting to beat each other into a bloody pulp. (*Desc.*)]

Kinky Boots (2005). Miramax Films/Harbour Pictures/Price Productions. Directed by Julian Jarrold; written by Geoff Deane and Tim Firth. [The untimely death of his father forces Charles Price to realize that the family business, Price & Sons Shoes, is failing. Charles meets a flamboyant drag queen cabaret singer, Lola, who suggests that Charles save the business by manufacturing men's fetish footwear.... Now this disparate lot must struggle at this unorthodox idea while dealing with the prejudice of the staff, Lola's discomfort in the small town, and the selfish manipulation of Charles' greedy fiancée. (Kenneth Chisholm, imdb.com)]

La Missión (2009). 5 Stick Films. Written and directed by Peter Bratt. ["OG" Che Rivera, born and raised in San Francisco's Mission District, works as a city bus driver and is respected by his peers for his strength, his street smarts, and his talent for building and restoring classic lowrider cars. A reformed inmate, recovering alcoholic, and single father, Che has worked hard to be a responsible breadwinner and a good father to his son, Jes, a senior at Mission High School. When he discovers that Jes is gay, Che reacts violently. The film explores whether Che will choose pride over the one thing that means the most to him—Jes. Interesting and grounded exploration of working-class San Francisco. (*Desc.*)]

Last Call at Maud's (1993). Maud's Project/Frameline. Directed by Paris Poirier. [Opened in 1966, Maud's was a San Francisco bar for working-class lesbians. The documentary traces lesbian history at mid-century, including the founding of the Daughters of Bilitis in 1955, police raids, and the need for alternatives to gay men's bars, and traces the social history of the bar through its closing in 1989. (*Desc.*)]

Last Match (La Partida) [The] (2013). Doce Gatos/El Azar/Malas Compañías. Directed by Antonio Hens; written by Abel González Melo and Antonio Hens. [A married, soccer-loving, male hustler falls in love with his best friend in their working-class Havana, Cuba, neighborhood. As secret gay lovers, they fight to lead a life together, but the journey is complicated: one is obsessed with earning money to support his wife and child; the other works as a collector for his father-in-law's loan shark outfit. (*Desc.*)]

Lavender Left, Part I: Homosexuality and Radicalism in 20th-Century U.S. (2012, 29 September). NYU Kimmel Center, New York. Bettina Aptheker, Queering The History of the Communist Party, USA; Dayo Gore, "My Pattern of Life": Gender, Sexuality and the Left In Pauli Murray's Political Vision; Aaron Lecklider, "To Be One With The People": Homosexuality in the Cultural Front; Avram Finkelstein, Silence=Death. Parts 1 & 2 available on Vimeo.com.

Lavender Left, Part II: Radical Exclusions and Inclusions. (2012, 29 September) Rosalyn Baxandall, Sexual Fluidity: Elizabeth Gurley Flynn, Marie Equi and the Communist Party Repression of Lesbians; David Waggoner, Homophobia in Marxist Ideology; Lisa Davis, Gay In The CPUSA: Angela Calomiris and Harry Hay; James Green, Exiles Within Exiles: Herbert Daniel, Brazilian Gay Revolutionary. Parts 1 & 2 available on Vimeo.com.

Leave It on the Floor (2011). Leave It on the Floor/Sheldon Larry Productions, Inc. Directed by Sheldon Larry; written by Glenn Gaylord. [At first glance, this is a slight, upbeat story of how pursuing an artistic dream (music, dance, and drag, in this case) redeems everything. But there is both more—and less—going on in this film. The filmmakers, both gay white men, set a love story amid the ballroom scene in a poor section of Los Angeles, where mostly black, mostly trans kids dream of "taking home tens" and trophies. *Leave It on the Floor* depicts the poverty, homelessness, and marginality of its characters' lives but somehow imagines those conditions as having no actual impact on their existences; they've been thrown out of their homes and done time in prison; no one has a job. And yet they happily fall in and out of love, treat each other reasonably well, and live in a sort of idyll of sister/brotherhood. There's not much "realness," but there is a kind of pushing back against "realistic" stories of ruined, gritty, miserable black lives, and that's a provocative stance, the film's glaring weaknesses notwithstanding. See discussion in this volume. ~WR]

Like It Is (1998). Channel Four Films/First Run Features. Directed by Paul Oremland, written by Robert Gray. [In bleak Northern England, Craig makes his living fighting illegal bare-knuckle bouts. When he falls for a record producer named Matt ... he finds his world turned upside down. (*Desc.*) Apart from the setting and the language, there's no specific exploration of class as class here, but the film places a gay relationship at the center of a story that is very much about work and the exploitation of workers, and there's a fine instance of working-class "getting over" in the denouement. ~WR]

Living End [*The*] (1992). Cineplex Odeon Films/Desperate Pictures/October Films. Written and directed by Gregg Araki. [*The Living End* is often referred to as a "gay *Thelma and Louise*" with the intent to be dismissive, but the film is actually a ground-breaking, violent, and intensely erotic exploration of the world in which gay men found themselves in the 1980s and 1990s, and is especially important considering Hollywood's refusal to deal with HIV/AIDS in that period. Luke, a dangerous, nothing-left-to-lose, hustler and drifter meets Jon, a (not accidentally) movie critic. Rage, hopelessness, frustration, romance, and gallows humor are explored in about equal measure. Araki's subsequent films all have something interesting to say about consumer-driven, pop-culture-addled America. ~WR]

Love is the Devil: Study for a Portrait of Francis Bacon (1998). Strand Releasing Home Video. Written and directed by John Maybury. ([A thief (Daniel Craig) breaks through a skylight and lands in the middle of an artist's studio. Peering at him from a slightly open door is the artist (Derek Jacobi). "Not much of a burglar, are you?" the artist says. "Take your clothes off. Come to bed. Then you can have whatever you want." The artist is Francis Bacon and the burglar is George Dyer, a working class, not-too-bright man thirty years younger than Bacon. They remained together from 1964 until Dyer's suicide in 1971.])

Midnight Cowboy (1969). Jerome Hellman Productions. Directed by John Schlesinger; screenplay by Waldo Salt. [In a career-making performance, Jon Voight plays Joe Buck, a naive Texas dishwasher who goes to New York to make his fortune as a hustler. Although enthusiastic about selling himself to rich ladies..., he quickly finds it hard to make a living and eventually crashes in a seedy dump with a crippled thief named Ratzo Rizzo.... [A]t its heart the movie is a sad tale of friendship between a couple of losers in the big city ... with an ending no studio would approve today. (Jim Emerson, Amazon.com)]

Monster (2003). Media 8 Entertainment/Newmarket Films. Written and directed by Patty Jenkins. [The true story of Aileen Wuornos, a woman with a tortured past who turns to prostitution for money, and who eventually turned her anger into a motive for murder, becoming one of America's most infamous serial killers. (*Desc.*)]

Mudge Boy [*The*] (2003). First Cold Press Productions/Showtime Pictures. Written and directed by Michael Burke. ([Duncan Mudge is a shy, isolated, sexually confused farm boy whose mother has recently died, leaving him under the supervision of a stern, depressed father.... Duncan likes to dress in his late mother's clothing, much to the distress of his confused father. The small, insular band of redneck teens that comprise adolescent social life in Duncan's world initially ostracize him, then allow him in to their circle only reluctantly, and largely for their own amusement. Duncan is beset with a profound sense of grief while trying to reconcile himself to a world in which he is a sexual alien. (*Desc.*)]

My Beautiful Laundrette (1985). Channel Four Films/Mainline Pictures. Directed by Stephen Frears, written by Hanif Kureshi. [Captures the contradictions of mid-'80s Thatcherism in a way that's as fresh today as when it was new. When the film was first released, it was the gay content that dominated the conversation, whereas now it seems a sensitive and multifaceted summation of its decade, exploring social, ethnic, and sexual issues and contradictions. Bringing together two such different characters as Omar—Asian, ambitious, for whom success is defined by wealth—and former childhood friend Johnny—white trash, ex-National Front—was inspired. [Harriet Smith, Amazon.com)]

Normal, Ohio (2000). Created by Bob Kushell, Bonnie Turner, and Terry Turner. Written by Bob Kushell, Bonnie Turner, Terry Turner, and others. Directed by Philip Charles MacKenzie and David Trainer. [The first seven episodes can be seen on YouTube; six others, filmed but not aired, are available on Hulu. See discussion in this volume. ~WR]

Paris is Burning (1990). Off White Productions. Directed by Jennie Livingston. [This ground-breaking, fascinating, and ultimately troubling documentary follows a group of participants in New York drag-ball culture" during the so-called "Golden Age" of the mid- to late-1980s. Livingston's informants are black and Hispanic gay men and transpeople, and almost all of them are desperately poor. Through membership in a "house" run by a "Mother" who cares for them and helps them prepare to "walk" in the balls, they find family, friendship, and support. Competition in the balls, though, is their major focus: through re-imagining themselves as white, rich, famous, heterosexual, or as "real" women, they temporarily inhabit fantasies of belonging in a world from which, as they are all quite aware, they are excluded. See discussion in this volume. ~WR]

Pit Stop (2013). Mile Marker Film/Vilcek Foundation. Directed by Yen Tan; written by David Lowery and Yen Tan. [In this perfectly crafted American drama, openly gay Ernesto and closeted Gabe grapple with the tribulations of being gay in a small, working-class Texas town. (*Desc.*)]

Pride (2014). Calamity Films, distributed by Pathé and BBC Films. Written by Stephen Beresford; directed by Matthew Warchus. [It's the summer of 1984. Margaret Thatcher is in power, and the National Union of Mineworkers (NUM) is on strike.... [A] group of gay and lesbian activists decides to raise money to support the families of the striking miners. But there is a problem. The Union seems embarrassed to receive their support.... [T]He activists ... decide to ignore the Union and go direct to the miners. They identify a mining village in deepest Wales and set off in a mini bus to make their donation in person. And so begins the extraordinary story of two seemingly alien communities who form a surprising and ultimately triumphant partnership. (*Desc.*)]

Queens Don't Cry (2002). Norddeutscher Rundfunk/Rosa von Praunheim Filmproduktion. Written and directed by Rosa von Praunheim. [This documentary follows four Berlin drag queens who met in the mid-1980s and went on to become Germany's most popular drag performers... Besides being performers, they are also political activists in AIDS awareness, anti-gay violence, the sex workers movement, and the struggle against the extreme right and racism. (*Desc.*) Von Praunheim's films are often intriguing for their explorations of "marginal" and "underground" queer life. Of note are the documentaries *Men, Heroes and Gay Nazis* (2005), which explores the mostly working-class gay men who align themselves with hard-core right wing skinheads, and *Rent Boys* (2011) in which von Praunheim explores the hustler culture that emerged in the 1960s at West Berlin's Bahnhof Zoo train station; he turns his lens on five grown men who spent their youths as rent boys there, revealing stories of abuse, drug addiction, and poverty but also of surprising tenderness and determination. ~WR]

Queer As Folk (1999-2000). Written by Sarah Harding, Charles McDougall, and Menhaj Huda; created and directed by Russell T. Davies. Distributed by Channel Four/C1TV Entertainment Television. [The original UK version of the series, ten episodes. ~WR]

Queer As Folk (2000-2005). Written by Ron Cowen, Daniel Lipman, Russell T. Davies, Michael MacLennan, Efrem Seeger, Brad Fraser, Del Shores, Shawn Postoff, and others. Directed by Michael DeCarlo, Kelly Makin, Kevin Inch, Alex Chapple, David Wellington, Bruce McDonald, Russell Mulcahy, Jeremy Podeswa, John Greyson, and others. [The American-Canadian Production in eighty-three episodes. See discussion in this volume. ~WR]

Rag Tag (2006). Muka Flicks. Written and directed by Adaora Nwandu. [Somewhat amateurishly staged and acted and occasionally overwrought with "they risked everything for love" melodrama, *Rag Tag*'s core story is worthwhile: two young men, both children of immigrant parents (Tag's are Nigerian; Rag's mother is from the West Indies), are inseparable as children, but take divergent paths as adults: the middle-class Tag pursues education and a law degree in London; Rag ends up in foster care in Birmingham, where he becomes involved in petty crime. When they rediscover each other a decade later, the question becomes whether their class and social differences will allow them to be the lovers they clearly want to be. ~ WR]

Red Dirt (2000). Sweet Tea Productions/Fox Lorber. Directed and written by Tag Purvis. [(T)he movie unwinds the story of Griffith, a young man who feels trapped in a small Southern town by the madness of his invalid aunt.... When a stranger seeks to rent a cottage on Griffith's property, they strike up a friendship that offers Griffith the possibility of escape. At first, *Red Dirt* threatens to drown in the tortured emotions of a Southern gothic novel, but the excellent performances slowly build a rich, affecting web of hope and passion. (Bret Fetzer, Amazon.com)]

Shameless (2004-2013). Company Pictures. Written by Paul Abbott, Ed McCardie, Tom Higgins, Jimmy Dowdall, Jack Lothian, Daniel Brocklehurst, Emma Frost, and others. Directed by Paul Walker, David Threlfall, Lawrence Till, Dearbhla Walsh, Gordon Anderson, Dominic

Leclerc, Andrew McDonnell, and others. [The British version of the series; 139 episodes. Set in Manchester, England, on the fictional Chatsworth council estate. ~WR]

Shameless (2011-). Bonanza Productions/John Wells Productions/ Warner Bros. Television/Showtime Networks/Sterling Films. Written by Paul Abbott, John Wells, LaToya Morgan, Nancy Pimental, Etan Frankel, Alex Borstein, Mike O'Malley, and others. Directed by Mark Mylod, Mimi Leder, John Wells, Anthony Hemingway, Sanaa Hamri, and others. [The American version of the series; eighty-four episodes through April 2014. See discussion in this volume. ~WR]

Shank (2009). Bonne Idée Productions. Directed by Simon Pearce. Written by Christian Martin and Darren Flaxstone. [Cal is a nineteen-year-old closeted gay gang member in Bristol, England, who has nothing in his life except drugs, sex, random acts of violence, and the secret he keeps hidden from his mates. When he chooses to protect one of his gang's intended victims, Olivier, a relationship develops and Cal is exposed to emotions ... he has never experienced. The gang isn't content to let Cal go, however, and violent retribution is exacted for Cal's "disloyalty." As the film ends, Cal and Olivier board a train together, severing once and for all Cal's links to the gang and his old life. A sequel, *Cal*, was released by Bonne Idée in 2012. ~WR]

Small Town Gay Bar (2006). View Askew Productions. Written and directed by Malcolm Ingram. [As the title suggests, this documentary explores life in and around small-town gay bars in rural Mississippi, a place Executive Producer Kevin Smith calls, "probably the hardest place in the world to be gay." In such an environment, the interviewees' use of words like "community" and "family" is anything but casual. Their concerns aren't marriage rights or gala fundraisers, but day-to-day survival, and their resourcefulness and resilience in the face of hostility and near-constant harassment and violence is both inspiring and illuminating. ~WR]

Soldier's Girl (2003). Bachrach/Gottlieb Productions. Directed by Frank Pierson; written by Ron Nyswaner. [The true story of the life and tragic death of soldier Barry Winchell. Winchell's love for Calpernia Addams, a beautiful transgendered nightclub performer, was misunderstood by fellow soldiers and eventually leads to his brutal death. (*Desc.*)]]

Stud Life (2012). New Lime Republic. Written and directed by Campbell Ex. [Set in East London, *Stud Life* traces the lives and loves of JJ, a stone-butch black lesbian and of her best friend, Seb, a willowy, punkish white boy. The rom-com aspects of the film are predictable, but the film includes an optimistic portrait of young, non-posh, gender-boundary-pushing queer folks figuring their lives out with very little "message film" drama. T'Nia Miller is particularly memorable as JJ. ~WR]

Sum of Us [*The*] (1994). Hallmark Entertainment. Directed by Kevin Dowling and Geoff Burton; written by David Stevens. [This light-hearted and somewhat earnest comedy, set in Sydney, Australia, features the not-yet-famous Russell Crowe as a working-class, twenty-something gay plumber who lives with his father, Harry, an open-minded "mate" who becomes obsessed with helping his semi-closeted son find a husband. ~WR]

Twist (2003). Strand Releasing. Directed by Jacob Tierney; written by Charles Dickens and Jacob Tierney. [A gay re-telling of Charles Dickens' classic *Oliver Twist*. Updated to current times and moved out of the poor house and onto the streets of Toronto, *Twist* is told from the point of view of The Artful Dodger.... Dodge takes (young Oliver) under his wing and instructs him in the unforgiving arts of drug abuse and prostitution. As Oliver's innocence dissolves, both young men confront inner and outer demons. (*Desc.*)]

Waters, John. Water's entire oeuvre is a lesson in consciousness of marginalization raised to the level of an art form. Whether his films are set in an actual or an imagined version of Baltimore's Hampden neighborhood, once a prototype of American working-class culture and today threatened by gentrification, Waters fixes his Überqueer gaze on trash, art, pop culture, gender, camp, and sex in a manner that is, according to one's tastes, either disgusting or revelatory. Though Waters' childhood was more leafy suburb than trailer park, he clearly grew up steeped in and fascinated with the people who inhabited the gritty neighborhoods, malls, and thrift shops that surrounded him, and he became a faithful, adoring chronicler of working-class language, tastes, grotesquery, irony, and messed-up lives, about which he refuses to be either critical or entirely serious. In many ways, his work parodies both the absurdity of capitalist, consumerist culture and the unlikelihood of escaping it or, as Australian critic Peter Conrad put it, "Squalor is [Waters'] chosen weapon against puritanical America." Any of Waters' many films showcases his unique sensibilities, but it may be best to start with early hits like *Pink Flamingos* (1972), *Female Trouble* (1974), and *Desperate Living* (1977) before moving on to *Pecker* (1998), *Cecil B. Demented* (2000), and *A Dirty Shame* (2004). His 2006 lecture/standup routine, *This Filthy World*, is also highly recommended. ~WR]

Web Sites

Web sites related to queers and class come and go—but mostly they go. Here are a few possibilities.

International Gay Rodeo Association: www.igra.com. [The largest such organization in the world, the IGRA coordinates rodeo events and specifically welcomes lesbian, gay, bisexual, transgender as well as heterosexual participants and spectators. (*Desc.*) Several states have local chapters as well. ~WR]

LGBT Labour: www.lgbtlabour.org.uk. [The Labour Campaign for Lesbian, Gay, Bisexual, and Transgender Rights is a socialist society affiliated with the UK Labour Party. Membership is open to any lesbian, gay man, bisexual or transgendered person in the Labour movement.]

Pride at Work: http://prideatwork.org. [An official constituency group of the AFL-CIO organized to mobilize mutual support between the organized Labor Movement and the LGBTQ Community.]

Queers for Economic Justice: www.q4ej.org. [The QEJ Project closed in 2014 because of a lack of funding, but their website and publications remain online, at least for the moment. ~WR]

Queers4Gears.com. "NASCAR and MotorSports—From a Queer Perspective."

RuralPride Campaign, National Center for Lesbian Rights: www.nclrights.org/ruralpride-campaign. [Aimed at increasing visibility of the LGBT community in rural America and identifying ways we can use federal advocacy to increase access to crucial services and resources for LGBT rural people and families. (*Desc.*)]

The Queer Working Class Zine Project (TQWCZP): queerworkingclasszineproject.tumblr.com and facebook.com/tqwzp. [UK-based; Facebook and Tumblr only. ~WR]

LGBTQ Literature: A Few Basics

Bronski, Michael (2013). *Pulp Friction: Uncovering the Golden Age of Gay Male Pulps.* New York: St. Martin's Griffin.

Castle, Terry (Ed.) (2003). *The Literature of Lesbianism: A Historical Anthology from Ariosto To Stonewall.* New York: Columbia University Press.

Coote, Stephen (Ed.) (1987). *The Penguin Book of Homosexual Verse.* New York: Penguin Group.

Donoghue, Emma (Ed.) (1999). *The Mammoth Book of Lesbian Short Stories.* Philadelphia: Running Press Book Publishers,

Faderman, Lillian (Ed.) (1994). *Chloe Plus Olivia: An Anthology of Lesbian Literature from the Seventeenth Century to the Present.* New York: Viking.

Fone, Byrne (1998). *The Columbia Anthology of Gay Literature: Readings from Western Antiquity to the Present Day.* New York: Columbia University Press.

Forrest, Katherine V. (2005). *Lesbian Pulp Fiction: The Sexually Intrepid World of Lesbian Paperback Novels 1950-1965.* Berkeley, CA: Cleis Press.

Galloway, David and Christian Sabisch (Eds.) (1982). *Calamus: Male Homosexuality in Twentieth-Century Literature: An International Anthology.* New York: Morrow.

Holden, N., Nestle, J., & Holoch, N. (Eds.) (1999). *The Vintage Book of International Lesbian Fiction.* New York: Knopf Doubleday.

Jones, Sonya L. (Ed.) (2014). *Gay and Lesbian Literature Since World War II: History and Memory.* New York: Routledge.

Leavitt, David and Mark Mitchell (Eds.) (1994). *The Penguin Book of Gay Short Stories.* New York: Viking.

Léger, Tom and MacLeod, Riley (Eds.) (2012). *The Collection: Short Fiction from the Transgender Vanguard.* New York: Topside Press.

Nestle, Joan & Holoch, Naomi (Eds.) (1990). *Women on Women: An Anthology of American Lesbian Short Fiction.* New York: Penguin.

Reynolds, Margaret (1994). *The Penguin Book of Lesbian Short Stories.* New York: Viking.

Ruff, Shawn Stewart (Ed.) (1996). *Go the Way Your Blood Beats: An Anthology of Lesbian and Gay Fiction by African-American Writers.* New York: Holt, Henry & Company.

Shewey, Don. (Ed.) (1988). *Out Front: Contemporary Gay and Lesbian Plays.* New York: Grove/Atlantic.

Working-Class Studies:
Places to Start

Center for Study of Working Class Life, Stony Brook University: www.stonybrook.edu/workingclass.

Class Dismissed: How TV Frames the Working Class (2005). Media Education Foundation. Written by Loretta Alper and Pepi Leistyna; directed by Loretta Alper. Study guide and ordering info from www.mediaed.org; portions are also available on YouTube. [*Class Dismissed* breaks important new ground in exploring the ways in which race, gender, and sexuality intersect with class, offering a more complex reading of television's often one-dimensional representations. (*Desc.*)]

Coles, Nicholas & Zandy, Janet (Eds.) (2007). *American Working-Class Literature: An Anthology.* New York: Oxford University Press.

Collins, Michael (2005). *The Likes of Us: A Biography of the White Working Class.* London: Granta Books. [Once they were portrayed as the salt of the earth. Nowadays, they ... expose their lives in TV documentaries; they love Gucci and hate the Euro—the broadsheets cast them as xenophobes and exhibitionists and mock their tastes and attitudes. Who are the white working class and what have they done to deserve this portrayal? (*Desc.*)]

Ehrenreich, Barbara (2001). *Nickel and Dimed: On (Not) Getting by in America.* New York: Metropolitan Books.

Foster, Gwendolyn Audrey (2005). *Class-Passing: Social Mobility in Film and Popular Culture.* Carbondale: Southern Illinois University Press. [From the construction worker in *Who Wants to Marry a Millionaire?* to the privileged socialites Paris Hilton and Nicole Richie of *The Simple Life*, Foster explores the fantasy of contact between the classes. (*Desc.*)]

Fussell, Paul (1989/1992). *Class: A Guide Through the American Status System.* New York: Touchstone Books.

hooks, bell (2000). *Where We Stand: Class Matters.* New York: Routledge.

Jensen, Barbara (2012). *Reading Classes: On Culture and Classism in America.* Ithaca : ILR Press.

Lauter, Paul and Ann Fitzgerald (Eds.) (2001). *Literature, Class, And Culture: An Anthology.* New York: Longman.

Lubrano, Alfred (2003) *Limbo: Blue-Collar Roots, White-Collar Dreams.* Hoboken, NJ: Wiley. [This country celebrates the idea that there is enormous opportunity to move up from one's station in life.... But for those who are the first from a traditionally blue-collar family to enter college and move into the white-collar workplace, there is a darker side ... when they find themselves alienated from both their (families) and their strange new middle-class world. [David Siegfried, Booklist]]

New York Times (correspondents) (2005). *Class Matters.* New York: Times Books. [From the series originally published in the *New York Times.* (E)xplores the ways in which class—defined as a combination of income, education, wealth, and occupation—influences destiny in a society that likes to think of itself as a land of opportunity." (*Desc.*)]

People Like Us: Social Class in America (2001). Public Broadcasting Service/Center for New American Media. Written and directed by Louis Alvarez and Andy Kolker. Available from CNAM Film Library, Harriman, NY. [*People Like Us* raises questions about the ways, large and small, in which Americans classify each other, how our inherited social class affects our self-perceptions and our expectations, and how race and other factors complicate an already complex arrangement of social distinctions in our society. (*Desc.*) See also www.pbs.org/peoplelikeus.

Sennett, Richard & Cobb, Jonathan (1993/1972). *The Hidden Injuries of Class.* New York: W. W. Norton & Company.

Smiley, Tavis & West, Cornel (2012). *The Rich And The Rest Of Us: A Poverty Manifesto.* New York: SmileyBooks. [(Smiley and West) take on the "p" word—poverty ... challeng(ing) all Americans to re-examine their assumptions about ... what (poverty) really is and how to eradicate it. (*Desc.*)]

Terkel, Studs (1974). *Working: People Talk About What They Do All Day and How They Feel About What They Do.* New York: Random House. [Available in many more recent reprint editions; *Working* was also turned into a graphic novel by Harvey Pekar in 2009. See YouTube for interviews with Terkel and other dramatizations of stories from the book. ~WR]

West End Press: www.westendpress.org. [Based in Albuquerque, New Mexico, West End Press is one of the very few remaining "people's publishers" and has been producing provocative fiction, poetry, memoir, and reportage by working-class writers since 1976. ~WR]

Working Class Studies Association: www.wcstudies.org.

Wray, Matt and Newitz, Annalee (Eds.) (1997). *White Trash: Race and Class in America.* New York: Routledge.

Zandy, Janet (2004). *Hands: Physical Labor, Class, and Cultural Work.* New Brunswick, NJ: Rutgers University Press.

Zandy, Janet (Ed.) (2001). *What We Hold In Common: An Introduction to Working-Class Studies.* New York: The Feminist Press at CUNY.

Zweig, Michael (2011). *The Working Class Majority: America's Best Kept Secret,* 2nd ed. Ithaca, NY: ILR Press. [Those who take (rather than give) orders at work are the working class; at 62 percent of the labor force, they are a majority distracted and diverted from its best interests for several generations. Zweig suggests the implications of this analysis for a number of key political issues, including the "underclass," "family values," globalization, and what workers get (and should get) from government. (Booklist)]

General Working-Class Fiction, Memoir & Anthologies

Bakopoulos, Dean (2005). *Please Don't Come Back from the Moon.* New York: Harper. ["When I was sixteen, my father went to the moon." Thus begins this debut novel about the mysterious disappearance of the men from a working-class suburb of Detroit.... As Bakopoulos writes in an author's note, the book is a kind of elegy for his father's generation of downtrodden working-class men, but their disappointments are tempered by the modest hopes and ambitions of their sons in this gentle and moving tale. (*PW*)]

Casares, Oscar (2003). *Brownsville: Stories.* Boston: Back Bay Books. ([At the country's edge, on the Mexican border, Brownsville, Texas, is a town much like many others. It is a place where men and women work hard to create better lives for their children, where people sometimes bear grudges against their neighbors, where love blossoms only to fade, and where the only real certainty is that life holds surprises. (*Desc.*)])

Coles, Nicholas and Janet Zandy, Janet (Eds.) (2007). *American Working-Class Literature: An Anthology.* New York: Oxford University Press.

Duval, Peter (2004). *Rear View: Stories.* New York: Mariner Books (Houghton Mifflin). [Starkly honest, gritty, and at times darkly humorous°... stories featuring blue-collar workers, lapsed Catholics, bullies, and smalltime thieves struggling with their jobs, their relationships, and their families.... Many of Duval's stories deal with both mundane and unexpected occurrences in a small working-class community. (*Desc.*)]

Gilb, Dagoberto (1994). *The Magic of Blood.* New York: Grove Press. [These plain-spoken stories take readers to construction sites and cheap rentals where chronically underemployed, necessarily mobile, struggling yet optimistic Texas Mexicans survive in an ungenerous world. (*LJ*) The *Magic of Blood* won the PEN/Hemingway award, but see also the author's many other collections of fiction and his volume of essays, *Gritos* (2003). ~WR]

MacDonald, Michael Patrick (1999). *All Souls: A Family Story from Southie.* Boston: Beacon Press. [This plainly written, powerful memoir details not only MacDonald's story of growing up in Southie, Boston's Irish Catholic enclave, but examines the myriad ways in which the media and law enforcement agencies exploit marginalized working-class communities.... MacDonald does not excuse Southie's racism, but he paints a frightening portrait of a community under intense economic and social stress. (*PW*)]

McIntosh, Matthew (2003). *Well.* New York: Grove Press. [Set primarily among the working class of a Seattle suburb called Federal Way, this highly original novel extols the lives of a large cast of characters lost in various modes of darkness and despair. Whether desperately alone or struggling to come together, they grapple with dark compulsions and heartrending afflictions. (*Desc.*)]

McPherson, James Alan (1969). *Hue and Cry: Stories*. Boston, Little, Brown. [McPherson's characters—gritty, jazzy, authentic, and pristinely rendered—give voice to unheard struggles along the dividing lines of race and poverty in subtle, fluid prose that bears no trace of sentimentality, agenda, or apology. (*Desc.*)]

Moehringer, J. R. (2005). *The Tender Bar: A Memoir*. New York: Hyperion. [(W)hile still tender of years, [Moehringer] was introduced to the culture, to the companionship and—yes—to the romance of ... a gin mill on Plandome Road where his Uncle Charlie was a bartender and a patron. On September 11, 2001, almost fifty souls [from] Moehringer's home town of Manhasset were killed in the terrorist attack on the World Trade Center.... Moehringer's lovely evocation of an ordinary place filled with ordinary people gives dignity and meaning to those lost lives, and to his own. (*PW*)]

Offutt, Chris (1992) *Kentucky Straight*. New York: Vintage Books. [The stories in this debut collection share ... a certainty and frankness of language that renders them powerful. Offutt, who grew up in the Kentucky Appalachians, offers taut stories filled with strained relationships and unarticulated desires. (*PW*)]

Perrotta, Tom (1994) *Bad Haircut: Stories of the Seventies*. Bridgehampton, NY: Bridge Works Publishing Company. [Set in the small New Jersey town of Darwin, these seamless, understated narratives (provide) insights into loneliness, societal violence, sexual identity, racism, mortality and much more. (*PW*)]

Ray, Janisse (1999) *Ecology of a Cracker Childhood*. Minneapolis: Milkweed Editions. [Ray ... takes a tough-minded look at life in rural southern Georgia in this blend of memoir and nature study. She presents detailed observations of her family members, most notably her grandfather Charlie, who was "terrifying, prone to violent and unmerited punishment"; her father, whose decision to buy a tract of land near Highway 1 and turn it into what became a massive junkyard with a house in the middle set in motion the key events in Ray's life; and her mother, whose total devotion to her family was tested when her husband began a three-year bout with mental illness.... What remains most memorable are the sections where Ray describes, and attempts to prevent, her own disconnection from the Georgia landscape. (*PW*)]

See, Carolyn (1996) *California Dreaming: Hard Luck and Good Times in America*. Berkeley: University of California Press. [In this bittersweet and beautifully written memoir, See embarks on nothing less than a reevaluation of the American Dream.... The story of See's family speaks for the countless people who reached for the shining American vision, found it eluded their grasp, and then tried to make what they had glitter as best they could. (*Desc.*)]

Sillitoe, Alan (1959/1992) *The Loneliness of the Long-Distance Runner*. New York: Plume Books.

Slezak, Ellen (2002) *Last Year's Jesus: A Novella and Nine Stories*. New York: Theia. [The stories in this affecting debut collection are populated by the sober, self-effacing members of Detroit's Polish-Catholic working class. Linked by place and characters, the stories create a world that feels both familiar and strange, where religion is a way of life, and traditions are carried down through the generations. (*Desc.*)]

Smith, Larry (2001). The American Working-Class Short Story. In Blanche H. Gelfant, Ed., *The Columbia Companion to the Twentieth-Century American Short Story*. New York: Columbia University Press, 81-93.

Viramontes, Helen María (1995). *Under the Feet of Jesus*. New York: Dutton. [With the same audacity with which John Steinbeck wrote about migrant worker conditions in *The Grapes of Wrath* and T.C. Boyle in *The Tortilla Curtain*, Viramontes presents a moving and powerful vision of the lives of the men, women, and children who endure a second-class existence and labor under dangerous conditions in California's fields.... (*Desc.*) See also her *The Moths and Other Stories* (1985) and *Their Dogs Came With Them* (2007).]

Zandy, Janet (Ed.) (1990). *Calling Home: Working-Class Women's Writings: An Anthology*. New Brunswick, NJ: Rutgers University Press.

Lightning Source UK Ltd.
Milton Keynes UK
UKHW021835110220
358551UK00014B/286